# CHEMICAL ASPECTS
## OF
# NUCLEAR REACTORS

ENGLAND:        BUTTERWORTH & CO. (PUBLISHERS) LTD.
                LONDON: 88 Kingsway, W.C.2

AFRICA:         BUTTERWORTH & CO. (AFRICA) LTD.
                DURBAN: 33/35 Beach Grove

AUSTRALIA:      BUTTERWORTH & CO. (AUSTRALIA) LTD.
                SYDNEY: 6–8 O'Connell Street
                MELBOURNE: 473 Bourke Street
                BRISBANE: 240 Queen Street

CANADA:         BUTTERWORTH & CO. (CANADA) LTD.
                TORONTO: 1367 Danforth Avenue, 6

NEW ZEALAND:    BUTTERWORTH & CO. (NEW ZEALAND) LTD.
                WELLINGTON: 49/51 Ballance Street
                AUCKLAND: 35 High Street

U.S.A.:         BUTTERWORTH INC.
                WASHINGTON, D.C.: 7235 Wisconsin Avenue, 14

# CHEMICAL ASPECTS

OF

# NUCLEAR REACTORS

J. K. DAWSON, Ph.D., F.R.I.C.

*Group Leader*
*Reactor Chemistry Group*
*A.E.R.E., Harwell*

R. G. SOWDEN, M.Sc., Ph.D., F.R.I.C.

*Principal Scientific Officer*
*Reactor Chemistry Group*
*A.E.R.E., Harwell*

Volume 1

Gas-Cooled Reactors

LONDON

BUTTERWORTHS

1963

*Suggested U.D.C. number : 621·039·5:54*
*Suggested additional number : 621·039·52·034·3*

*Printed in Great Britain by*
*Spottiswoode, Ballantyne & Co. Ltd.,*
*London and Colchester*

# FOREWORD

R. Spence, C.B., Ph.D., D.Sc., F.R.S.

Deputy Director, A.E.R.E., Harwell

THE technology of nuclear power reactors has developed rapidly in recent years. It is a technology compounded of physics, chemistry, metallurgy and engineering in varying amount. The early plutonium production reactors, which were largely the creation of physicists and engineers working with materials which had been developed by chemists and metallurgists during the Second World War, presented few chemical problems. Temperatures, pressures, power densities and fuel burn-up were low, giving little opportunity for significant chemical change to take place. The subsequent attempt to produce heat of a quality which can be economically converted to electricity has changed this situation quite drastically. Operating conditions have been pressed as far as existing designs and knowledge of materials will allow, but, though fuel costs are low, capital costs are still at least twice as great as those of stations using carbonaceous fuel. Only by the most skilful utilization of materials, the properties of which are well understood, can further progress be made.

High temperature, high radiation intensity and high fuel burn-up create conditions favourable for chemical change, either by reaction between moderator or fuel cladding and coolant, or by generation of fission products and their subsequent migration and reaction. The astonishing variety of reactor types has given rise to a large number of new fields of research; it is one of the aims of this book to bring these together and to distinguish the unifying chemical features.

The authors have had long experience in the field of reactor chemistry and their views have been moulded by a great deal of discussion with colleagues in Britain and in other countries. Of the many books published on atomic energy this will, I believe, be among the most valuable.

# PREFACE

IT IS a common complaint that the output of scientific literature is expanding so rapidly that even the specialist finds it difficult to keep abreast of developments in his own limited field. The sciences and technologies concerned with the development of nuclear reactors have been well to the fore in the production of this spate of new information. Traditional journals have grown thicker, newer publications have sprung up to absorb the overflow, and a welter of detailed material has been made available in the specialist reports of the various government agencies and commercial laboratories.

We make no apology for increasing the literature still further. It is our aim, in fact, to assist its digestion and appreciation in two ways:

1. To present to scientists and technologists working in the nuclear field a comprehensive and up-to-date account of the chemical background to problems encountered in the design of nuclear reactors. To this end we have endeavoured to review critically the available information, and to assemble it within a single work with sufficiently detailed references to enable the reader to consult the original literature where he so desires.

2. To indicate to chemists working in other fields the role of chemistry in the nuclear power industry. The vital role of the chemist in the development of nuclear theory and in the discovery of fission itself is widely accepted. We seek to show that the chemist makes no less a contribution to the problems of commercial exploitation. Conversely, the technological requirements of the nuclear industry have been a means of enriching our knowledge of chemistry and chemical metallurgy, and have provided the stimulus for new studies of many materials under unusual conditions.

We have confined ourselves primarily to considerations of the chemical and metallurgical aspects of the cores and primary coolant circuits of nuclear reactors. Fringe subjects, such as water chemistry in secondary coolant circuits, have been excluded on the grounds that in general they do not pose problems which arise specifically from the use of nuclear fission as a source of heat.

Two important chemical topics related more indirectly to nuclear reactors, the processing of irradiated fuel and the disposal of radioactive waste, are considered to be outside the scope of this book, though integral chemical processing in fluid-fuelled reactors has been dealt with briefly where it seemed appropriate. For the rest, the choice of classification and order of presentation of topics has been somewhat subjective, but we hope that the sub-division into three volumes (Volume 1, Gas-Cooled Reactors; Volume 2, Water-Cooled Reactors; Volume 3, Miscellaneous Topics) will be generally acceptable. The reader may consider that some anomalies have arisen here and there. For example, the chapter on ceramic fuels falls perhaps incongruously under the main heading of 'Gas-Cooled Reactors'. Although ceramic fuels have been adopted for both sodium-cooled and water-cooled reactors in other countries, and no doubt may be so used in the United Kingdom at a later date, their development and first use in the U.K. has been for a gas-cooled reactor—the AGR.

The scope of the field embraced by what may be loosely called 'nuclear reactor chemistry' is very wide, and it is difficult to find a single unifying chemical thread linking the diverse topics covered. Nevertheless certain features have a recurrent importance:

*Radiation.* The inevitable presence of ionizing radiation in the core of a nuclear reactor can bring about peculiar and sometimes embarrassing effects in reactions involving all three conventional states of matter. Radiation chemistry is not only one of the most important aspects of nuclear reactors *per se*; it appears also to have a particular potential to stimulate fundamental research. Thus the basic radiation chemistry of water has gained greatly from an interest in aqueous reactors, both heterogeneous and homogeneous, while the growing concern with the compatibility of materials and with ceramic fuels shows signs of stimulating basic studies in the radiation chemistry of the solid state.

*Unusual ambient conditions.* Aside from radiation, reactor technology often demands the study of chemical reactions under unusually severe conditions of temperature and pressure. For example, studies of aqueous solutions and suspensions have been carried out close to the critical point of water, and the compatibility of solids at temperatures around 2,000°C has assumed considerable importance. Reactions at phase boundaries become significant in many cases, and surface chemistry will receive a considerable stimulus as the problems become more clearly defined.

*State of materials.* Many illustrations of the importance of the physical state and purity of materials will be met in this book. The names 'graphite' and 'uranium dioxide', for example, can cover a multitude of materials with a host of significantly divergent properties. Technological materials tend to be comparatively inhomogeneous substances; full of voids, localized concentrations of impurities and complex dislocation networks. The diffusion of foreign atoms or ions through the medium of these heterogeneities is a recurrent theme.

We have attempted to review the state of knowledge as it stands in 1961–62. Since the study of nuclear reactor chemistry started in the early 1940's, this has involved an assessment of the progress made on a wide front over a period of about 20 years. We have tried to sift out that part of the early work which has lasting value and to eliminate that which has subsequently been found to be invalid for reasons such as insufficient control over the many variable parameters involved. Where earlier review papers were available, these have usually been taken as the starting point and special emphasis has been laid on recent developments.

Considerable reliance has been placed upon Nuclear Science Abstracts in surveying the literature. For each chapter the aim has been to include all major references up to a particular issue of NSA, but in such a wide field it has not been possible to make a single date valid throughout the work. In some of the topics covered very rapid progress is being made at the time of writing, two outstanding examples being the development of ceramic fuel materials (Chapter 4) and the aqueous oxidation of metals (Volume 2, Chapter 5). The specialist reader will therefore find the following list of value if he wishes to follow up subsequent developments:

| Chapter | Last issue of NSA consulted |
|---------|------------------------------|
| 1 | 31 December 1961 |
| 2 | 30 June 1961 |
| 3 | 30 June 1961 |
| 4 | 30 September 1961 |
| 5 | 30 September 1961 |

It has been possible to make use of many later references owing to the excellent Information Service of the A.E.R.E. Library and to personal communications, but complete coverage may not have been achieved beyond the dates given.

We wish to acknowledge the willing cooperation in this project which has been accorded to us by many of our colleagues at A.E.R.E. and by our associates at Oak Ridge National Laboratory and at the KEMA laboratories, Arnhem. Many of them have allowed us to use previously unpublished work. Whilst the selection of material and the conclusions drawn in each chapter remain the responsibility of ourselves alone, we wish particularly to acknowledge valuable comments received on various parts of the manuscript from the following: Drs. A. R. Anderson, C. B. Amphlett, W. G. Burns, B. Cox, N. Hodge, D. A. Landsman, G. Long, L. E. J. Roberts, W. Wild, Messrs, G. N. Walton, J. Wright (Chemistry Division, A.E.R.E.); Drs. L. E. Russell, B. R. T. Frost, Messrs. J. N. Wanklyn, J. Williams (Metallurgy Division, A.E.R.E.); Dr. H. A. Kearsey (Chemical Engineering Division, A.E.R.E.); Mr. M. S. T. Price (U.K.A.E.A., Winfrith Heath); Dr. D. M. Donaldson (U.K.A.E.A., Dounreay); and M. E. A. Hermans (N. V. KEMA, Arnhem).

Individual acknowledgements for permission to reproduce illustrations are given under the appropriate diagrams.

J. K. DAWSON
R. G. SOWDEN

*March, 1963*

# CONTENTS OF VOLUME 1

CONTENTS

CHAPTER 1

# INTRODUCTION TO GAS-COOLED REACTORS

MANY fluids have been used, or are potentially available, for removing heat from the cores of nuclear reactors. They can be grouped conveniently under the three main sub-divisions of this work: gaseous coolants, water and non-aqueous liquids. The present chapter will describe the status of gas-cooled reactors and indicate in broad outline the principal grounds on which the choice of a particular gas may be made for a given reactor. The chemical problems will then be discussed in detail in the subsequent chapters devoted to graphite, corrosion of metals, ceramic fuels and special safety problems.

## 1.1 THE GAS-COOLED REACTOR PROGRAMME

Gas-cooling for large nuclear power reactors has been established not only as feasible, but further as a technique possessing considerable potential for future development. The principal countries engaged in this development are Great Britain and France, with an expanding programme relating to advanced concepts of gas-cooling also arising in the U.S.A. *Table 1.1* lists the important gas-cooled reactors either completed, or having planned completion dates which are reasonably certain: the systems are sub-divided according to the coolant gas used.

The establishment of gaseous coolant technology in Western Europe, in contrast to the water coolant technology developed in the U.S.A., arose principally from two causes. The first gas-cooled graphite moderated power reactors were the only type using relatively familiar and readily available construction materials, and furthermore they did not require isotopic enrichment of either the fuel or the moderator. This was an important factor when the decision was made in 1947 to build the large-scale gas-cooled reactors at Windscale. The research reactor, BEPO, had been designed previously for erection at Harwell: with a heat output of no more than 6 MW it was possible to cool this reactor with air at normal pressure. The fact that the much larger Windscale plutonium production reactors were also cooled by air arose from considerations of siting in addition to the limit set by the physical or chemical properties of the various possible coolants. The first Windscale reactor was originally intended to be water-cooled, as were the American plutonium-producing reactors at Hanford. However, the requirements for a very large supply of pure water plus the adoption of the American safety principle that such reactors should not be sited nearer than 50 miles to any town soon led to considerable difficulty in finding suitable sites in Great Britain.

1

TABLE 1.1

PRINCIPAL GAS-COOLED REACTORS

| Coolant | Designation | Location | Number of reactors | Output per reactor (MW)* | Purpose | Moderator | Gas outlet temperature (°C) | Date of full power operation |
|---|---|---|---|---|---|---|---|---|
| Air | ORNL-X.10 Area graphite reactor | Oak Ridge, U.S.A. | 1 | 3·5(T) | Research | Graphite | 80 | 1943 |
| | BEPO | Harwell, England | 1 | 6(T) | Research | Graphite | 95 | 1949 |
| | Windscale | England | 2 | — | Pu production | Graphite | 210 | 1950 (now closed down) |
| | BGRR | Brookhaven, U.S.A. | 1 | 20(T) | Research | Graphite | 160 | 1951 |
| | G-1 | Marcoule, France | 1 | 38(T) | Pu production | Graphite | 135 | 1956 |
| | BR-1 | Mol, Belgium | 1 | 4(T) | Research | Graphite | 75 | 1957 |
| $CO_2$ | Calder Hall and Chapel Cross | England and Scotland | 8 | 200(T) 38(E) | Pu and Power | Graphite | 336 | 1956–60 |
| | G2, G3 | Marcoule, France | 2 | 200(T) 32(E) | Pu and Power | Graphite | 350 | 1959 |
| | EDF-1 | Chinon, France | 1 | 68(E) | Power | Graphite | 355 | 1962 |
| | AGR | Windscale, England | 1 | 100(T) | Experimental power production | Graphite | 500–575 | 1962 |
| | Berkeley | Gloucestershire, England | 2 | 138(E) | Power | Graphite | 345 | 1962 |
| | Bradwell | Essex, England | 2 | 150(E) | Power | Graphite | 390 | 1962 |
| | Latina | Italy | 1 | 200(E) | Power | Graphite | 390 | 1962 |
| | Hinkley Point | Somerset, England | 2 | 250(E) | Power | Graphite | 375 | 1963 |
| | EDF-2 | Chinon, France | 1 | 195(E) | Power | Graphite | 365 | 1963 |

| Coolant | Identification | Location | | Output | Type | Moderator | | Year |
|---|---|---|---|---|---|---|---|---|
| | Hunterston | W. Glasgow, Scotland | 2 | 150(E) | Power | Graphite | 555 | 1965–4 |
| | EL-4 | Monts D'Arree, France | 1 | 80(E) | Prototype | $D_2O$ | — | 1964 |
| | Trawsfynydd | Wales | 2 | 250(E) | Power | Graphite | 400 | 1964 |
| | Tokai Mura | Japan | 1 | 158(E) | Power | Graphite | 398 | 1965 |
| | 'HWGCR' (KS-150) | Bohunice, Czechoslovakia | 1 | 150(E) | Power | $D_2O$ | 425 | 1965 |
| | EDF-3 | Chinon, France | 1 | 375(E) (gross) | Power | Graphite | 385 | 1965 |
| | Dungeness | Kent, England | 2 | 275(E) | Power | Graphite | 400 | 1965 |
| | Oldbury | Gloucestershire, England | 2 | 280(E) | Power | Graphite | — | 1966 |
| | Sizewell | Suffolk, England | 2 | 190(E) | Power | Graphite | 410 | 1966 |
| | Wylfa | Anglesey, Wales | 2 | 400(E) | Power | Graphite | — | 1967–8 |
| $N_2$ | EL-2 | Saclay, France | 1 | 2(T) | Research | $D_2O$ | 130 | Now converted to $CO_2$-cooling |
| | GCRE | Idaho, U.S.A. | 1 | 2(T) | Experimental (relating to ML-1) | $H_2O$ | 550 | 1960 |
| | ML-1 | U.S. Army | 1 | 0·45(E) | Mobile, power | $H_2O$ | 650 | 1961 |
| He | EGCR | Oak Ridge, U.S.A. | 1 | 22(E) | Experimental | Graphite | 565 | 1963 |
| | EBOR | Idaho, U.S.A. | 1 | 10(T) | Experimental | BeO | 700 | 1963 |
| | HTGR | Peach Bottom, U.S.A. | 1 | 40(E) | Power | Graphite | 750 | 1964 |
| | Dragon | Winfrith Heath, England | 1 | 20(T) | Experimental | Graphite | 750 (926 from hottest channel) | 1964 |
| (He/Ne)? | AVR (Krupp-Brown Boveri) Turret | Julich, Germany | 1 | 15(E) | Experimental | Graphite | 850 | 1964 |
| | (UHTREX) | Los Alamos, U.S.A. | 1 | 3(T) | Experimental (for process heat) | Graphite | 1,300 | 1964 |

* (T) = thermal output   (E) = net electrical output

3

At the same time, it was realized that the proposed large reactors for plutonium production could still be cooled by air at atmospheric pressure provided that fins of low neutron cross-section aluminium were fitted to the fuel cans to improve their heat transfer characteristics. Moreover, on nuclear grounds, the gas-cooled reactor was considered to be inherently more stable (and hence safer) than a water-cooled reactor. The final decision was made to build two air-cooled plutonium production reactors, and some design effort was also continued at Risley on the possibility of a reactor cooled by a gas under pressure and working at a temperature sufficiently high to generate electric power.

It is well known that air cannot be used to operate at high temperatures in graphite-moderated reactors owing to rapid oxidation of the graphite. Carbon dioxide has been chosen, therefore, as the gaseous coolant for the majority of power reactors to be constructed in the early 1960s. Even this gas, however, is too oxidizing towards both graphite and most constructional metals at temperatures required to enter the gas turbine field of electricity generation. Consequently there are now a number of projects for the investigation of more inert gases, particularly helium, for this very high temperature operation (see *Table 1.1*). Nitrogen is receiving some attention in the U.S.A. for the GCRE and ML-1 reactors. Ultimately it is hoped that it may be possible to replace the nitrogen by air in future versions of these mobile reactors: the problem of incompatibility with graphite will not arise since the reactors will be of a pressure-tube design and moderated by light water.

Nothing could be cheaper or more convenient as a coolant than air at atmospheric pressure for reactors which do not have to operate above about 150°C. For higher temperatures, it is necessary to take into account the physical and chemical properties of each of the possible gases. Those gases which have received most attention from reactor designers are air, carbon dioxide, hydrogen, helium and nitrogen. Gases which have received more limited attention include neon, benzene, ammonia, sulphur dioxide and the Freons. Steam has attractive heat transfer properties and has been the subject of a number of reactor design studies, but no reactor has yet been built utilizing steam cooling alone.

Gaseous uranium hexafluoride has also been seriously considered as a reactor coolant, but since it would also act as the fuel its use would lead to quite different problems from the non-fissile gases and it is considered separately in Volume 3 Chapter 4.

## 1.2 FACTORS AFFECTING THE CHOICE OF COOLANT

The main considerations which govern the choice of coolant for a particular reactor are:

Nuclear properties
Physical and heat transfer properties
Chemical properties, including stability and compatibility

There is no 'best gas' for all possible nuclear applications: the choice for each reactor must inevitably be a compromise between conflicting requirements which appear under the various headings.

## 1.2.1 Nuclear Properties

The nuclear properties of coolant gases are important for three reasons. If the neutron absorption cross-section is high and the gas is to be used under high pressure, additional enrichment of the fuel in fissile isotopes may be required with a consequent increase in the fuel cost. The excess nuclear reactivity which would subsequently be created as a result of a loss-of-coolant accident also requires careful consideration. Thirdly, undesirable radioactive species may be created in the gas during irradiation, leading to increased health hazards in the surrounding areas arising from leakage of gas or from the requirements of maintenance.

*Helium* is outstanding amongst the gases considered as possible coolants since it has a thermal neutron absorption cross-section of only a few millibarns. None of the problems mentioned in the previous paragraph arise. Special attention must be paid to maintaining a low content of argon in order to reduce activity in the outer reactor circuit due to $^{41}Ar$ (except for some possible designs of the DRAGON-type reactor in which fission product activity from the fuel is allowed deliberately to enter the coolant gas: this would, of course, swamp out any induced argon activity). The argon content of commercially available helium in the U.S.A. (obtained from natural gas) is in the range 0·2–2 p.p.m., and this appears to be tolerable.

*Neon* is three times as abundant as helium in the atmosphere and the extraction of a neon–helium mixture from air might be relatively convenient. The total cross-section of neon for fast neutrons amounts to several barns, but that for thermal neutrons is only about 0·4 barn. However, no significant amounts of radioactivity would be induced by exposure to neutrons. A reactor cooled by a neon–helium mixture has been proposed for construction in Germany, see *Table 1.1* (German Patent, 1959).

*Carbon dioxide* is almost as good as helium from the nuclear viewpoint. Both its constituent atoms have very low cross-sections for thermal neutrons, moreover most of the possible neutron captures result in further stable nuclides. From a health physics viewpoint, $^{14}C$ is an important long-lived constituent of the circulating gas when the latter is released to atmosphere by leakage or during blow-down. The principal source of $^{14}C$ in the reactors at Calder Hall has been found to be an (n, p) reaction on the nitrogen impurity (up to 100 p.p.m.) in the carbon dioxide. The second largest source of $^{14}C$ is an (n, α) reaction on the $^{17}O$ constituent of the carbon dioxide in reactors which have been operating for less than ten years: beyond that time it is predicted that an (n, γ) reaction on the $^{13}C$ of the moderator graphite, followed by reaction with carbon dioxide, will produce the second largest contribution (RILEY, 1960).

The circulating gas in the Calder Hall reactors has been found to become radioactive during operation due primarily to $^{16}N$ produced by an (n, p) reaction on $^{16}O$, and to $^{41}Ar$ produced by an (n, γ) reaction on $^{40}Ar$ which is present to the extent of about 3 p.p.m. in the carbon dioxide (DAVEY, GAW-THROP and MARSHAM, 1958).

The $^{16}N$ activity is troublesome also in the operation of water-cooled reactors, where it arises from the interaction between neutrons and the $^{16}O$ in the water molecules. Nitrogen-16 emits a very hard (7 MeV) gamma radiation which is difficult to attenuate, but since the half-life is only 7 sec no long-term activation is involved, and the activity in the external parts of the coolant circuit falls

5

rapidly after reactor shutdown. The longer half-life of $^{41}$Ar (109 min) is sufficient to prevent access to the coolant circuit for several hours after reactor shutdown.

*Air* presents a similar $^{16}$N problem when it is used as a reactor coolant. The argon content of air is as high as 0·9 per cent and the $^{41}$Ar activity can also become comparatively high. Leakage of irradiated air into a confined space could render the latter temporarily unfit for human occupation. It is necessary to pass the exit gas from a reactor cooled by air on a once-through system up a high stack to obtain suitable dispersion of the activity. Carbon-14, arising from an (n, p) reaction on $^{14}$N, will also be produced by irradiation of air. This isotope will present the most serious long-lived hazard (half-life 5,600 years), but in relatively low-power research reactors the use of a stack, required to disperse the $^{41}$Ar activity, will also disperse the $^{14}$C to tolerable concentrations. High power reactors using air at high pressure have not been built, and so the resultant problems of leakage of $^{41}$Ar and $^{14}$C into the surrounding area, together with long-lived contamination of the circuit by $^{14}$C, have not yet arisen in practice.

*Argon* itself is by far the most abundant inert gas in air and it is extracted commercially on a large scale. However, the consequences of the leakage of induced $^{41}$Ar activity from a reactor circuit weigh heavily against the choice of argon as the coolant medium.

*Nitrogen* gives rise to the problem of long-lived $^{14}$C production, as in the irradiation of air. There will also be some contribution from $^{41}$Ar to the activity in the coolant circuit, from the few p.p.m. of argon present in commercially available nitrogen. Moreover, with a neutron cross-section of 1·88 barn, the use of nitrogen at high pressure would introduce a significant amount of neutron absorber into the reactor core, with consequent problems of the sudden availability of excess nuclear reactivity in an accident involving loss of coolant.

*Steam* has been considered as a reactor coolant in a number of design studies. It differs from the other gases in having both neutron absorbing and neutron moderating properties. The problem of induced short-lived radioactivity from $^{16}$N, $^{17}$N, and $^{18}$F will be similar to that encountered in pressurized-water and boiling water reactors (see *Table 6.4*, Volume 2). The use of steam is usually considered in conjunction with a pressure-tube design of reactor core, the tubes being surrounded by heavy water or graphite moderator. Although this arrangement removes the problem of compatibility between steam and graphite, the heterogeneous arrangement of moderating material (including the steam) gives rise to considerable problems in the neutron physics of the system.

The proportion of the total moderation of neutrons which occurs in the steam coolant will depend upon the density of the steam and upon its degree of 'wetness'. Very wet steam, containing a high proportion of liquid droplets, has attractive heat transfer properties, but its use would require careful consideration of the nuclear consequences of a loss-of-coolant accident.

*Hydrogen* has a relatively high neutron capture cross-section, 0·33 barn. The primary disadvantage of this would be a slight increase in the required enrichment of the fuel compared with a reactor cooled by, say, carbon dioxide. Natural hydrogen contains 99·985 per cent $^{1}$H; neutron capture will give stable $^2$H and will not give rise to excessive radioactivity in the coolant circuit. Radioactive $^3$H will be formed by neutron capture in $^2$H, but the capture cross-section is less than 1 millibarn and no serious hazard can result. Impurities in the hydrogen would probably make a larger contribution to the circuit activity.

The relative merits of the various possible coolant gases are summarized later in *Table 1.2* in relation to each of the topics considered in the text.

### 1.2.2 Physical Properties

The primary disadvantages of gases compared with liquids as coolants for nuclear reactors are their rather poor heat transfer characteristics and their low volumetric specific heats. These properties can lead to a relatively high proportion of the reactor power output being used for circulating the coolant, with a consequent deleterious effect upon the overall economics.

The physical properties of the coolant gases have recently assumed greater significance and have attracted considerable attention now that reactor technology has advanced sufficiently for designs to be aimed at closed-cycle gas turbine installations.

A good coolant must be able to accommodate high rates of heat transfer from the fuel element surfaces, for which a good thermal conductivity is essential. For efficient removal of heat from the reactor channels the gas must also have a high specific heat. These two requirements are not necessarily both met in a single gas: thus helium has a high thermal conductivity but a low volumetric specific heat.

Several attempts have been made to compare the coolant gases on these grounds: the most desirable gas usually being considered to be the one requiring the least pumping power for its circulation. This is based on the lowest value of the expression $1/p^2C_p^3$, or at constant pressure $M/C_M^3$, where $p$ is the density, $M$ is the molecular weight and $C_p$ and $C_M$ are the specific heats per gram and per mole respectively. Several important assumptions are involved in using these expressions, however:

(a)  A fixed geometry of the fuel channels.
(b)  A constant temperature rise as the gas passes through a coolant channel.
(c)  The Prandtl number is constant and has the value unity.

SAMUELS (1958) has shown that the use of this expression can be very misleading in evaluating the merits of different gases. For a reliable comparison it is necessary to adjust the channel geometry to suit the needs of each particular gas. At Oak Ridge National Laboratory (ORNL STAFF, 1959) it has been considered that the best basis for the comparison of different coolant gases is the unit net power cost of the system optimized separately for each gas, care being taken that no parameter is allowed to vary except as required by specific coolant properties. The report quotes results obtained on this basis relating to a reactor with a gas inlet temperature of 230°C and an outlet temperature of 540°C. The use of helium gave power costs consistently lower than those for carbon dioxide; the difference was small at heat ratings of about 0·8 MW(t) per channel, but the costs diverged rapidly at higher ratings.

A comparison study between helium and carbon dioxide as coolants for a maritime gas-cooled reactor by GENERAL DYNAMICS CORPORATION (1958) showed that within practical limitations of design the thermodynamic plant performance was almost identical for the two gases. It was concluded that thermodynamic considerations alone did not provide sufficient grounds for the choice of fluid. A study of a closed-cycle gas-turbine reactor by WINKLER (1957) also showed that whether the working fluid was helium, carbon dioxide or nitrogen had no significant effect upon the power plant efficiency.

In contrast to ABLITT (1958), FORTESCUE (1957) has pointed out that pumping power alone is not the most relevant characteristic of a gaseous reactor coolant. As nuclear power plant is characterized by relatively high capital cost and low fuel cost, a compromise must be made between conflicting requirements of plant efficiency and output, the compromise being weighted heavily in favour of high output. Since pumping power considerably above the minimum possible will be required, therefore, the size of the gas circulators becomes an important consideration. Fortescue showed that, for constant channel geometry and temperature, the circulator volume would be related to the specific heat and the molecular weight in such a way that gases composed of molecules of high molecular weight (e.g. $CO_2$, $N_2$ or $CF_4$) would be more advantageous than low molecular weight hydrogen or monatomic helium.

In conclusion, the physical properties of the coolant gases, though of considerable importance, cannot be used as the sole basis for selecting the best coolant for a particular reactor: a very involved optimization of the whole reactor circuit must be carried out for each gas. Consequently it is not considered appropriate to present extensive values of physical properties here, as they should not be considered in isolation. A useful summary of the relevant physical properties (thermal conductivity, heat capacity and viscosity) has been compiled by TIPTON (1960).

### 1.2.3 Chemical Properties

*Stability.* The thermal stability of the gases commonly considered as reactor coolants—He, $H_2$, $N_2$, air, $CO_2$ and steam—is quite satisfactory up to the temperatures envisaged for reactor operation. Carbon dioxide tends to dissociate into carbon monoxide and oxygen as the temperature is increased, but even at $1,000°K$ the equilibrium concentration of carbon monoxide at a pressure of 10 atmospheres would be only about 3 p.p.m. according to the data of WAGMAN et al. (1945). In a reactor in which the carbon dioxide comes into contact with the graphite moderator, the resultant concentration of carbon monoxide would be greater than this on account of chemical reaction with the graphite.

Steam also undergoes thermal dissociation into hydrogen and oxygen as the temperature is raised, but again at $1,000°K$ and a pressure of 100 atmospheres the equilibrium concentration of hydrogen would not exceed about 1 p.p.m.

In assessing reactor systems, however, due account must be taken of the possibility that the steady state attained under irradiation may differ from the thermodynamic equilibrium. Moreover, heterogeneous chemical reactions between some of the decomposition products and the constructional materials, particularly graphite, must also be considered.

8

In some instances true chemical equilibrium would never be achieved. Thus although carbon tetrafluoride is known to be very stable towards thermal degradation, and moreover it is chemically inert and might therefore be considered as a possible coolant gas, appreciable amounts of fluorine are produced under pile irradiation (DAVIDGE, 1955). This fluorine would react immediately with hot graphite and with the constructional metals and so prevent the establishment of an equilibrium.

The possibility of not attaining thermodynamic equilibrium might be turned to good account in the case of hydrogen. Thermodynamic data indicate that at equilibrium the concentration of methane in a hydrogen/graphite system at temperatures of interest for reactor operation might be as high as 10–20 per cent, i.e. considerable attack of the graphite might take place. There is evidence to show, however, that even under irradiation at 600°C the rate of reaction is sufficiently slow that the thermodynamic equilibrium would not be attained in a reasonable time (CORNEY and THOMAS, 1958).

*Compatibility.* The various problems of compatibility between the coolant gases and the constructional materials used in reactors are discussed in detail in subsequent chapters. Helium is outstanding in its inertness towards all the constructional materials, but other generalizations are difficult to make. Thus, nitrogen could probably be used in contact with graphite up to a temperature of 2,000°C, but it would not be significantly better than air, carbon dioxide or steam in contact with beryllium or zirconium alloys.

The compatibility relationships of each reactor must be considered individually and no very precise limits can be laid down for the range of temperatures over which a particular combination of materials may be used regardless of other conditions. The decision on the most desirable gas from a compatibility viewpoint is bound to be somewhat subjective. Important factors which will affect such a decision will be:

(a) The definition of rate of penetration or of loss in weight acceptable over a working life for the reactor of 20–30 years will be arbitrary, and will depend upon the degree of optimism of the engineering design team.

(b) Impurities in either the gas or the solid materials can markedly affect the compatibility relationships. The purity of a gas in a reactor circuit may be very different from that obtainable in a laboratory system; moisture in particular is difficult to reduce to very low levels of concentration.

(c) The effects of radiation are difficult to predict or to extrapolate to power reactor conditions from experiments necessarily carried out in lower radiation fluxes.

All of the gases will produce short-lived chemical species under irradiation: these will be potentially very reactive and may have an important effect in terms of compatibility of the coolant with the constructional material. Not even helium may be exempt from this effect. Under irradiation some $He^+$ ions will be produced; this species has a hydrogen-like structure and might have a half-life sufficiently long for its chemical reactivity to become a technological problem.

ONSLOW-MACAULAY and TOMLINSON (1960) have investigated briefly the possible attack by irradiated helium on graphite and the subsequent transfer of carbon around a reactor coolant circuit. With energy absorbed in the gas from a microwave generator at a rate considerably greater than would be experienced in a reactor, they could observe no significant attack on films of pyrolytic carbon. They also calculated theoretically that even if every excited helium atom and helium ion produced in a reactor channel were to remove one atom of carbon from the graphite structure, the loss of graphite would probably remain within tolerable limits over the life of the reactor.

Hydrogen would introduce the special problem of the possible embrittlement of low-alloy steels used in reactor pressure shells. This may arise as physical embrittlement due to the diffusion and accumulation of hydrogen at grain boundaries (below 200°C) or by chemical attack on the carbon in the steel at higher temperatures. The effect of irradiation on both forms of embrittlement requires investigation, although out of irradiation it is known that the embrittlement may be avoided by using steels of the austenitic type. The extensive use of austenitic stainless steel in any reactor, however, presents an economic penalty which tends to offset other advantages which may arise.

The fuel in a hydrogen-cooled reactor would probably have to be a relatively inert ceramic such as uranium dioxide rather than a metal: the latter would react with hydrogen which might diffuse through the cladding metal. An assessment of the seriousness of this reaction must await experimental data on diffusion rates through the metals of interest.

The general situation arising in an operating nuclear reactor is complicated by the unavoidable presence of impurities in the coolant gases. For a Calder Hall reactor cooled by carbon dioxide, a typical composition of the circulating gas has been given by DAVEY, GAWTHROP and MARSHAM (1958) as:

|  | CO | Ar | $H_2O$ | $H_2$ | $O_2$ | $N_2$ | $CH_4$ | $C_2H_6$ |
|---|---|---|---|---|---|---|---|---|
| p.p.m. in $CO_2$ | 3,800 | 3 | 10 | 16 | 17 | 94 | 13 | 1 |

The hydrogen presumably arises by the reduction of water vapour with CO, but an equilibrium is established which still leaves some water vapour in the gas mixture. The technological implications of the presence of moisture in the carbon dioxide have been discussed briefly by DENNIS (1957) and an attempt to calculate equilibrium concentrations in the system graphite–carbon dioxide–water vapour has been reported by RAGONE (1960). The latter author suggested that very small traces of hydrogen might suppress the transport of carbon by the carbon dioxide.

The effect of impurities is particularly important in helium. Normally this gas is considered to be chemically inert, but very small traces of oxidizing impurities, such as water vapour or oxygen, could seriously affect the graphite components of the core of a very high temperature reactor. The maximum tolerable concentration of oxygen in the coolant of a DRAGON-type reactor may be less than 1 p.p.m.

The elucidation of problems arising from such impurities has often taken a large amount of research effort and it is important that due emphasis should be placed on them when proposals are made for the construction of a new design of reactor. Consideration of the coolant as a simple, pure gas is quite unrealistic.

The compatibility of a range of possible coolant gases with ceramic materials (mainly oxides) has been studied by LEVY and FOSTER (1961). They concluded that nitrogen was potentially more attractive than carbon dioxide, steam, air or hydrogen.

In view of the lack of more general experimental data, the tabulation of respective merit of the gases under the heading of Compatibility in *Table 1.2* must be considered tentative and subject to possible change.

### 1.2.4 Containment

Standard engineering practice in construction leaves the possibility of some leakage through the walls of the containment system. Normally this is accepted in conventional steam circuits, but a much higher standard is required for nuclear plant for two reasons.

Some coolant gases may produce hazardous constituents by nuclear reactions (such as $^{41}$Ar from air), and in other reactors fission products may be allowed deliberately to diffuse into the coolant stream (e.g. DRAGON): obviously leakage of such gases from the reactor must be avoided on safety grounds.

Secondly, where helium is used as coolant, leakage must be minimized in the interests of economy. Since the U.S.A. is the only large-scale producer of helium in the Western World, and transportation to a European country would approximately double the cost, unavoidable losses by leakage must be eliminated. The extraction of large quantities of helium from the atmosphere, in which it occurs only at very low concentrations, cannot compete with the U.S.A. source from natural gas, although the extraction of a helium–neon mixture might be more competitive.

The problem of containment of helium has received considerable attention, and the possibility of attaining a leak rate as low as 0·1 per cent of the system volume per day has been considered feasible at Oak Ridge (ORNL STAFF, 1959). The high rate of diffusion of helium through leaks renders this figure a difficult target to achieve, however. The leakage of carbon dioxide from Calder Hall reactors has been made as low as about 0·1 per cent per day and this is considered to be probably the practical limit for this gas without considerable redesign of the coolant circuits (CUNNINGHAM, 1958). Such a rate is equivalent to the escape through a hole of less than 0·03 in. diameter in a total surface area of about 250,000 ft².

Several studies of the application of hydrogen as a coolant have been made and attention has been focused on the possibility of explosions arising from hydrogen–air mixtures after leakage of the gas from the reactor system (GARAY, 1960; BRADLEY, 1960). However, these studies indicate that this aspect of the use of hydrogen may have been over-emphasized previously: the chemical industry in general has quite a wide experience of handling hydrogen at higher pressures and temperatures than those contemplated in nuclear reactors. There is probably a considerable factor of safety inherent in the low density hydrogen; any leaks into the ambient atmosphere will under most circumstances be rapidly dispersed upwards away from possible sources of ignition. A useful summary of safe conditions for handling hydrogen has been given by SHAPIRO and GIFFEN (1952).

## 1.3 SUMMARY

An attempt has been made in *Table 1.2* to allot an order of merit under the various headings discussed in this chapter to six possible coolant gases for large power reactors. This classification must inevitably be subjective and the respective merits may change as more experimental information is accumulated. However, the Table does show that in the opinion of the authors the most desirable gas is helium. Hydrogen comes rather low in the order of merit, despite its good heat transfer properties. There is reason to believe that the inclusion of placings based upon physical properties would not affect the overall position of the first and second gases (helium and carbon dioxide) although steam might displace nitrogen as third choice.

It should be emphasized also that *Table 1.2* refers to the use of the various gases in large power reactors. For special applications (e.g. propulsion reactors) the order may be different.

TABLE 1.2

RELATIVE MERIT OF COOLANT GASES FOR USE IN LARGE NUCLEAR POWER REACTORS*

| Gas | Nuclear properties | Physical properties | Compatibility | | | Containment | Overall placing† |
|---|---|---|---|---|---|---|---|
| | | | Out-pile circuit | Graphite moderator | Water moderator | | |
| He | 1 | Insufficient | 1 | 1 | 1 | 5 | 1 |
| $Co_2$ | 2 | evidence on | 2 | 3 | 2 | 3 | 2 |
| $N_2$ | 5 | optimized | 5 | 2 | 3 | 2 | 3 |
| Steam | 4 | complete | 3 | 5 | 4 | 4 | 4 |
| $H_2$ | 3 | reactor | 4 | 4 | 5 | 6 | 5 |
| Air | 6 | systems | 6 | 6 | 6 | 1 | 6 |

* 1 represents the most desirable gas, 6 the least desirable.
† Equal weight given to each sub-assessment.

The choice of helium as the most suitable gas has been made also by PFLAUM and REIHER (1960) for a nuclear reactor–gas turbine combination, although a similar assessment by GODWIN and DENNISON (1959) did not produce a clear-cut decision between helium and carbon dioxide.

It should be observed finally that gas-cooling for reactors is capable of considerable additional development. Apart from the obvious advantages of improving reactor designs by using higher pressures and temperatures, the main disadvantage of gaseous coolants, low thermal capacity, might be alleviated by the device of dust-cloud cooling. The addition of finely divided material of high thermal capacity, such as powdered graphite, to the gaseous coolant could produce very good heat transport properties, and preliminary assessments of such a system have been published (SCHLUDERBERG, 1955, 1961;

RHODE et al., 1960). There are many problems to be investigated before advantage could be taken of such an improvement, however; in the chemical field these would include the effect of ionizing radiation upon the surface properties of finely dispersed graphite and a study of the rate of approach to chemical equilibrium with reactive species in the coolant gas. Both of these considerations could affect the state of dispersion and the stability of the particle size distribution in a circulating system, upon which the heat transfer properties will depend.

Further advantages might be gained also in closed-cycle turbine systems by the use of a gas which will dissociate endothermically in the reactor core and recombine exothermically in the external circuit. A major problem will be to find a multi-atomic gas which would dissociate and recombine sufficiently rapidly. No very satisfactory suggestions have yet appeared; the equilibrium reaction

$$PCl_5 \rightleftharpoons PCl_3 + Cl_2 \pm 30 \text{ kcal}$$

has been mentioned in a patent on the grounds that it would be in favour of $PCl_3$ at 130°C but $PCl_5$ at 300°C (BABCOCK and WILCOX, 1960). Dissociation would be suppressed by an excess pressure of $PCl_3$, however.

## REFERENCES

ABLITT, J. F. (1958). 'Selecting the reactor coolant.' *Atomics and Nuclear Energy*, **9**, 316

BABCOCK and WILCOX (1960). British Patent 847,984. 'Improvements in and relating to heat exchangers.' Granted to Société Française des Constructions Babcock and Wilcox

BRADLEY, D. (1960). 'Hydrogen as a power reactor coolant.' *Nucleonics*, **18**, No. 7, 84

CORNEY, N. S. and THOMAS, R. B. (1958). 'The effect of pile radiation on the reaction between hydrogen and graphite.' U.K.A.E.A. Report, AERE C/R 2502

CUNNINGHAM, J. B. W. (1958). 'Current re-designs of Calder Hall.' *Proc. Second Geneva Conf.*, **8**, 416

DAVEY, H. G., GAWTHROP, J. and MARSHAM, T. N. (1958). 'Operating experience at Calder Hall.' *Proc. Second Geneva Conf.*, **8**, 10

DAVIDGE, P. C. (1955). 'The decomposition of ammonia and carbon tetrafluoride by pile irradiation.' U.K.A.E.A. Report, AERE C/R 1569

DENNIS, W. E. (1957). 'Chemical problems in coolant gases.' *Nuclear Engng*, **2**, 321

FORTESCUE, P. (1957). 'Coolant choice for the v.h.t. reactor.' *Nuclear Power*, **2**, 381

GARAY, P. N. (1960). 'Hydrogen as a reactor coolant.' *Nuclear Power*, **5**, (51), 96

GENERAL DYNAMICS CORPORATION (1958). 'Evaluation of coolants and moderators for the maritime gas-cooled reactor.' U.S.A.E.C. Report, GA-570

GERMAN PATENT No. DAS 1,058,164 (1959). 'Neon as coolant for graphite-moderated high temperature reactors'

GODWIN, R. P. and DENNISON, E. S. (1959). '(Nuclear) Gas-turbine progress report.' *J. Engng for Power*, **81** (A), 352

LEVY, A. and FOSTER, J. F. (1961). 'The compatibility of gas coolants and ceramic materials in coated-particle nuclear fuels.' U.S.A.E.C. Report, BMI-1530

ONSLOW-MACAULAY, I. N. and TOMLINSON, M. (1960). 'On the possibility of radiation induced transport of carbon in helium.' U.K.A.E.A. Report, AERE-R 3262

ORNL STAFF (1959). 'Gas-cooled reactor coolant choice.' U.S.A.E.C. Report, ORNL-2699

PFLAUM, W. and REIHER, D. (1960). 'The suitability of various gases as working media for a nuclear reactor–gas turbine combination.' *Engng Digest*, **21**, No. 2, 94

RAGONE, D. V. (1960). 'Equilibrium concentrations of several gaseous species in equilibrium with graphite at very low hydrogen and oxygen levels.' U.S.A.E.C. Report, GA-1109

RHODE, G. K., ROBERTS, D. M., SCHLUDERBERG, D. C. and WALSH, E. E. (1960). 'Gas-suspension coolants for power reactors.' *Proc. Amer. Power Conf.*, **22**, 130

RILEY, C. J. (1960). Unpublished work, U.K.A.E.A., Risley

SAMUELS, G. (1958). 'Comparison of gases for use as the coolant in gas-cooled reactors.' U.S.A.E.C. Report, ORNL-CF-58-4-108

SCHLUDERBERG, D. C. (1955). 'The application of gas-ceramic mixtures to nuclear power.' U.S.A.E.C. Report, ORNL-CF-55-8-199

SCHLUDERBERG, D. C., WHITELAW, R. L. and CARLSON, R. W. (1961). 'Gaseous suspensions—a new reactor coolant.' *Nucleonics*, **19**, No. 8, 67

SHAPIRO, Z. M. and GIFFEN, R. H. (1952). 'Safe practice in the handling of hydrogen.' U.S.A.E.C. Report, WAPD-RM-158

TIPTON, C. R. (1960). *Reactor Handbook*, 2nd Ed., Vol. I. Interscience Publ., New York

WAGMAN, D. D., *et al.* (1945). 'Heats, free energies and equilibrium constants of some reactions involving $O_2$, $H_2$, $H_2O$, C, CO, $CO_2$ and $CH_4$.' *J. Res. Nat. Bur. Stand.*, **34**, 143

WINKLER, W. (1957). 'Closed-cycle gas-turbine reactor power plant.' U.S.A.E.C. Report, NP-6652

# Chapter 2

# GRAPHITE

GRAPHITE is by no means a new material: it occurs in nature and the small deposits in Cumberland are known to have been worked commercially as early as 1564. The principal deposits are in Ceylon, Madagascar, Germany and the U.S.A. Natural graphite is relatively impure, however, and very extensive purification procedures would be required in order to allow its use in a nuclear reactor.

All graphite-moderated reactors which have been built to date have been constructed using material produced artificially. Artificial graphite has been employed for many years as electrodes in the chemical and metallurgical industries, and by the time the first nuclear reactors were constructed there was already a demand for the fabrication of electrodes of increasingly large dimensions. Much of the basic technology for the production of graphite moderator blocks was already established, therefore, although the requirements for nuclear use proved to be more stringent than those for other applications. Considerable research effort has been expended in order to achieve the desired low impurity content coupled with the highest possible density, and recently a further requirement of very low permeability to gases has been added.

The advent of the nuclear industry has given rise to a vast increase in our knowledge of the production and properties of this interesting material whose properties are partly metallic, partly ceramic. The total annual demand for nuclear-grade graphite in Western Europe has been predicted to be not less than 40,000 tons by 1965 (PERRET, 1959).

The properties of graphite which are particularly advantageous when it is considered for use in reactor construction are: ease of fabrication of special shapes, high thermal conductivity, resistance to thermal shock, and the possibility of obtaining a very high purity. In terms of these properties graphite is much superior to industrial carbon.

Ideal graphite would be composed of layers of hexagonally packed carbon atoms (essentially giant molecules) bound by strong covalent bonds and spaced 1·42 Å apart (*a*-axis). Much weaker binding, by van der Waals' forces only, occurs between neighbouring planes which are spaced 3·35 Å apart (*c*-axis). Each layer is displaced by half a unit hexagon with respect to its neighbours, and the stacking sequence *ababab* produces exact correspondence only between alternate layers.

Some natural graphite approaches this idealized structure, but individual samples of the material deviate to a greater or lesser extent. Artificial graphite made on a large scale has a lower degree of perfection than natural graphite. According to FRANKLIN (1951) the deviations take the form of random orientation of adjacent layer planes, so that an imperfect graphite will consist of a mixture of pairs of planes of correct and random orientation

15

statistically distributed along the $c$-axis of the crystal. The inter-layer spacing increases to 3·44 Å for random orientation.

A further complication arising in artificial graphite is the cross-linking which takes place with variable amounts of intercrystalline carbon. Moreover, on a macroscopic scale there will be left in the manufactured material residual pores covering a wide range of sizes. The physical and mechanical properties of graphite are therefore difficult to define accurately: they will vary from batch to batch and even at different points in a single block. Another peculiarity is the marked anisotropy of the physical and mechanical properties on a macroscopic scale. This is discussed in detail in Section 2.2.

Since the mechanical, physical and chemical properties of the finished product are all dependent upon the nature of the raw materials and upon the processes employed during fabrication, Section 2.1 will contain a discussion of the manufacture of graphite and the variations which may be introduced.

## 2.1 PRODUCTION OF GRAPHITE

The production of artificial graphite is not an exact science, there is still an element of craft about it and many of the details of each company's processes are obscured by commercial secrecy. The basic principles are readily available, however, and have been described by CURRIE, HAMISTER and MACPHERSON (1955) in relation to the process carried out in the U.S.A. by the National Carbon Company. The successive stages are shown in general outline in *Figure 2.1*.

A specially chosen grade of petroleum coke from oil refineries is fired at a temperature of about 1,300°C in order to remove the gaseous hydrocarbons which still remain. The primary reason for this step is to preshrink the coke to minimize changes of volume during subsequent stages in the manufacture of the large blocks of graphite required for reactor construction.

After firing, the coke is crushed to give particles in the size range 2–1,000 microns. Several sieving and milling operations are usually performed in order to obtain the required distribution of particle sizes.

The coke 'flour' is then mixed with pitch which will act as a binder in subsequent operations. A grade of pitch with a melting point below 100°C is usually chosen and the blending process is performed at about 165°C, i.e. with the pitch relatively fluid. A small quantity of a petroleum oil is sometimes also added at this stage to act as a lubricant during extrusion into bars.

Either extrusion or moulding (at about 100°C) may be used to form the 'green' bars which are then fired at about 750°C. During the latter process, the bars are packed tightly in granular coke so that they will not distort while they are heated through the range in which the pitch is molten (up to about 450°C). Copious amounts of gaseous hydrocarbons are evolved during firing, and the bars undergo considerable shrinkage due to decomposition of the pitch. A complete firing cycle in the large furnaces used for this work may extend up to a period of six weeks.

The bars are still of relatively low density and high porosity after this treatment. In order to increase the density, they are heated to 250°C and immersed in pitch at a pressure of 100 p.s.i. so that the molten pitch may penetrate all the pores. These impregnated bars are again fired to decompose the pitch and are then subjected to a graphitization process. They are stacked in a furnace and interspersed with layers of granular coke: the latter act as the heating elements using electrical power fed to graphite electrodes at each end of the furnace.

The carbon bars become heated to temperatures between 2,600 and 3,000°C in the graphitization furnace and require to be cooled for about two weeks before they may be unloaded in the atmosphere. The purity of the final

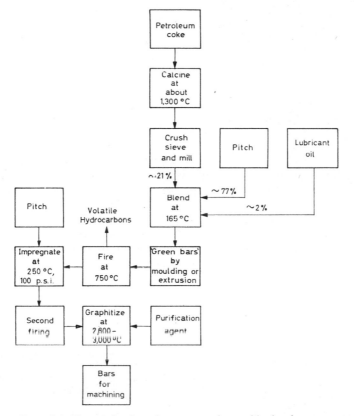

*Figure 2.1.* The production of reactor-grade graphite by the process described by Currie, Hamister and MacPherson (1955).

graphite depends markedly on the purity of the particular batches of coke and pitch which have been used in its formation, but a final purification can be achieved during the graphitization step (see p. 23).

The pitch impregnation step, followed by firing, may be repeated several times in order to achieve a somewhat higher density, but a limit is soon reached above which the small incremental increases in density become uneconomic.

The mechanism of graphitization is imperfectly understood. A recent discussion of the molecular and atomic processes involved has been given by MROZOWSKI (1959). The mechanism is certainly different from anything known to occur in other solid materials. At temperatures about 1,200°C, when most of the gaseous products have been expelled from the coke, a structure appears which is composed of groups of parallel planes of aromatic rings together with a disordered carbon phase which forms a matrix surrounding these groups. The groups form turbostratic crystallites, i.e. there is random stacking of the planes, as illustrated in *Figure 2.2.*

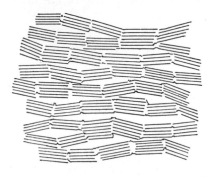

*Figure 2.2.* Schematic representation of the structure of a graphitizing (but non-graphitic) carbon (Franklin, 1951b) (by courtesy of the Royal Society).

When the temperature is raised even higher, the number of planes in a group increases and the individual planes increase in width by incorporating carbon atoms from the disordered phase. The neighbouring planes of aromatic rings begin to become arranged in ordered relative positions above 1,700°C, i.e. the typical graphite structure then begins to appear. The means by which these final atomic rearrangements occur are not yet known: there is evidence which shows that at temperatures even as high as 2,500°C neither atomic diffusion nor sublimation are responsible.

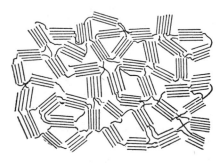

*Figure 2.3.* Schematic representation of the structure of a non-graphitizing carbon (Franklin, 1951b) (by courtesy of The Royal Society).

Certain types of carbon are difficult to transform into graphite. According to FRANKLIN (1951b) these carbons are formed from substances which contain little hydrogen or much oxygen. They contain a considerable amount of cross-linking which immobilizes the structure and unites the crystallites in a rigid but highly porous mass. The crystallites are in random orientation (*Figure 2.3*).

The overall process having been described in general, the most important technological aspects will be treated in more detail in the following sections, together with modifications which may be introduced for special purposes.

The nomenclature of the various grades of artificial graphite is confusing, since each manufacturer uses his own system of designation. Some representative types which will be met later in the chapter are shown in *Table 2.1*.

TABLE 2.1

NOMENCLATURE OF SOME REPRESENTATIVE TYPES OF ARTIFICIAL GRAPHITE

| Manufacturer | Designation | Type | Purity |
|---|---|---|---|
| National Carbon Co. | AGR | Acheson graphite, regular | Not specially purified |
| | AGX | Acheson graphite, extra dense by impregnation | |
| | AGOT | Standard reactor moderator in U.S.A. | No purification, but special selection of raw materials. |
| | AGOT-W (etc.) | The second designation refers to the source of coke | Blocks selected from centre of graphitizing furnace |
| | GBF | Impregnated and re-baked; fine grain | Chemical purification during graphitization |
| | TS–GBF (etc.) | The first designation refers to the the source of coke | |
| Supplied through U.K.A.E.A. | Pile grade A | British reactor grade material | Specially selected raw materials |
| Morgan Crucible Co. | EY 9 | Fine grain material | Chemical purification not usually applied |
| A.E.R.E., Harwell | HX–10 (etc.) | Experimental materials originating in the Harwell plant. This particular material is made using powdered graphite instead of coke | Not specially purified |

## 2.1.1 Raw Materials

*Coke.* In principle graphite could be manufactured from a wide variety of organic substances which have a high carbon content and a low content of impurities such as sulphur, boron and the lanthanide elements. The purest material available in sufficient quantity at a relatively low cost is petroleum coke, and this has always been used as the major raw material.

However, as pointed out by LOCH and SLYH (1954), petroleum coke is a low-profit item from petroleum refineries, and refining methods are continually being aimed at the lowest possible production of coke. Moreover, the coke which is produced can vary greatly in its properties since these are affected both by changing techniques and by the nature of the crude petroleum. The assessment of suitable batches of coke for graphite production consequently requires considerable skill and it is usually necessary to perform test runs on small samples before acceptance.

Coke particles can show considerable eccentricity and this has been attributed to a tendency of the aromatic molecules of the original petroleum to become aligned with the planes of the benzene rings parallel to the cellular walls of the solid material as coking proceeds. It has been claimed by SHEA (1956), however, that the particle eccentricity can be altered by varying the method of coking.

An electron micrograph study by KMETKO (1956) has shown that all *soft* cokes (i.e. those formed by the pyrolysis of liquid hydrocarbons) break up on grinding into platelets and that the platelets are stacked in lamellar bundles. This microcrystalline orientation can be destroyed by milling the coke. On the other hand, *hard* cokes (formed by the pyrolysis of solid hydrocarbons) all break up into jagged, approximately equiaxial particles.

Thus cokes from different sources can have a different degree of particle eccentricity which can subsequently exert a profound effect upon the properties of the finished graphite. The reason is that during extrusion of the coke-pitch mixture the coke particles tend to become aligned with their longest dimension parallel to the direction of extrusion. The finished graphite will then have better mechanical properties and a higher thermal conductivity parallel to the resultant grained structure than across the grain. Moulding, on the other hand, tends to align the particles with their longest dimension perpendicular to the moulding force and the physical properties of the graphite will then show anisotropy which is different from that of extruded material.

The selection of suitable batches of petroleum coke depends not only upon the type of particle which they contain, but also upon their chemical purity. Since the slowing down length for fast neutrons in graphite is large, reactors employing this moderator are bulky and contain large quantities of the material. Moreover they usually also utilize uranium of natural isotopic composition, so that economy of neutrons is very important. The absorption cross-section for neutrons is 0·0032 barn (CURRIE, HAMISTER and MACPHERSON, 1955). The best commercial graphite always has an absorption cross-section somewhat higher than this, usually about 0·004 barn. *Table 2.2* shows the effect which the presence of 1 p.p.m. of certain impurity elements can have on the absorption cross-section of graphite. An increase of $5 \times 10^{-4}$ barn in the absorption cross-section can lead to an increase of about 8 per cent in the critical radius of the reactor and a proportional increase in the fuel investment (LOCKETT, 1957).

Atmospheric nitrogen and water vapour which can become adsorbed on the surfaces of permeable graphite, and which can be trapped in the pores,

TABLE 2.2

THE EFFECT OF SOME IMPURITIES ON THE NEUTRON ABSORPTION CROSS-SECTION OF GRAPHITE
(after O'Driscoll and Bell, 1958)

| Element | Change in cross-section in mb for 1 p.p.m. | Element (natural composition) | Change in cross-section in mb for 1 p.p.m. | Element (natural composition) | Change in cross-section in mb for 1 p.p.m. |
|---|---|---|---|---|---|
| Boron | $8 \cdot 38 \times 10^{-1}$ | Hydrogen | $3 \cdot 93 \times 10^{-3}$ | Samarium | $4 \cdot 28 \times 10^{-1}$ |
| Caesium | $2 \cdot 62 \times 10^{-3}$ | Krypton | $4 \cdot 02 \times 10^{-3}$ | Scandium | $6 \cdot 41 \times 10^{-3}$ |
| Chlorine | $1 \cdot 07 \times 10^{-2}$ | Lithium | $1 \cdot 23 \times 10^{-1}$ | Tantalum | $1 \cdot 41 \times 10^{-3}$ |
| Cobalt | $7 \cdot 54 \times 10^{-3}$ | Lutecium | $7 \cdot 41 \times 10^{-3}$ | Terbium | $3 \cdot 32 \times 10^{-3}$ |
| Dysprosium | $8 \cdot 13 \times 10^{-2}$ | Manganese | $2 \cdot 89 \times 10^{-3}$ | Thulium | $8 \cdot 37 \times 10^{-3}$ |
| Erbium | $1 \cdot 19 \times 10^{-2}$ | Neodymium | $3 \cdot 83 \times 10^{-3}$ | Tungsten | $1 \cdot 25 \times 10^{-3}$ |
| Europium | $3 \cdot 63 \times 10^{-1}$ | Niobium | $1 \cdot 42 \times 10^{-3}$ | Vanadium | $1 \cdot 20 \times 10^{-3}$ |
| Gadolinium | $3 \cdot 52$ | Nitrogen | $1 \cdot 61 \times 10^{-3}$ | Ytterbium | $2 \cdot 50 \times 10^{-3}$ |

contribute a considerable amount to the total cross-section when other impurities have been removed to the lowest possible level.

The very high temperatures used in the graphitization process are beneficial in removing many of the metallic impurities, but special attention has been needed to the behaviour of boron ($B_4C$ is comparatively stable even at these temperatures). Moreover, some sources of coke have levels of boron impurity which are unacceptably high. The impurity levels of the type of coke which has been used for the manufacture of reactor graphite in the U.S.A. are shown in *Table 2.3*.

TABLE 2.3

IMPURITIES IN CALCINED COKE (Currie, Hamister and MacPherson, 1955)

| Impurity | Usual range (p.p.m.) | Typical value (p.p.m.) |
|---|---|---|
| Silicon | 50–1,300 | 300 |
| Iron | 270–2,000 | 500 |
| Vanadium | 5–270 | 70 |
| Titanium | 2–55 | 10 |
| Aluminium | 15–340 | 150 |
| Manganese | 0–180 | 20 |
| Nickel | 0–85 | 40 |
| Calcium | 130–5,200 | 260 |
| Magnesium | 10–230 | 50 |
| Boron | 0·2–0·9 | 0·4 |
| Total ash | 1,000–20,000 | 7,000 |

A study of the production of low-boron graphite in Poland has been reported by BURAS (1955). He found that hand selection of small batches of coke to eliminate pieces which had been next to the walls of the coking retort reduced the total residual ash of the resultant graphite by a factor of three and the

21

boron content by a factor of four. He also observed that the boron content of the graphite was lowered by raising the graphitizing temperature. This is difficult to explain owing to the known stability of boron carbide; Buras suggested that the effect may have been due not directly to the higher temperatures but to the unavoidably longer heating times associated with them, giving more time for the boron to diffuse away from the high temperature region.

Buras pointed out also that not only must the raw coke be selected for low boron content, but the boron content of the materials of construction of the graphitizing furnaces must be low. He reported that fireclay bricks used in the construction of normal graphitizing furnaces could be quite rich in boron and recommended their replacement by a magnesite refractory of much lower boron content. DAVIDSON (1958) has investigated by autoradiography the distribution of impurities in graphite and has shown that they occur not only evenly distributed but also in discrete localized particles. It was suggested that the latter were introduced during grinding of the coke.

ISKANDERIAN (1960) found that the boron impurity level of graphite used in the TREAT reactor was as high as 7·6 p.p.m. The origin of this boron lay in the baking of the graphite fuel tubes in contact with borated ($\sim 2$ wt.%) stainless steel separators. At the baking temperature, some of the boron was not in stable solution in the steel and migrated from it to the graphite.

*Pitch.* The pitch which is used as a binder during extrusion or moulding has much less effect on the ultimate properties of the graphite than has the coke filler. The property of the graphite which remains most susceptible to the characteristics of the pitch is density. To produce the highest density it is necessary for the density and the coking value of the pitch to be as high as possible.

The coking value is defined as the percentage of pitch left as carbon after heating to 1,000°C. In commercial operation it has a value of about 65 per cent (CURRIE, HAMISTER and MACPHERSON, 1955). It can be increased by some 6 per cent by the addition of 2 per cent polyvinyl chloride to the pitch to increase the amount of condensation reactions taking place during coking, and this may possibly lead to an increase of about 0·02 g cm$^{-3}$ in the apparent density of the final graphite( JUEL *et al.*, 1952). The benefits obtained as a result of adding organic chlorides to pitch are not universally acknowledged, however. DARNEY (1957) has reported that the improvement in carbon electrodes by the use of carbon tetrachloride was insufficient to justify the additional cost.

Pitch for the manufacture of graphite is obtained from coal by distillation processes. Destructive distillation of coal to give gas and coke also produces coal tar as a by-product. Subsequent distillation of the coal tar leaves a residue of pitch. Its detailed composition is unknown and variable: the material available in different countries may have significant variations according to whether it is derived from coke ovens or from vertical retorts (McNEIL and WOOD, 1957). The control of quality of the pitch is primarily in terms of the fraction insoluble in benzene and in quinoline, an approximate indication of the distribution of molecular sizes.

The behaviour of boron impurity during the distillation processes for the formation of pitch has been studied by SAWAI *et al.* (1958). Various samples of the coal which they used as a raw material contained between 2 and 25 p.p.m. of boron, but most of this was retained by the coke in the first distillation and only about 0·5 p.p.m. was found in the tar. Almost all of this boron remaining in the tar was non-volatile and remained in the pitch after the second distillation. These authors pointed out that although the production of pitch having a very low boron content would be possible by the selection of low-boron coal as the raw material, in practice this is usually not possible as pitch is only a by-product of the manufacture of coke and gas. They investigated several chemical methods for removal of the boron from pitch before its use in graphite manufacture. Good results were obtained by leaching of the pitch with water at temperatures of 150–200°C, and this would certainly be the most economic of the methods investigated.

BURAS (1955) showed that although the boron is involatile, it is not primarily associated with those insoluble impurities which can be separated readily by the filtration of coal tar. In agreement with Sawai et al., he found that the washing of coal tar with aqueous acids would reduce the boron content. A practical difficulty was the ready formation of emulsions which were difficult to break.

For the use of pitch as a binder, such purification is not required. If the pitch were to be used as an alternative source of coke, however, a lower boron content would be essential. Pitch coke has been used to a limited extent in Germany for the manufacture of non-nuclear grades of graphite, but it has not found widespread application for this purpose.

A comparison between 53 materials as binders for graphite production has been reported by BRADSTREET (1959). Furfuryl alcohol compared very favourably with the coal tar pitch used as the standard binder, yielding a graphite of somewhat higher density and lower porosity. Moreover, the specimens showed a smaller deviation in structure from the mean than those from any other binder investigated. Furfuryl alcohol would be more expensive than coal tar pitch for use on a commercial scale, but it might have the additional advantage of higher purity.

Bradstreet also suggested that the use of phenol-benzaldehyde as a binder could produce a graphite with a relatively high degree of porosity, and that the porosity would be comparatively uniform.

### 2.1.2 Purification

Although a considerable increase in the purity of the final graphite can be achieved by the rejection of impure raw materials, it is sometimes necessary to introduce a special purification procedure at the graphitization stage. High purity is required in order to minimize the neutron absorption and to eliminate possible catalysts which could enhance the chemical reactivity.

The purification of small graphite electrodes for spectrographic work had been investigated during the early 1930s, but a process for the purification of large blocks of graphite was not introduced until 1947. It was developed by the United Carbon Products Co., Inc., at Bay City, Michigan and has been described by SERMON (1948).

The graphite bars to be purified are packed into an all-carbon granular resistance furnace and the purification reagent gases may be introduced through perforated graphite pipes in a bed of coke immediately underneath the bars. When heating of the furnace begins, carbon tetrachloride in nitrogen carrier gas is passed until the bars are at about 2,000°C. The carbon tetrachloride is then discontinued and is replaced by a stream of dichlorodifluoromethane (Freon F-12; the process is sometimes known as the F-process) while the temperature is raised to about 2,400°C. The Freon is not added at the lower temperatures in order to avoid the formation of carbon tetrafluoride by reaction with the graphite.

Most of the halide salts of the important impurities (e.g. europium, samarium, vanadium and calcium) are volatilized from the graphite during this treatment by reaction with chlorine produced by thermal decomposition of the carbon tetrachloride. Some of the less volatile salts are deposited in the coke insulating bed, but there is apparently no recontamination of the graphite by diffusion of the impurities during the subsequent cooling period. The use of dichlorodifluoromethane is specifically for the removal of boron by its reaction with fluorine. A purified graphite can be produced in which the boron content is less than 0·1 p.p.m. and the total ash content is less than 10 p.p.m. (from an initial graphite with levels of 0·6 and 600 p.p.m. respectively). The dimensions of the bars remain unaffected and the density is reduced by less than 0·1 per cent.

Details of the development of the same process at the Morganton factory of the National Carbon Co. (subsequently taken over by the Great Lakes Carbon Co.) have been described by WEST (1949) and LEPPLA and MARKEL (1951). Possible improvements to the original process were reported by JUEL (1952). These consisted principally of the replacement of Freon-12 by either carbon tetrafluoride or sulphur hexfluoride. Sufficient purification was obtained on a pilot plant scale using either of these materials alone, without the addition of carbon tetrachloride; the major disadvantage was an increased rate of attack on the tubes used to introduce the reagents into the purification furnace.

An attempt was made also to introduce a 'self-purifying' raw material. A calcined petroleum coke was produced which contained about 2 per cent of combined chlorine. A low ash content was formed upon subsequent graphitization, but not sufficiently low for nuclear reactor application. It was pointed out by Juel that although the principles of the purification process were known from a technological viewpoint, comparatively little was known concerning the mechanisms and rates of the various chemical reactions involved.

The F-process for purification, which depends upon the diffusion of chlorine and fluorine into the pores of the graphite and the subsequent diffusion of the volatile impurities out of the pores, can be applied successfully to graphite of relatively high permeability. The application of the process becomes increasingly difficult as the permeability is reduced.

Studies in Japan have shown that dichlorodifluoromethane may be used without the pretreatment with carbon tetrachloride for the purification of graphite (SAWAI et al., 1958). This is to be expected, since pyrolysis of this compound produces both chlorine and fluorine. These authors pointed out, however, that it is a comparatively expensive reagent, and they subsequently investigated the suitability of certain inorganic halides as cheaper substitutes. They claimed that a substantial reduction in the cost of purification would be obtained by the use of calcium fluoride.

24

Inorganic fluorides, particularly sodium fluoride, are used in the French process for purification (LEGENDRE, GUERON and HERING, 1958; CORNAULT and des ROCHETTES, 1957). The sodium fluoride is laid in a horizontal bed above and about 200 cm from the graphite blocks in the purification furnace. This separation ensures that vaporization does not occur until the temperature of the graphite is at least 2,600°C.

### 2.1.3 High Density Graphite

The density of perfect graphite is 2·27 g cm$^{-3}$. Normal reactor-grade graphites have a density of only 1·65–1·75 g cm$^{-3}$, however, as would be expected from the presence of a considerable void volume within the structure. The voids are largely inter-connected, so that the graphite is permeable to gases and to liquids of low viscosity. As mentioned previously, advantage is taken of this fact to increase the density by impregnation with pitch. A single impregnation, even under pressure, will not completely fill the voids since there is about 50 per cent decrease in volume of the pitch on subsequent heating to carbonization temperatures. Successive re-impregnations then become increasingly more difficult owing to partial blocking of the pores in the graphite.

An alternative approach is to add, in the initial stage of mixing the raw materials, sufficient very fine particles to obtain a maximum packing density. Carbon black has been used for this purpose (NATHANS, 1954) and has enabled the production of graphite with a density of 2·0 g cm$^{-3}$ to be achieved by otherwise conventional processing techniques (including two impregnations with pitch). The resulting material contains internal cracks and flaws. Graphite approaching this density becomes increasingly difficult to manu-facture in large pieces, since the decomposition gases produced during baking and graphitization cannot readily diffuse out of the mass. The F-process for purification is also difficult to apply for the same reason.

According to KMETKO (1956) the carbon black particles are polyhedra whose faces are the basal planes of graphite crystallites joined at the edges. They are thus closed systems with respect to crystal growth and cannot grow out into the carbon matrix in which they are embedded.

Japanese workers (SAWAI et al., 1958) have also reported that additions of carbon black up to 30 per cent produced corresponding increases in the density of the final graphite. They attributed this to a greater ease of contraction during baking when carbon black was present. They found that extra mixing stages were necessary to ensure uniformity, and obtained best results when mixing, kneading and extrusion were performed under vacuum to remove occluded gases.

Coke milled to particles of less than 5 microns diameter was found by Sawai et al. to be as effective as carbon black for use as a filler.

The production of graphite with a density greater than 2 g cm$^{-3}$ by the compaction at room temperature of crushed, chemically purified natural graphite has been described briefly by WIRTZ (1955).

### 2.1.4 Low Permeability Graphite

Attention has been drawn in the preceding sections to the fact that nor-mal reactor-grade graphite is permeable to gases and liquids owing to its

25

interconnected pore structure. Most types of reactor which employ graphite as a moderator or a structural material would benefit by a reduction in this permeability, especially if it can be shown that it leads to a lower rate of oxidation by coolant gases. The problem of producing impermeable material is particularly important for high temperature gas-cooled reactors of the DRAGON type (see p. 61).

The flow of gas through normal reactor-grade graphite is predominantly of the viscous type, the mean size of the pores lying well outside the mean free path of the gas molecules at the pressures of interest. At lower permeabilities, the slip flow component becomes significant, and with very small pores it may be necessary also to take into account capillary condensation.

The permeability coefficient $(K)$ for a particular gas is expressed by the D'Arcy relationship:

$$Q = K . \frac{A}{L} . \Delta p$$

where $Q$ = gas flow expressed in (say) cm$^3$ atm sec$^{-1}$; $A$ = area of the sample normal to the flow of gas (cm$^2$); $L$ = length of the sample; and $\Delta p$ = pressure difference across the sample (atm).

For the flow of various gases through a commercial fine-grain graphite perpendicular to the axis of extrusion, the permeability coefficient has been shown by HUTCHEON, LONGSTAFF and WARNER (1957) to be given by

$$K = \frac{B_0}{\eta} . P_m + \frac{4}{3} K_0 \left( \frac{8RT}{\pi M} \right)^{1/2}$$

where $\eta$, $P_m$ and $M$ are the viscosity, mean pressure and molecular weight of the gas and $T$ is the absolute temperature. $B_0$ and $K_0$ are the permeability coefficients for viscous and slip flow, and are constants characteristic of the material: typical values for standard reactor-grade material are $10^{-9}$ cm$^2$ and $3 \times 10^{-6}$ cm respectively.

In a further paper, HUTCHEON and PRICE (1960) have shown that the permeability is proportional to the open voidage raised to the power of 3·5.

Several methods which have been investigated for the reduction of permeability will be described below.

*Impregnation with pitch.* Multiple impregnations of porous graphite with pitch are used widely as a means of increasing the density. It is of interest that there is a simultaneous reduction of the permeability (EATHERLY *et al.*, 1958) but the reduction is by a comparatively small factor, less than 100 after four impregnations (PRICE, 1959, see *Figure 2.4*). There may be a factor of more than 10 variation in permeability between various blocks of normal graphite from a single batch (BOYLAND, 1959). Much larger factors of reduction have been found possible by other methods.

There is not necessarily any general relationship between density and permeability: the relationship will depend upon the type of impregnant used and on the pore shape.

*Replacement of coke by graphite.* Coke particles occupy a large proportion by volume of the fabricated carbon before graphitization. Since the coke particles are very porous, their replacement by milled artificial graphite should produce a considerable decrease of permeability. The development at Harwell of a graphite designated HX-10 using this technique has been described by PRICE (1959b).

Graphite powder arises in considerable quantity as a result of the machining of normal reactor-grade graphite. This was suggested by Price as an economic source, presumably on the grounds that the requirement for low permeability material would be much smaller than for normal graphite. The powder is mixed with carbon black (to improve the packing of particles) and pitch; great care is necessary to obtain a homogeneous distribution. Subsequent stages are similar to the manufacture of normal graphite, except that it has been found advantageous (but not essential) to perform the baking operation under gaseous pressurization.

HX-10 has a permeability which is appreciably lower than that of normal reactor graphite, the value of $B_0$ being about $2 \times 10^{-12}$ cm$^2$ and $K_0$ about $0.94 \times 10^{-7}$ cm. A further improvement may be made by means of an impregnation with sugar, furfuryl alcohol or gaseous hydrocarbons.

*Alternatives to pitch for impregnation.* The use of a concentrated aqueous solution of sugar as an impregnating agent has been described by BOYLAND (1959). Sugar may be obtained with high purity and upon thermal decomposition in an inert atmosphere it could yield theoretically 40 per cent of its weight as carbon. The density of this carbon is less than that obtained from calcined pitch, and so for the same weight of impregnation taken up in the pores the reduction of permeability is much greater. A single impregnation of normal reactor graphite with sugar can reduce the permeability 50-fold, provided that the initial graphite is of uniform texture and does not contain an excessive number of large pores. Four or five successive impregnations, each followed by a baking step, can reduce the permeability by a factor of $10^6$ (compare *Figure 2.4*).

Sugar-impregnated sleeves in the fuel element channels of the Hunterston reactor have been considered for reducing the access of carbon dioxide coolant to the graphite moderator.

Boyland observed that in the later stages of multiple impregnations with sugar, it becomes increasingly difficult for the sugar to penetrate into the graphite. Furfural is a penetrating liquid and has a higher content of carbon than that of sugar. Its use leads to a corresponding reduction in permeability. However, although furfuryl is widely used in the artificial resin industry, it is more difficult than sugar to purify.

Furfuryl alcohol, $C_5H_6O_2$, has been used successfully to reduce the permeability of graphite tubes (WATT et al., 1959; CONWAY-JONES, 1960). This liquid may be polymerized with a catalyst to give a solid resin which yields 50 per cent carbon upon subsequent thermal decomposition. A graphite tube is impregnated with furfuryl alcohol plus the catalyst from one side only. The resin in the pores is next heated to at least 1,000°C for carbonization. The tube is then impregnated from the opposite side and carbonization is repeated. This two-stage process is necessary to avoid bursting of the graphite by the gaseous decomposition products during the carbonization. Apart from the catalyst, a further material (unspecified) is added for the second impregnation to reduce the surface tension of the impregnant and so assist its flow into pores which have been made smaller as a result of the first impregnation.

A reduction by a factor of at least $10^4$ in the permeability of tubing $2\frac{1}{4}$ in. o.d. and $\frac{3}{8}$ in. wall thickness can be obtained by using two impregnations.

*Replacement of pitch as a binder.* PRICE (1959) considered that the high permeability of normal graphite could be attributed partly to the fusible nature of the pitch used as binder. This allows some dilation of the material to

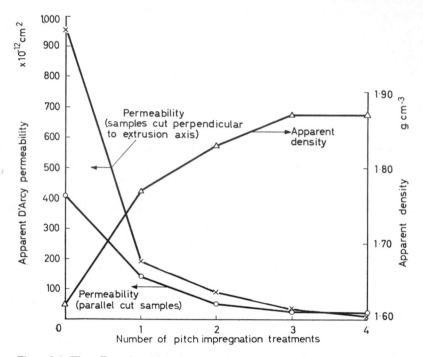

*Figure 2.4.* The effect of multiple impregnation of normal reactor-grade graphite with pitch upon permeability and apparent density (Price, 1959).

take place under the pressure of decomposition gases during the baking stage. He suggested that infusible binders would give graphite with a lower permeability.

Furfuryl alcohol was considered to be suitable as a replacement for pitch. It is a liquid of low viscosity which may be mixed readily with graphite powder and carbon black. It is then polymerized *in situ* at slightly elevated temperatures to give a resin which remains completely infusible. The addition of a small quantity of hydrochloric acid catalyses the polymerization and substantially increases the carbon residue.

The permeability of graphite produced in this way at Harwell (designated HX-12) is $10^4$–$10^5$ times lower than that of normal reactor-grade graphite and $10^2$ lower than HX-10. It may be reduced even further by impregnation with furfuryl alcohol or with sugar. For unimpregnated HX-12, $B_0 = 0.027 \times 10^{-12}$ $cm^2$ and $K_0 = 0.06 \times 10^{-7}$ cm.

According to BRADSTREET (1960), the best results are obtained by pre-polymerization to a material having the composition of the dimer, before mixing with the coke together with $p$-toluene sulphonic acid as a catalyst.

WATT et al. (1959) have also investigated this process at the Royal Aircraft Establishment, Farnborough, but no details of the product have been published. A general review of the types of synthetic and natural polymers which might be suitable alternatives for this process has been published by BOOCOCK and HOLDSWORTH (1958). An experimental study of a wide variety of types of synthetic binder material led RIESZ and SUSMAN (1960) to conclude that furfuryl alcohol was the most promising material for the production of high density and low porosity.

*Impregnation with gases.* The use of thermally unstable hydrocarbon gases for reducing the permeability of graphite by impregnation has been reported by WATT et al. (1959). The example they quoted was that of heating permeable graphite in a mixture of nitrogen and benzene. At high temperatures, the rate of pyrolysis of the benzene is sufficiently rapid that only surface coatings are obtained. These deposits have a density which approaches the theoretical maximum for graphite and they are therefore of very low permeability. Close control of the conditions of deposition is necessary to obtain a coating which will remain crack-free and impermeable during subsequent thermal cycling. At lower temperatures ( < 800°C) the benzene is able to diffuse into the inner structure of the graphite before it decomposes and a decrease of permeability in depth is obtained.

An interesting method for obtaining metal carbide coatings on graphite has been described by BLOCHER and CAMPBELL (1958). They pointed out that for a variety of halides of transition metals and some other elements (e.g. silicon) there exists, at any given temperature, a transitional range of pressure in which carbide formation can take place by reactions such as:

$$TiI_4(g) + C(s) \rightarrow TiC(s) + 4I(g)$$

in preference to the deposition of metal by thermal decomposition reactions such as:

$$TiI_4(g) \rightarrow Ti(s) + 4I(g)$$

Furthermore, provided, that there is an adequate supply of halide vapour within this pressure range, the rate of carbide coating formation is controlled by the rate of difusion of carbon atoms through the carbide, i.e. the rate of coating formation becomes a function primarily of temperature and uniform coatings are comparatively easy to achieve. Coatings of NbC, TaC and ZrC were produced experimentally and they were found to be stable to thermal cycling. No measurements of permeability were made.

A process for obtaining a coating of metallic nickel has also been described (DAVIDSON and RYDE, 1960). This consists of allowing nickel carbonyl to permeate throughout the graphite at room temperature, thereby depositing nickel over the internal surfaces and offering some protection against oxidation. No information is available on the subsequent chemical or physical properties of such material, but the method would appear to be more attractive than those which produce coatings only on the external surface of the graphite (e.g. RAWSON and BAYNTON, 1959).

29

It is evident that there is a considerable number of ways for reducing the permeability of graphite to the required extent for special reactor applications. Current development of these processes is aimed at scaling them up for application to large size blocks or tubes, and at determinations of the chemical and physical properties of the resultant graphites. It is possible, for instance, that carbon deposited in the pores of the graphite might be more chemically reactive than the matrix.

## 2.2 PHYSICAL PROPERTIES

Graphite shows considerable variability in its properties, since the latter depend to a marked extent upon the characteristics of the raw materials used and upon details of the method of manufacture. Moreover, many of the physical and mechanical properties are anisotropic to an extent which also depends upon the raw materials and the method of fabrication. In the following sections, therefore, the values quoted should be taken as representative of the general ranges observed rather than as absolute and invariable quantities.

Under irradiation, some of the carbon atoms become displaced from their normal lattice sites to positions of higher potential energy between the layer planes. The number of displacements increases with increase in the fast neutron flux and the time of irradiation, but decreases with increasing temperature. The energy stored by these displaced atoms may be released after irradiation by raising the temperature sufficiently to promote thermal migration back to sites in the layer planes.

Radiation damage will be discussed only in so far as it affects the properties of graphite. The mechanism of damage and of its thermal annealing are adequately treated elsewhere (HENNIG and HOVE, 1955; DIENES and VINEYARD, 1957; NIGHTINGALE and FLETCHER, 1957; HENNIG, 1958).

### 2.2.1 Density

Reactor-grade graphite for use as a moderator usually has a density within the range 1·65–1·75 g cm$^{-3}$. A more precise value quoted for a specific type

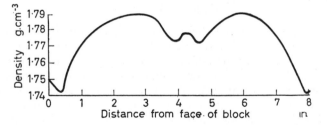

*Figure 2.5.* Density profile of a block of reactor-grade graphite, traversed perpendicular to the extrusion direction (Davidson, 1958) (by courtesy of The General Electric Company).

of graphite will only be an average over considerable variations within the sample itself, as illustrated in *Figure 2.5.* Measurements of the density distribution of powdered Type-TS.GBF graphite have been reported by KORETZKY *et al.* (1959).

Methods of improving the density of artificial graphite for special purposes have been described in Sections 2.1.3 and 2.1.4.

The density of artificial graphite decreases upon irradiation in a flux of fast neutrons and at the same time there is a decrease in the surface area and a shrinkage in the pore size. The change in surface area is not necessarily accessible to measurement by nitrogen adsorption (SPALARIS, BUPP and GILBERT, 1957; WOODLEY, 1957).

### 2.2.2 Expansion

The thermal expansion of powdered natural (Ceylon) graphite over the temperature range 15–800°C has been measured using x-ray diffraction data by NELSON and RILEY (1945) and by MATUYAMA (1958). Their results for the c-axis crystal direction are shown in *Table 2.4*.

TABLE 2.4

THERMAL EXPANSION OF NATURAL GRAPHITE ALONG THE c-AXIS

| Authors | Temperature variation of d, the interlayer spacing (Å) | Average expansion coefficient $\dfrac{d_2 - d_1}{d_1 . T °C} \times 10^6$ |
|---|---|---|
| Nelson and Riley | $d = 3·3525 + 90·54 \times 10^{-6} T + 6·33 \times 10^{-9} T^2$ (°C) | 28·5 |
| Matuyama | $d = 3·3535 + 82·41 \times 10^{-6} T + 10·30 \times 10^{-9} T^2$ | 27·0 |

Several laboratories have reported results for the c-axis expansion of powdered artificial graphite containing various degrees of disordered stacking of the layer planes, and there is general agreement that the expansion coefficient of individual crystallites does not differ significantly from that of the more perfect natural material (WALKER, McKINSTRY and WRIGHT, 1953; CURRIE, HAMISTER and McPHERSON, 1955; STEWARD and COOK, 1960).

The extreme anisotropy of graphite is illustrated by the fact that the coefficient of expansion along the a-axis (i.e. within the planes) is markedly different from that along the c-axis. Nelson and Riley found that the a-axis thermal expansion was negative at room temperature, with an average value for the coefficient of $-15 \times 10^{-7}$ °C⁻¹ between 15° and 150°C. The coefficient becomes more positive with increasing temperature and reaches zero at about 300°C. Within the range 600° to 800°C it has the mean value of $+9 \times 10^{-7}$ °C⁻¹, still over thirty times lower than the expansion between the layer planes.

There is no direct correlation between the crystal expansion coefficients and those of bulk graphite. In general, the more random the arrangement of crystallites within the material the closer the coefficient of expansion will be to a value about one third that of the c-axis expansion of a single crystal. For the oriented types of graphite, however, the sum of the coefficients of expansion in three mutually perpendicular directions is less than the single crystal coefficient. This appears to be associated with the presence of voids within the artificial graphite structure, but the means by which they exert their effect is not clear (HOVE, 1958).

Currie, Hamister and McPherson have suggested that for practical engineering purposes the increase in thermal expansion with temperature is the same for all types of graphite in common use. According to O'DRISCOLL and BELL (1958) determinations made in the Culcheth Laboratories of the U.K.A.E.A. on a large number of samples of nominal density $1 \cdot 75$ g cm$^{-3}$ may be represented by the relationships:

$$l_T = l_0(1 + 1 \cdot 6 \times 10^{-6}\, T + 1 \cdot 6 \times 10^{-9}\, T^2) \quad \text{Parallel to extrusion}$$

$$l_T = l_0(1 + 3 \cdot 4 \times 10^{-6}\, T + 1 \cdot 4 \times 10^{-9}\, T^2) \quad \text{Perpendicular to extrusion}$$

OKADA (1960) has studied the variation of thermal expansion of pitch-bonded graphites as a function of binder content and particle size distribution of the filler. He proposed that the binder pitch impregnated the surface region of the coke filler particles to some depth, and when coked it created a region with a thermal expansion coefficient differing from both the un-impregnated regions and the ordinary binder coke formed between the filler particles. The impregnation of normal reactor-grade graphite with sugar solution, to reduce the permeability to gases, does not significantly affect the coefficient of thermal expansion (LOSTY, 1960).

*Dimensional changes under irradiation.* It is probable that irradiation has a negligible effect upon the temperature coefficient of thermal expansion of reactor-grade graphite (WOODS, BUPP and FLETCHER, 1955). There is, however, an important independent effect of irradiation upon the physical dimensions of bulk graphite.

Such distortion is caused primarily by the displacement of carbon atoms from their normal lattice sites to interstitial positions between the layer planes as a result of their interaction with fast neutrons. The *c*-axis spacing of individual crystals increases and at high levels of irradiation the crystallites begin to break up. The process has been aptly described as de-graphitization. BACON (1960) has reviewed the x-ray crystallographic evidence on this type of irradiation damage in graphite.

The dimensional changes of two types of bulk graphite during irradiation at 30°C in a Hanford reactor are illustrated in *Figure 2.6*. The data were subsequently extended to much higher levels of exposure: about 11,000 MWd/at*. After this exposure, samples of CSF graphite continued to expand in the transverse direction at the rate of about $0 \cdot 26$ per cent per 1,000 MWd/at, the rate being apparently constant between 5,000 and 11,000 MWd/at. The contraction rate of samples parallel to extrusion was $0 \cdot 08$ per cent per 1,000 MWd/at between 5,000 and 11,000 MWd/at (ALBAUGH, 1960). The difference in behaviour between the two graphites shown in *Figure 2.6* appears to be due to the more perfect development of the graphite structure in the CSF material (graphitized at 2,800°C compared with 2,450°C for the TSGBF). KINCHIN (1959) has confirmed this trend independently at Chalk River.

* This unit is the amount of irradiation received by a sample during the time required for the ton of uranium adjacent to it to generate 1 MWd of fission energy.

The expansion of bulk material during low temperature irradiation appears not to be related directly to the lattice expansion along the $c$-axis of the individual crystals. Below 1,000 MWd/at it is only a small fraction of the $c$-axis expansion, a large part of the latter being accommodated by voids within the structure. Above 6,000 MWd/at, the $c$-axis expansion reaches saturation and the bulk expansion must be due to another cause.

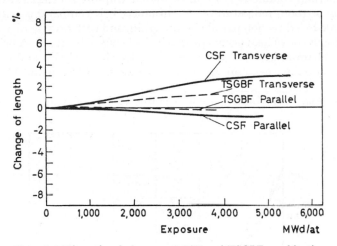

*Figure 2.6.* Dimensional changes of CSF and TSGBF graphites irradiated at 30°C (Woodruff, 1957) (by courtesy of U.S.A.E.C.).

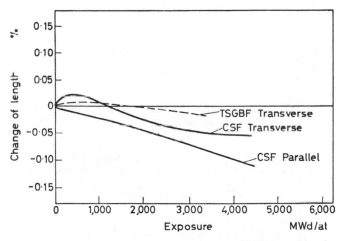

*Figure 2.7.* Dimensional changes of CSF and TSGBF graphites irradiated at 400–500°C (Woodruff, 1957) (by courtesy of U.S.A.E.C.).

The observed changes in dimension during irradiation depend markedly upon the temperature of exposure. This effect is illustrated by *Figure 2.7* in comparison with *Figure 2.6*. WOODRUFF (1957) has reported that contraction occurs in both the transverse and parallel directions at irradiation

33

temperatures between 300 and 750°C. Data for temperatures below 350°C are given by Woods, Bupp and Fletcher (1955), Simmons (1957) and Davidson, Woodruff and Yoshikawa (1959) for bulk material, and by Nightingale and Fletcher (1957) for the $c_0$ spacing within crystals.

### 2.2.3 Thermal Conductivity

The thermal conductivity of unirradiated graphite is comparatively high, especially at·room temperature; for instance, it is comparable with that of aluminium in a direction parallel to the grain, and with brass across the grain. The transmission of heat occurs primarily by lattice vibrations. A brief review of the mechanism involved has been given by Hove (1957) and the experimental results have been summarized by Currie, Hamister and McPherson (1955).

Currie *et al*. show that for a considerable variety of types of graphite it is

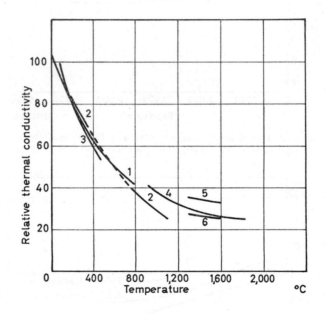

*Figure 2.8.* Dependence of the thermal conductivity of graphite on temperature, expressed as a percentage of the value at 25°C (Currie, Hamister and Macpherson, 1955) (by courtesy of National Carbon Company).

(1) Powell (1937).
(2) Powell and Schofield (1939).
(3) Odening and Zaffarano, unpublished data.
(4) Jain and Krishnan (1954).
(5) and (6) Micinski and Downey, unpublished data.

reasonable to calculate the thermal conductivity at 25°C from the more easily measured electrical resistivity by means of the relationship:

$$K \text{ (cal cm}^{-1} \text{ sec}^{-1} \text{ °C}^{-1}) \times \rho \text{ (ohm cm)} = 3 \cdot 1 \times 10^{-4}$$

34

The thermal conductivity at room temperature of British reactor-grade graphite of density 1·75 g cm$^{-3}$ has been quoted by O'DRISCOLL and BELL (1958) as:

Parallel to extrusion,          0·7 ± 0·05 cal cm$^{-1}$ sec$^{-1}$ °C$^{-1}$

Perpendicular to extrusion,   0·34 ± 0·04 cal cm$^{-1}$ sec$^{-1}$ °C$^{-1}$

These authors pointed out that variation of density had a marked effect on thermal conductivity.

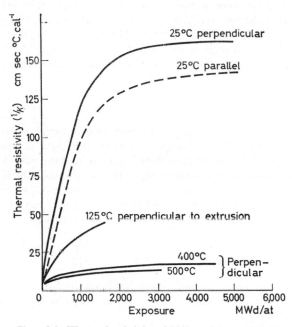

Figure 2.9. Thermal resistivity of CSF graphite as a function of time and temperature of irradiation. Data compiled from Woods, Bupp and Fletcher, 1955; Nightingale, Davidson and Snyder, 1958.

The thermal conductivity falls rapidly with increasing temperature, and Figure 2.8 summarizes the experimental data up to 1955. Several investigators have reported measurements since that date; although these have generally been on special types of graphite, the results have not differed significantly from the earlier work (SUTTON, 1960; LUCKS, DEEM and WOOD, 1960).

The thermal conductivity over the range 200–3,000°C depends upon the characteristics of both the binder and the filler used in the manufacture of the graphite (MROZOWSKI, 1958; STRAUSS, 1960). Strauss also observed a dependence of thermal conductivity on the ambient gas pressure, slight for graphite of density 1·54 and more marked at a density of 1·24. The electrical conductivity was unaffected by gas pressure.

*The effect of irradiation.* Irradiation introduces lattice defects which scatter the thermal waves arising during heat transmission and so reduce the thermal

35

conductivity of graphite. Short irradiations in a fast neutron flux are sufficient to produce large decreases in the thermal conductivity at room temperature, and the conductivity continues to decrease at a lower rate with prolonged irradiation. The effect is illustrated for type-CSF graphite in *Figure 2.9*.

It is evident that the damage effected by fast neutrons, in so far as it affects thermal conductivity, becomes saturated at about 3,000 MWd/at over a considerable range of exposure temperatures. The effects of irradiation are also lower in magnitude the higher the temperature.

A discussion and summary of data on the effects of irradiation at temperatures below 25°C has been presented by HOVE (1959). The effect of fission fragment bombardment on the thermal conductivity, using uranium-impregnated graphite, has been studied by HUNTER (1959). He concluded that the rate of radiation dosage is important in determining the final damage effect, and that the particle size of the embedded fuel material also has a major effect.

### 2.2.4 *Vapour Pressure*

The determination of the vapour pressure of graphite has proved to be a difficult experimental task. Interpretation of the data is rendered more difficult by the possible variation in the composition of the gas. Mass spectrometric techniques indicate that the composition at about 2,400°K is a mixture of $C_1$ atoms and $C_3$ molecules, with a smaller amount of $C_2$ molecules.

Effusion experiments by THORN and WINSLOW (1957) have indicated that the partial pressures at 2,400°K of the various species are:

|  | $C_1$ | $C_2$ | $C_3$ |
|---|---|---|---|
| $P$ (atm) ($\times 10^{-8}$) | 4·29 | 1·13 | 10·5 |

The total pressure of all species present has been predicted to be one atmosphere at 4,200°K by GLOCKLER (1954) and at 4,630°K by BREWER, GILLES and JENKINS (1948).

The heat of sublimation was for many years a controversial topic. Recent determinations by several investigators give a mean value (at 0°K) of 170 kcal mole$^{-1}$.

### 2.3 CHEMICAL PROPERTIES

### 2.3.1 *Diffusion of Fission Products*

The penetration of graphite by fission products is an important problem in several types of reactor. It is most acute, however, in high temperature reactors such as DRAGON where the fuel is a uranium-impregnated graphite. In this system, it is desired to reduce the emission of fission products into the coolant gas stream to the lowest possible level by such means as the application of an 'impermeable' graphite cladding to the fuel elements. An alternative concept which may be considered feasible in the future is to attempt to increase the diffusion rates to such an extent that the important neutron poisons are removed rapidly from the reactor core. Despite its attractions this may invoke severe penalties in the form of a fission product handling system of extremely high activity, and loss of some of the delayed neutron emitters upon which nuclear control of the core is normally based.

For the gaseous fission products it is necessary to distinguish between two quite distinct barriers to the emission which may be present in a fuel element. Firstly there may be diffusion within the matrix fuel material: this will be discussed in the present section. Secondly, there may be cladding of relatively impermeable graphite around the matrix. The permeation of gases through this material has been discussed briefly in Section 2.1.4.

The porous nature of artificial graphite may be used for the purpose of impregnating it with a uranium-bearing fluid, such as molten uranyl nitrate. The latter may then be decomposed thermally and the uranium fuel left as a coating on the walls of the pores in the graphite: it will remain as an oxide at relatively low firing temperatures, but will be converted to carbide above about 1,500°C. Further details of the impregnation process are given in Chapter 4.

In such a fuel system, the mechanism and rate of diffusion of fission product atoms will depend upon their distribution with respect to the graphite structure. Some of them may have recoiled a distance up to 20 microns into the graphite crystallites, and may be accommodated interstitially between the layer planes of carbon atoms. Other fission products may have expended most of their recoil energy within the fuel particles and then, being unable to penetrate the graphite lattice, will be adsorbed on the pore surfaces. A third fraction will remain in the fuel particles.

The prediction of overall diffusion constants in such a complex system is difficult, and experimental work has been performed in a number of laboratories in attempts to deduce the mechanism of diffusion for various fission products.

*Diffusion of rare gases.*

The xenon isotopes are important fission products from the viewpoint of neutron economy of a reactor, and fortunately they are the simplest ones to study owing to their chemical inactivity. The work of FINDLAY (1958, 1960) has been performed with uranium-impregnated graphite irradiated by neutrons sufficiently to produce tracer quantities of $^{133}Xe$; the uranium fuel was then leached out with nitric acid, leaving some 80 per cent of the xenon still embedded in the graphite phase. It was considered that the leaching step was insufficient to alter the pore structure of the graphite. Moreover, the measured diffusion was not significantly different in a control experiment in which the uranium fuel particles were allowed to remain in the graphite as in the earlier work of CUBICCIOTTI (1952). The diffusion of xenon from the graphite structure was investigated by annealing the specimens at controlled temperatures and collecting the radioactive gas evolved.

Cubicciotti showed that the diffusion of xenon through AUF graphite in the temperature range 1,000–1,600°C was independent of the size of sample. The rate-controlling step at these temperatures must therefore be diffusion within the graphite grains. Subsequent diffusion along the grain boundaries and within the pores is comparatively rapid.

A difficulty arises, however, over the intercomparison of the graphites used in the experimental work, and over extrapolating the results to other grades

37

of graphite which may be used for reactor construction. Various mathematical solutions to Fick's general diffusion equation are available, depending for instance upon whether the structural unit controlling the diffusion is assumed to be approximately cylindrical or spherical in shape. Both Cubiciotti and Findlay assumed a cylindrical unit on the basis that interlamellar diffusion was much more probable than diffusion across the carbon layers. The choice of a spherical diffusion unit would lower the calculated diffusion constants by about a factor 2, which is not really a significant change in this type of work. However, the actual value of the leading dimension of the diffusion unit remains considerably in doubt.

Since the diffusion coefficient $(D)$ and the radius of the diffusion unit $(a)$ appear in the solutions of the diffusion equation in the ratio $D/a^2$, the results for each particular type of graphite are often expressed in this way as an 'apparent diffusion coefficient' $(D')$. Herein lies the difficulty: the results cannot be used in relation to other types of graphite unless the value of $a$ is known. FINDLAY and LAING (1960) have measured the rate of diffusion at 800°C of xenon from samples of graphite which were ground to successively smaller mean particle diameter. The apparent diffusion coefficient remained unchanged over the range 0·1 to 25 micron diameter particles, and within this range the absolute diffusion coefficient may be calculated using the measured grain size as the dimension of the unit controlling the diffusion.

Above 25 microns diameter, the diffusion release appeared to be independent of particle size. This figure is approximately the same as the range of penetration of fission fragments into graphite. It is suggested that the calculation of absolute diffusion coefficients for rare gases in graphite of large grain size should be made using the penetration range of about 25 microns as the size of the rate-controlling unit, and not the measured grain size (for example, 70 microns in the experiments of Cubicciotti).

The structure of British pile-grade graphite has been studied by DAWSON and FOLLETT (1959) using electron microscopy. They found that the grains were composed of crystallites of about 0·3 micron diameter, separated by boundaries about 50 Å wide and pores 400–800 Å diameter. BACON (1958), on the other hand, found by studies of x-ray line broadening that the crystallite diameter was as small as 0·05 micron. Whichever value is correct, they are both smaller than the size of the unit controlling diffusion at 800°C found by Findlay and Laing. It is concluded, therefore, that the mechanism which controls diffusion at this temperature does not take place within the crystallites in an interlamellar fashion, but rather it is located along the inter-crystallite boundaries and subpores within the grains. This conclusion may not be valid at higher temperatures, since there is some evidence that the mechanism of diffusion may then be different (see below).

Some support is afforded by the further observation by Findlay and Laing that the diffusion coefficient of xenon in Magecol 888, a carbon black of small particle size, differs little from that in pile graphite of the same particle size, i.e. that the difference in lattice structure within the crystallites appears to be unimportant.

The results of RILEY, SUNDERMAN and DUNNINGTON (1959), though not very extensive, have shown that the value of $D'$ for the diffusion of xenon in graphite is not significantly affected by neutron irradiation at 600°C.

The investigations of Findlay and Laing on pile-grade artificial graphite, extended over the temperature range 500–1,400°C (*Figure 2.10*), show that there is an apparent change at about 1,000°C in the mechanism controlling diffusion. The combination of these results with the value for the absolute diffusion coefficient obtained with graphite powders at 800°C gave the

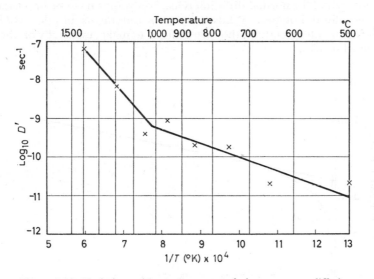

*Figure 2.10.* Variation with temperature of the apparent diffusion coefficient for xenon in British pile-grade graphite. (The values are calculated from the linear portion of the emission curve of the type shown in *Figure 2.11.*) (Findlay and Laing, 1960)

following relationship for the variation of diffusion coefficient with temperature in the range 500–1,000°C.

$$D = 3{\cdot}0 \times 10^{-12} \exp -\frac{17,000}{RT} \ \mathrm{cm^2\ sec^{-1}}$$

The activation energy of 17 kcal mole$^{-1}$ is low for lattice diffusion and is consistent with a boundary-type diffusion process. Between 1,000–1,400°C the activation energy is about 40 kcal mole$^{-1}$. Cubicciotti found a value of 49 kcal mole$^{-1}$ but this result is less reliable since his measurements were made over relatively short time periods in which it is now known that the diffusion laws are not obeyed.

The release of xenon from graphite at elevated temperatures is a two-stage process as shown in *Figure 2.11*. There is a rapid initial release ('burst') upon first attaining a given temperature, followed by normal diffusion behaviour after about 30 hours. The magnitude of the burst is defined by the intercept **I** on *Figure 2.11*. Qualitatively the same effect is observed in fission gas release from ceramic fuels and from metals, and limited evidence suggests that it may apply also to some other fission products. The significance of the initial burst has not been fully explained, but in the post-irradiation studies on diffusion in graphite it is most probably due to the accumulation of xenon atoms on the surface of the smaller pores during irradiation. In order to predict in-pile diffusion and emission rates from the post-irradiation experiments it may be necessary to allow considerable significance to the burst release. For the release of fission products of half-lives less than one hour the burst release is over-riding, and the normal diffusion release only appears to be important for the longer-lived isotopes. Whilst direct measurements in-pile avoid this complexity of interpretation, they are difficult to make, especially on the very short-lived species.

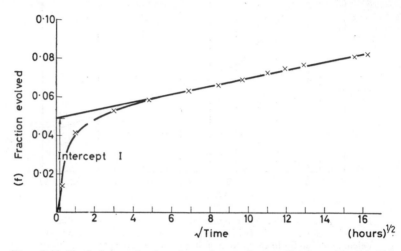

*Figure 2.11.* Typical curve for the release of xenon from artificial graphite in which it has been embedded by fission recoil (Findlay and Laing, 1960). The same effect has been reported also by Nakai *et al.* (1960).

Allowance must be made for the burst release in attempting to compare the results of different investigations: they must be compared only over corresponding time intervals. In particular, the early work of Cubicciotti was performed for exposure times of only 3 hours, entirely in the burst release range. As would be expected from the foregoing discussion, the change in diffusion mechanism apparent in *Figure 2.10* is not observed when the results relate to short annealing times (3 hours). Good agreement is obtained in comparing the results of Cubicciotti with those of Findlay and Laing for 3 hour exposures, indicating that the burst release is insensitive to the type of graphite used.

### Diffusion of other species

*Iodine and tellurium.* The diffusion of these fission products in graphite was found by DOYLE (1953) to be similar to each other at 1,500–1,900°C. FINDLAY (1958) later showed that there was no significant difference between the apparent diffusion coefficients of the two elements and that of xenon for post-irradiation annealing at 800°C. Evidently the temperatures are too high for

40

the formation of stable compounds of iodine or tellurium with other fission products or with impurities in the graphite, and these elements diffuse in an uncombined state like xenon.

*Lanthanides and transition elements.* At lower temperatures, the apparent diffusion coefficient for these fission products is considerably lower than that of xenon. FINDLAY (1958) found that $D' < 8 \times 10^{-12}$ for lanthanum and cerium, and $D' < 7 \times 10^{-16}$ sec$^{-1}$ for niobium and zirconium in pile-grade graphite at 800°C during post-irradiation annealing. Doyle and SMITH and YOUNG (1951) found that zirconium and molybdenum were held very tenaciously by graphite at 1,900°C. Such low diffusion constants may reflect the relatively high thermal stability of the carbides of these elements, although Doyle pointed out that the very small traces of the fission products produced in the experiments can hardly form the crystal lattices on which macro-stability depends.

A comparison of the rates of emission of the whole series of lanthanides at 1,600–2,400°C has been made by ORTH (1961). Samarium, europium and ytterbium showed the largest emission for a given set of conditions, and Orth pointed out that these were also the lanthanides with the lowest boiling points of the metals. There is no independent confirmation that these three lanthanides could exist in the metallic state under such conditions, but further evidence may become available from studies of the mechanism of formation of the corresponding actinide carbides from oxides (Chapter 4).

Unexplained differences in the mobility at lower temperatures of the various lanthanide fission product species have been observed in recent studies at Harwell (LARGE et al., 1961).

Yttrium was found by YOUNG (1953) to diffuse considerably faster at 1,500°C in uranium-impregnated graphite under deuteron bombardment than in the post-irradiation experiments of Doyle. This was believed to be due to enhanced transport by the short-lived strontium-91 precursor of yttrium-91.

*Strontium, caesium and barium.* The work of SMITH and YOUNG (1951) and of DOYLE (1953) showed that the diffusion of fission product barium in artificial graphite was dependent upon sample size at temperatures about 1,700°C. Evidently barium diffuses by a mechanism different from that of xenon, iodine, tellurium, etc., and the rate-controlling step appears to be a process taking place in the larger pores between grains rather than diffusion within the grains. It is expected, therefore, that the diffusion and emission of barium will be much more dependent than that of other fission products upon the physical characteristics of the graphite, and the prediction of the behaviour in one graphite from observed results in another graphite will be extremely tentative until more is known of the nature of the rate-controlling step.

Doyle found that the diffusion of caesium and strontium was independent of graphite sample size. Agreement between his results at 1,500–1,900°C and those of Smith and Young at 1,560–1,760°C was good, the apparent diffusion coefficient being of the order of $3 \times 10^{-4}$ sec$^{-1}$ at 1,700°C. The later results at 800°C ($D' \sim 10^{-13}$ sec$^{-1}$) of FINDLAY (1958), however, lie well below the value predicted by extrapolating Doyle's results to lower temperatures. It is concluded, therefore, that for these elements there is a change in the mechanism of diffusion somewhere between 800 and 1,500°C.

It should be noted that at the higher temperatures the value of the apparent diffusion coefficient for caesium is higher than that for the larger xenon atom. This would be consistent with the supposition that above 1,500°C the rate controlling step is diffusion between the layers of carbon atoms in the crystallites. Transport in the gas phase through the larger pores in the graphite structure is rapid under these conditions. At 800°C the diffusion coefficient for caesium is much lower than for xenon, and surface migration within the pores of the graphite structure may be important. Another possible factor contributing to the slow diffusion at low temperatures may be the tendency to trap small numbers of caesium atoms between the planes of carbon atoms or at crystal imperfections: the known lamellar compounds of graphite with the alkali metals decompose at about 400°C (CROFT, 1960) but there is no previous information relating to such dilute concentrations as those encountered in the tracer diffusion studies. Impurities in the graphite might also combine selectively with chemically reactive atoms such as caesium, and so reduce diffusion. Strontium may readily form its oxide at the temperatures envisaged for high temperature reactor operation.

*Further studies*

It is evident that much work is still required to elucidate the mechanism of diffusion of the most important fission products in graphite; until the mechanism is known, the prediction of diffusion properties in the newer types of graphite remains little better than guesswork.

The post-irradiation annealing technique which has been the basis of the majority of the investigations described above is eminently suitable for such further work; however, in-pile diffusion experiments are needed also in order to highlight effects which may be due to precursor diffusion. A specific example has been given above that the in-pile diffusion of yttrium may be high because of initial transport as the intrinsically more mobile precursor [91]Sr. The precursor effect can also produce variations of the apparent diffusion of different isotopes of the same element: YOUNG (1953) and WALTON (1962) found that [141]Ce diffused faster than [144]Ce owing to enhanced transport by the more mobile precursor [141]Ba.

Other effects on which little information is yet available are:

(a) Impurities in the graphite reacting with fission products.
(b) Interaction between fission products as their concentration builds up at high irradiation times, especially at lower temperatures where the thermal stability of their compounds is greater.
(c) Oxidizing impurities in the coolant or sweep gas forming fission product oxides with low diffusion constants.

*2.3.2 Degassing of Graphite*

It is important to consider artificial graphite not as a chemically pure substance, whose reactions may be predicted from a knowledge of thermodynamic functions and of physical chemistry, but as a technological material of variable composition and containing substantial amounts of impurities. Chemically reactive gaseous contaminants are liberated when the temperature of the graphite is raised, and these can not only affect the oxidation of the graphite itself but can also have serious effects on other components of a reactor system. In reactors which rely upon the use of an inert gas such as helium as the coolant, it becomes essential to employ a purification system, and before this can be designed it is necessary to have information on the composition and rate of evolution of gases from the graphite.

The first major study of the degassing of graphite was reported by NORTON and MARSHALL (1944). However, their results are of only limited application since they used an unspecified commercial graphite anode material.

Some years later a more detailed study was made in North American Aviation laboratories. The graphite samples were heated by induction over various temperature steps up to 1,800°C, and it was observed that the major components of the desorbed gas were hydrogen, nitrogen, carbon dioxide and

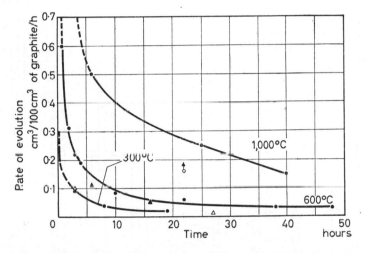

*Figure 2.12.* Rate of evolution of gas by TSF graphite (Overholser and Blakely, 1960) (by courtesy of Oak Ridge National Laboratory).

carbon monoxide (EGGLESTON *et al.*, 1955; SIEGEL *et al.*, 1955). The time of heating at each temperature was only 8 minutes, however, and the quantitative aspects of the evolution of gas are therefore likely to be misleading.

*Figure 2.12* shows that even at 1,000°C graphite continues to evolve gas at times much greater than in the experiments of Eggleston. OVERHOLSER and BLAKELY (1960) have compared the evolution of gas from AGOT graphite (purification by raw materials selection and by volatilization during normal graphitization up to 2,800°C) with that from TSF graphite (purified by high temperature treatment with halogens, p. 23). The results are summarized in *Figure 2.13*.

The total quantity of gas evolved from TSF graphite was lower, and there was a higher ratio of $H_2$ to $(CO + CO_2)$, than from the AGOT graphite. Variations between specimens of the same material were noted also, however; the amount of gas evolved differing by as much as 50 per cent for samples machined from the same bar. A transient peak in the gas production rate was

43

observed each time the sample temperature was raised, a phenomenon observed also in fission product diffusion studies in graphite (pp. 39–40).

It will be noted from *Figure 2.13* that no differentiation was made between nitrogen and carbon monoxide, since analyses were made by mass spectrometry. Other work by these authors showed, however, that at 1,000°C the gas fraction with mass number 28 was mainly CO, and that nitrogen only became an appreciable fraction below 400°C.

Gas release from a TSF-type graphite has been compared with an electrode graphite up to 1,300°C by REDMOND and WALKER (1960). Their analyses

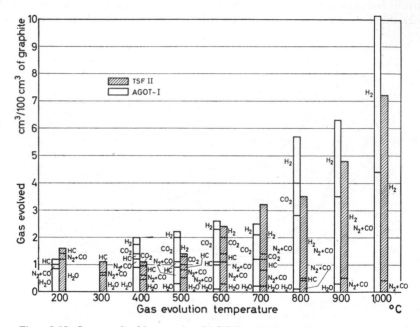

*Figure 2.13.* Gases evolved by samples of AGOT and TSF graphites upon heating to temperatures up to 1,000°C (Overholser and Blakely, 1960) (by courtesy of Oak Ridge National Laboratory).

showed significant amounts of the following hydrocarbons evolved: at low temperatures, $C_2H_4$ predominant with smaller quantities of $C_2H_2$, $C_2H_6$, $CH_4$ and *iso*-$C_4H_8$, at high temperatures $C_2H_2$ predominant. They were not able to infer unambiguously what fraction of the hydrocarbons resulted from reaction of the graphite with desorbed hydrogen which may have been ionized by the high frequency induction heating coil.

A detailed study of the degassing of graphite has been made at Harwell by ASHER *et al.* (1960). For samples of pile-grade graphite, which had been previously heated to 2,600°C in argon and then stored in air, they observed the evolution of gas shown in *Figure 2.14*. It was noted that little gas was evolved over the range 2,000–2,200°C, but above this temperature gas evolution recommenced at the same time as measurable sublimation of the graphite itself. These authors also differentiate between the *primary* desorbate (continuous high vacuum maintained around sample), and the *equilibrium* desorbate (evolved gas left in contact with sample), *see Figure 2.15*. The main difference between the two conditions is that methane does not survive above 700°C in the equilibrium state (being replaced by hydrogen) and that the $CO/CO_2$ ratio is much lower at equilibrium below 600°C. Both the primary and the equilibrium gas above 1,500°C consist almost entirely of an equimolar mixture of hydrogen and carbon monoxide.

The quantitative relationships observed by Asher and co-workers for the relative proportions of the various gases in the desorbate showed that, provided the graphitization and subsequent cooling to room temperature are both performed in a pure inert gas atmosphere, then water vapour adsorbed during subsequent exposure to air is the main source of the desorbate. The physical

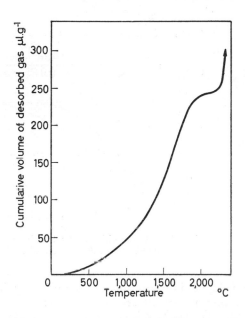

*Figure 2.14*. Evolution of gas from British pile-grade graphite up to 2,300°C (Asher *et al.* 1960).

adsorption of water vapour on graphite at room temperature had been studied previously by HORTON and ROBERTS (1958). These workers found that pile graphite adsorbed about $1 \times 10^{-4}$ w/w from air at 80 per cent humidity and at 25°C. SPALARIS (1953) has also reported results on the variation of adsorption of water vapour as a function of pressure. These latter investigations were made in order to determine the effect on nuclear reactivity in air-cooled reactors due to changes in the amount of adsorbed water on the graphite moderator as a result of humidity and temperature variations of the coolant air. The effect was comparatively small for normal climatic variations.

Asher *et al.* considered that over a period of months of exposure to air a considerable amount of chemisorption of water also occurred on the graphite. They regarded the graphite surface as inhomogeneous, being covered by various types of complex derived from chemisorbed water. This gives rise to a distribution of activation energies for desorption and to the changes in the

45

composition of the primary desorbate as the temperature is raised to 1,000°C. Chemisorbed oxide complexes on the surface can desorb as both carbon monoxide and dioxide simultaneously. Chemisorbed hydrogen appears to desorb as methane, although hydrogen also appears to be a primary product below 600°C.

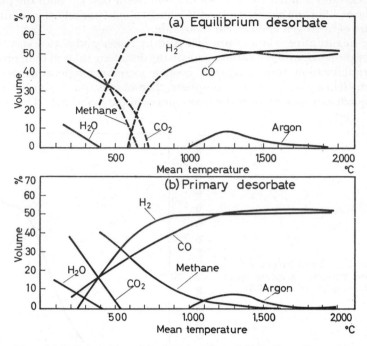

*Figure 2.15.* Composition of the desorbate from British pile-grade graphite heated in 200 or 300°C steps to 2,000°C (Asher *et al.*, 1960).

Changes in composition of the primary desorbed gas and the equilibrium gas mixture are due to the reactions:

$$CO_2 + C \rightleftharpoons 2CO$$
$$2H_2 + C \rightleftharpoons CH_4$$
$$H_2O + C \rightleftharpoons CO + H_2$$

These reactions are discussed in more detail in later parts of this chapter. The equilibrium positions are dependent not only on temperature but also on pressure since they all involve changes in volume. As a result, the composition of the equilibrium gas is shown in *Figure 2.15a* only by dotted lines where there may be differences in detail at other pressures.

*Effect of radiation*

FELDMAN (1951) has shown that irradiated graphite subsequently heated to temperatures up to 2,000°C releases gas more readily than unirradiated material. Details of these experiments are lacking, however, such as the conditions of irradiation and the ratios of the various gases evolved at each temperature.

ASHER *et al.* (1960) found that the irradiation for 25 days at 80°C in BEPO of samples of pile graphite, previously degassed by heating to 400°C, did not release any substantial amount of gas. They concluded that at fluxes about $10^{12}$ neutrons $cm^{-2}$ $sec^{-1}$ the effect of irradiation could be neglected. Similar irradiations by COPESTAKE and CORNEY (1961) also showed that the effect of irradiation was quite small: about $0 \cdot 05$ $cm^3$ gas was evolved per 100 $cm^3$ of graphite during a thermal neutron dose of $3 \cdot 5 \times 10^{18}$ nvt. The ratio $CO:CO_2$ in the desorbed gas was very variable.

### 2.3.3 Compatibility with Helium

There should be no thermal reaction between graphite and pure helium. The lack of attack, even of a physical nature, has been verified experimentally for helium moving at sonic velocities impingeing on graphite at 1,370°C (THOMPSON, 1956). Even under irradiation, when ionized and excited helium atoms may be produced, it has been shown by ONSLOW-MACAULAY and TOMLINSON (1960) that the attack of graphite is not significant. However, the helium in a reactor circuit is likely to contain appreciable amounts of reactive impurities from a number of sources: evolution from metal surfaces, evolution from the graphite if the latter is unclad (Section 2.3.2), introduction of impurities with each new fuel element, etc.

Attack of the graphite by these impurities is likely to be of considerable importance, and the reactions have been studied in several laboratories. ANTILL and PEAKALL (1959) have given details of investigations performed out of pile using argon instead of helium. They found that the rates of reaction of the impurities with graphite decreased in the order: oxygen, water vapour, carbon dioxide. The reaction rates increased with temperature up to 1,000°C and with the partial pressure of the oxidizing gas; hydrogen and carbon monoxide inhibited the attack. These authors concluded that the permissible concentrations of oxygen, water vapour and carbon dioxide depend upon the concentrations of carbon monoxide and hydrogen in the gas; as the latter increase the specification for the reactive gases may be relaxed. For gas containing no carbon monoxide or hydrogen they predicted that the gas in a reactor circuit must not be allowed to contain more than 10 vpm of carbon dioxide and water vapour or more than 1 vpm of oxygen. They pointed out, however, that such predictions are based on experiments performed out of a radiation field: in a reactor the impurities may well become activated and increase the rate of attack. Suitable in-pile experiments have not been reported.

The beneficial effect of hydrogen confirms the prediction by RAGONE (1960) that hydrogen could counteract the tendency of oxygen to transport carbon from regions of high temperature to regions of lower temperature. The latter author attempted to calculate the concentrations of mixtures of CO, $CO_2$, $CH_4$, $H_2$ and $H_2O$ in equilibrium with graphite under conditions applicable in a high temperature reactor.

An important observation of Antill and Peakall was that a graphite impregnated with furfuryl alcohol and treated at comparatively low temperatures ($\sim 1,000$°C) was attacked to a greater extent than unimpregnated material. Although the higher density and lower permeability of such impregnated material may appear to be desirable characteristics, it is by no means certain that these properties will be retained, owing to the apparently greater chemical reactivity of the char produced from the impregnant in the pores of the matrix graphite. Heat treatment to much higher temperatures after impregnation may alleviate this difficulty.

Further data will be obtained under reactor operating conditions from the Dragon reactor.

It will be necessary to include purification beds in the coolant circuits of inert gas-cooled reactors in order to keep down the concentrations of impurities to the levels predicted by Antill and Peakall's work.

DAVIDGE, HODGE and STOCKDALE (1960) have discussed the use of metallic uranium at 650–725°C for the removal of CO, $CO_2$, $O_2$ and $H_2O$. The uranium will not remove hydrogen impurity from inert gases at these temperatures, and a separate bed of zirconium–titanium alloy would be necessary (see, for instance, PASCARD and FABRE, 1958).

Alternatively, all impurities except hydrogen may be removed by passing the inert gas stream through a comparatively small bed of activated charcoal at about liquid nitrogen temperature. The residual hydrogen could be removed by conversion to water using copper oxide, followed by absorption in a molecular sieve bed. The charcoal beds could be used also for removal of fission product gases from a reactor circuit in which these may contaminate the inert coolant, the major design problem then being the minimization of fission product heating in the traps by the use of suitable delay beds of charcoal at higher temperatures to precede the low temperature traps.

### 2.3.4 Compatibility with Nitrogen

Pure nitrogen may react with graphite to form cyanogen:

$$2C + N_2 \rightleftharpoons (CN)_2$$

Thermodynamic data show that the equilibrium is overwhelmingly in favour of the uncombined elements at s.t.p. and that detectable amounts of cyanogen should not be formed below about 2,000°C.

The first detailed study of the thermal reaction was made by FINK and WROUGHTON (1945). They derived the following expression for the equilibrium concentrations up to about 2,300°C:

$$\log \frac{[CN]_2}{[N_2]} = 15,530/T + 0.855 \log T + 7.65 \times 10^{-5} T \,(°K) - 0.50$$

It is evident that at temperatures about 1,000°C, such as may be required in a nitrogen-cooled reactor, the thermally induced reaction should be very slight. Fink and Wroughton observed that the presence of water vapour or of hydrogen in the nitrogen gave rise to the formation of HCN and that appreciable amounts were formed at much lower temperatures ($\sim 1,500$°C) than for cyanogen.

There is some possibility that the rate of reaction between graphite and nitrogen might be enhanced under irradiation by the formation of ionized or excited nitrogen atoms  No detectable enhancement of the rate of reaction at

600°C has been observed in experiments performed in DIDO (WRIGHT, 1960), and no cyanogen was observed as a result of passing nitrogen activated by an electrodeless discharge over spectroscopic carbon at 800°C (ZINMAN, 1960). The latter author found, however, that the addition of only 30 p.p.m. of hydrogen to the nitrogen gave rise to a considerable yield of HCN. This compound was found also by GIBERSON (1961) when microwave-activated nitrogen reacted with CSF graphite at an unspecified temperature: its formation was probably due to the presence of adsorbed impurities in the graphite. Giberson also concluded that para-cyanogen was produced in his experiments, i.e. there was some evidence for enhancement of the direct reaction under the influence of energy deposited in the gas.

Cyanogen is thermally unstable at high temperatures and a mechanism for the transport of carbon around a reactor coolant circuit can therefore be foreseen. Even though the forward reaction would probably proceed only very slowly in the conditions of the reactor core, the possible extent of carbon transport remains unknown and would have to be checked experimentally before a reactor could be built with confidence. Moreover, the experimental investigations show that impurities in the coolant would play a major role in the compatibility with graphite in a nitrogen-cooled reactor.

### 2.3.5 Compatibility with Hydrogen

The reaction between carbon and hydrogen results in the formation of methane:

$$C + 2H_2 \rightleftharpoons CH_4$$

Substantial equilibrium concentrations of methane are possible as the pressure is increased at temperatures below 1,200°C. Therefore if rates of reaction are high the conditions in a power reactor could be quite unacceptable, leading to rapid depletion of the graphite moderator. For example, in the absence of radiation, the equilibrium gas mixture at 10 atmospheres pressure and 727°C would contain 3·8 atmospheres partial pressure of methane. Although the temperature variation of the equilibrium indicates that mass transport of carbon from the core to the cooler parts of the reactor system would not occur, nevertheless substantial losses of carbon could take place by leakage, reactor blow-downs, etc. There may also be radiation-induced decomposition of the methane.

The literature on the thermally induced reaction is not particularly applicable to predicting the rates at which it may occur about 800°C. BARBER (1936) has studied the sorption of hydrogen on graphite and diamond, and BARBER and RIDEAL (1935) also investigated the sorption on charcoal. The rate of reaction was found to be controlled by chemisorption of hydrogen on the carbon surface, an activation energy of about 34 kcal mole$^{-1}$ being approached at high surface coverage of the graphite. The chemisorbed hydrogen was in all respects similar to the C—H linkage in a hydrocarbon. The decomposition of the chemisorbed hydrogen–carbon complexes to give gaseous methane proceeded only slowly under normal conditions, although it was facilitated by the presence of hydrogenation catalysts.

The sorption of hydrogen on nuclear grades of graphite at temperatures above 1,000°C has been studied by REDMOND and WALKER (1960). They observed a considerably higher value of the activation energy, and concluded that adsorption of hydrogen took place on carbon atoms at the edges of crystallites rather than by intracrystalline adsorption.

BLACKWOOD (1959) found no reaction between natural graphite and hydrogen at 30 atm pressure and 650°C. The rate of formation of methane from non-graphitic carbons under the same conditions depended upon the oxygen content of the carbon: it was suggested that the oxygen was present in chromene and benzpyran groups which acted as activation sites for methane formation without themselves being consumed.

CORNEY and THOMAS (1958) have examined directly the rate of reaction between low pressure hydrogen and graphite at 500–600°C under irradiation in BEPO. Methane was found to constitute 98 per cent of the gaseous product and the reaction appeared to proceed through short-lived intermediate species formed by the action of radiation on the hydrogen, i.e. the mechanism was different from that of the thermal reaction and resembled that of other radiation-induced reactions between graphite and gases. The rate of reaction was proportional to the pressure of hydrogen and was controlled by the rate of deposition of radiation energy in the gas.

The rate of reaction observed by Corney and Thomas was greater under irradiation than the thermally induced reaction, although the difference between them diminished as the temperature was raised.

At temperatures above about 700°C it is possible that the thermal reaction rate would be too great to be acceptable in a power reactor: whether the radiation induced reaction would be significant below this temperature requires elucidation by further experiments under conditions of temperature, pressure, flow and radiation flux appropriate to a reactor core.

### 2.3.6 Compatibility with Steam

The reaction between various types of carbon and steam is of great industrial importance. The rates are probably too high to contemplate the deliberate contact between graphite and steam as a nuclear reactor coolant, but the reaction must be considered in the event of accident or of the possible use of water for fire-fighting in a reactor.

The principal reactions taking place at the surface of graphite in contact with steam are:

$$C + H_2O \rightleftharpoons CO + H_2$$
$$C + 2H_2O \rightleftharpoons CO_2 + 2H_2$$
$$C + CO_2 \rightleftharpoons 2CO$$

In addition, the reaction

$$CO + H_2O \rightleftharpoons CO_2 + H_2$$

may occur either entirely in the gas phase or heterogeneously on the graphite surface. The relationships between these reactions, and the mechanisms by which they take place have been summarized elsewhere (WALKER, RUSINKO and AUSTIN, 1959; KNOTT, 1954).

MAYERS (1934) studied the reaction between steam at high velocity and Acheson electrode graphite. His work can be used to predict the rate of production of inflammable gas ($CO + H_2$) from a graphite reactor structure upon the introduction of water. At temperatures below about 850°C, the major source of hydrogen production might be exposed uranium metal fuel elements, but above this temperature the graphite would become the major source.

### 2.3.7 The Graphite–Carbon Dioxide System

The reaction between graphite and carbon dioxide has assumed great technological importance from the choice of this gas as the coolant for a considerable number of large nuclear power reactors (*Table 1.1*). For the reactors at Calder Hall, the temperatures are such that the thermally induced reaction is small enough to be acceptable over a 20-year life, but considerable attention has had to be given to the radiation induced reaction. As the desire to increase operating temperatures becomes greater for future reactors, so a more detailed study of the thermal reaction is becoming important.

The study of the reaction has not developed entirely as a result of the needs of the atomic energy programme: it was investigated by LANGMUIR as long ago as 1915 and by BROOM and TRAVERS in 1932. The results obtained, together with those of GADSBY et al. (1948), BONNER and TURKEVICH (1951) and of ERGUN (1956), show that the mechanism by which the reaction takes place is a complex one involving chemisorption of carbon dioxide on to active sites ($C_f$) on the graphite to form surface oxides:

$$C_f + CO_2(g) \rightleftharpoons C(O) + CO(g) \tag{1}$$

$$C_f + C(O) \rightleftharpoons C(CO) \tag{2}$$

$$C(CO) \rightleftharpoons CO(g) + C_f \tag{3}$$

An extensive discussion of these equilibria has been given by WALKER, RUSINKO and AUSTIN (1959).

COPESTAKE, DAVIDSON and TONGE (1959) have shown that not every carbon atom on the graphite surface is necessarily an active site for chemisorption and that carbon dioxide itself can activate the surface at about 625°C. Below this temperature the principal reaction is the formation of a stable surface oxide (reaction 1), a process which does not involve loss of carbon from the graphite. The gasification reaction (4) was detectable at 650°C.

$$C + CO_2(g) \rightleftharpoons 2CO(g) \tag{4}$$

In the absence of irradiation, the (gasification) reaction between carbon dioxide and graphite has been studied by WALKER, FORESTI and WRIGHT (1953), PETERSEN and WRIGHT (1955), and BURTON (1959). Their results were obtained at temperatures above 900°C, however, and extrapolation to about 600°C gives predicted rates of reaction which differ by two orders of magnitude. This is due to the fact that according to Petersen and Wright the rate-controlling process changes at about 900°C. Above this temperature the rate is sufficiently fast to be controlled by gaseous diffusion within the pores of the graphite, whereas at low temperatures chemical reaction on the graphite surface of the pores becomes overriding. A subsequent investigation by

51

BLAKELEY (1959) showed that the transition between the two types of oxidation occurred over a range of 500°C or more:

Transition range at low velocity,    1,000–1,500°C

Transition range at high velocity,   1,500–2,500°C

The transition will also depend upon the pore structure of the graphite.

Direct experiments at low temperatures were made by BOND, SPENCER and TEE (1960) and by COPESTAKE *et al.* (1959). The latter authors found that at 500°C the gasification rate was sufficiently low to lead to a weight loss from the graphite of less than 0·1 per cent in 20 years. It was concluded also that above 650°C the gasification reaction was strongly inhibited by carbon monoxide since the equilibrium gas compositions calculated from thermodynamic data were not attained even after thousands of hours (see also Gow and MARSH, 1960). However, the loss of carbon from the solid phase at 650°C is probably sufficient to rule out the use of normal pile-grade graphite at this temperature on the basis of the thermal induced reaction alone. It is possible that less reactive forms of graphite may be developed, but their application on a large scale will depend upon a balance between higher costs of production and the benefits of higher temperatures of reactor operation.

## The effect of irradiation

Once the limit for the graphite temperature is set from considerations of the thermal reaction with graphite, the available data on the system below this temperature are of little value in assessing the extent of reaction in a nuclear power reactor. This situation arises from the fact that the mechanism of the radiation enhanced reaction has been found to be entirely different from that of the thermal reaction.

The effects of irradiation on the graphite in promoting reaction with carbon dioxide are small in comparison with the effects produced by radiation in the gas. DAVIDGE and MARSH (1955) studied the reaction under irradiation in BEPO at comparatively low pressures. They found that the rate of reaction was proportional to the intensity of the radiation and increased with increasing pressure of the gas. Water vapour did not affect the rates observed. A steady state concentration of CO in $CO_2$ could be achieved upon prolonged irradiation.

Davidge and Marsh deduced the following set of reactions to explain their data:

$$\text{(Ionization) } CO_2 \rightsquigarrow CO_2^+ + e^- \rightarrow CO + O \tag{5}$$

$$\text{(Excitation) } CO_2 \rightsquigarrow CO_2^* \rightarrow CO + O \tag{6}$$

$$O + O + M \rightarrow O_2 + M \tag{7}$$

$$O_2 + O + M \rightarrow O_3 + M \tag{8}$$

$$C + O \rightarrow CO \tag{9}$$

$$C + O_3 \rightarrow CO + O_2 \tag{10}$$

The M in equations 7 and 8 represents a third body, such as a gas molecule or the graphite surface, which is required to take up the excess energy released in the combination reactions. The extent of the recombination reaction:

$$CO + O + M \rightarrow CO_2 + M \qquad (11)$$

was believed to be insignificant in the presence of an extensive graphite surface.

A negligible steady state concentration of molecular oxygen was observed by Davidge and Marsh. No direct proof of the presence of ozone as an intermediate was obtained either, but its probable formation was inferred from previous suggestions by GROTH (1937) concerning the photochemical decomposition of carbon dioxide and by HIRSCHFELDER and TAYLOR (1938) for its decomposition induced by alpha particles. In a nuclear reactor, the primary source of energy deposition in carbon dioxide is from gamma radiation, with a smaller contribution from fast neutrons. It is probable that the effects of these two sources of energy deposition in the gas are very similar to each other (DAVIDGE and MARSH, 1955; COPESTAKE and CORNEY, 1960).

Other effects must also be taken into account in assessing the overall reactions between carbon and graphite. For instance, HARTECK and DONDES (1955, 1957) found that irradiation of carbon dioxide at low temperatures gave material which was believed to be polymerized carbon sub-oxide. The products of the radiolysis of CO include $CO_2$ and polymeric carbon sub-oxides which WOODLEY (1954, 1955) suggested were formed by reactions such as:

$$CO + C + M \rightarrow C_2O + M$$
$$C_2O + CO + M \rightarrow C_3O_2 + M$$
$$C_3O_2 + CO + M \rightarrow C_4O_3 + M$$

The most well known carbon sub-oxide is $C_3O_2$, which is gaseous in the monomeric state at room temperature. It very readily polymerizes to 'red carbon', a process investigated in detail by SCHMIDT, BOEHM and HOFMANN (1957). The extent to which the carbon sub-oxides enter into the processes occurring in a nuclear power reactor operating at high temperatures remains to be assessed by future experiments. According to HARTECK and DONDES (1955, 1957) it is possible that $C_3O_2$ could play an essential part in the re-formation of $CO_2$ from its radiolytic products by reactions such as:

$$C_3O_2 + O \rightarrow CO_2 + C_2O$$
$$C_3O_2 + O_3 \rightarrow CO_2 + C_2O + O_2$$

The reader is referred to WRIGHT (1960b) for a more detailed discussion of the various mechanisms of the radiolysis of $CO_2$ and CO.

The effect of pile irradiation on the $CO_2$-graphite system in sealed tubes has been studied in considerable detail by COPESTAKE and CORNEY (1960). They found that the rate of formation of carbon monoxide decreased with increasing dose of radiation: the initial rate depended on the amount and geometry of the carbon and on the amount and pressure of the carbon dioxide. It did not depend markedly on the nature of the carbon, a conclusion confirmed in further work by TOMLINSON (1961).

A further significant observation was that the deposition of radiation energy in the gas within the pores of the graphite outweighed in importance that deposited in the bulk of the gas surrounding the graphite. The relative importance of these two regions may not be the same when the gas is flowing rapidly (as in an operating reactor circuit).

COWEN and LIND (1960) made investigations at high radiation intensities of the reaction between graphite and slowly flowing carbon dioxide under pressure. They confirmed that the pore structure of the graphite was of considerable importance and they found that partial oxidation could lead to an opening of the pore structure with a consequent increase in the rate of oxidation. It appeared possible to account for the increase by the deposition of radiation energy in the larger amount of carbon dioxide within the graphite after the opening up of the pore structure. Cowen and Lind suggested that if this explanation were substantiated the increase in oxidation should become less marked after the pore structure becomes fully open.

*Effect of temperature.* The radiation-induced production of carbon monoxide from carbon dioxide and graphite varies by only a factor of 2 over the range 100–600°C, i.e. up to the region in which thermal processes begin to be important (Gow and MARSH, 1960).

## The prediction of in-pile performance

The important technological problem with which chemists have been confronted has been the prediction of the rate of loss of graphite from the cores of nuclear reactors operating at radiation fluxes beyond those which could be reached in experimental reactors. The reactor designer is interested in the smallest possible rate of reaction extended over periods of 20–30 years, which also involves very long extrapolations from normal experimental data.

The complexity of making these predictions will have been evident from the brief discussion given above. Variable parameters which must be taken into account are:

> Radiation intensity
> Gas flow rate and geometrical factors of the system
> Temperature
> Pressure
> Type of graphite (especially pore structure)
> The build-up of CO concentration in the coolant
> Effect of impurities in the coolant
> Effect of impurities, possibly having catalytic effects, in the graphite
> Elapsed time

When the design of the Calder Hall reactors was being considered, it was found impossible to predict quantitatively the extent and distribution of weight changes in the graphite by extrapolation from small scale experiments such as those of Davidge and Marsh. It was necessary, therefore, to adopt a more empirical approach and to build a loop for operation in BEPO which could simulate as closely as possible the conditions to be experienced in the power reactors. The results have been described by ANDERSON *et al.* (1958).

It was predicted from this work that the net loss of graphite from the Calder Hall reactors would be about 0·1 per cent per year. The deduction was made also that carbon deposition on heat exchanger surfaces, arising from the radiolysis of CO, would probably be insignificant.

Results subsequently obtained in the Calder Hall reactors and quoted by the same authors agreed reasonably well with those predicted from the loop experiment which had been performed at a flux level five times lower and a flow rate one half of that in the reactor.

An important result from the loop work was the attainment of a steady state concentration of carbon monoxide controlled by:

(a) the rate of CO production,
(b) the leak rate of gas from the system,
(c) the carbon deposition reaction.

It was pointed out, therefore, that in future reactors designed for higher power ratings and lower leakage rates the steady state CO concentration might be raised considerably and the carbon deposition reaction could then become of much greater significance.

A beneficial effect of the presence of CO upon the weight loss of small samples of graphite has been found by several investigators (e.g. DAVIDGE and MARSH, 1955; ANDERSON *et al.*, 1958; O'DRISCOLL *et al.*, 1960; COWEN and LIND, 1960). Owing to a possible limiting effect of gas diffusion through the pores, however, the concentration of carbon monoxide may vary by a considerable amount in different parts of a large block of graphite, and may bear no direct relationship with the concentration in the main gas stream. It also remains for further experiments to clarify whether the reduction of weight loss of the graphite, if there is any, is due to interference by CO molecules in the diffusion of O atoms to the carbon surface (by capture to form $CO_2$) or to deposition of carbon by the reverse of equation 4. DOMINEY (1961) has shown by the use of $^{14}C$ tracer that under some conditions CO can inhibit the transport of carbon from the solid to the gas phase, but it is not possible to extrapolate his results to the conditions expected in an operating power reactor. The difference between the two mechanisms may have a technological significance, in that the structure of the graphite, on a microscopic scale, remains unchanged by the first possibility but may be altered by the second possibility.

### 2.3.8 Oxidation by Oxygen

The reaction of various forms of carbon with oxygen is the major source of our energy production, and it has been the subject of a considerable amount of investigation outside the atomic energy industry. It became particularly important in the latter when the decision was made to build graphite-moderated reactors cooled by air (see *Table 1.1*).

An interesting discussion of the mechanism of the reaction has been given by LEWIS and UBBELODHE (1960). They point out that although many authors claim that the first step in the reaction is the formation of a relatively uniform 'surface oxide', the evidence for this is not complete. In a carbon with a highly developed graphite structure they consider that the first step is the removal of volatile molecules such as CO from sites at the edges of hexagonal networks where impurity atoms have been chemisorbed, followed by further attachment and removal of molecular oxygen. Such attack may also take place near the sites of foreign atoms incorporated in the carbon network. HEDLEY (1960) has observed with an electron microscope that for natural graphite in air at 600°C, attack occurs preferentially at crystal edges and cleavage steps.

It seems generally agreed that both carbon monoxide and carbon dioxide are primary products of the reaction. The ratio of these two products varies with temperature (see also *Figure 2.15*).

At temperatures below about 300°C, the rate of the thermally induced reaction is controlled by an activated chemisorption of oxygen on to the graphite surface. The attack occurs throughout the graphite structure and the whole internal surface of the pores becomes involved. The experimentally determined variation of the rate with change of temperature shows an energy of activation which varies considerably but has an average value about 58 kcal mole$^{-1}$. This is very close to the dissociation energy of an oxygen molecule, 59 kcal mole$^{-1}$ (WALKER, RUSINKO and AUSTIN, 1959).

Above about 400°C the rate of gasification of the surface oxide complexes increases and the reaction can become controlled by transport processes in the gas phase. Moreover, there is evidence for a change in mechanism at 1,200°C within the transport-controlled region (OKADA and IKEGAWA, 1953). Under some conditions, water vapour can have an inhibiting effect on the reaction (DUVAL, 1961).

### Oxidation in large structures of graphite

DODSON (1960) has made a theoretical approach to the oxidation of graphite in the transport-controlled region of temperature. For large blocks of material the oxygen will be first consumed more rapidly than it can diffuse into the interior: the concentration in the body of the material will fall until the rate of reaction equals the rate of diffusion of the oxidizing gas inwards or the products of oxidation outwards. If $D$ is the effective diffusion coefficient of oxygen through the gas in the pores of the graphite, and $k$ is the reaction rate constant in terms of the volume of oxygen consumed, then a depth of oxidation $L$ may be defined as:

$$L = \left(\frac{D}{k}\right)^{1/2}$$

When $L$ is much less than the dimensions of the graphite block, the total rate of oxidation is the same as would occur if the oxygen penetrated freely to a depth $L$ over the whole surface of the block, with no oxidation below this depth. The apparent activation energy under these conditions will be half the true activation energy and the rate of reaction will be proportional to the square root of the oxygen pressure (it is directly proportional to pressure at lower temperatures).

An important difference between the oxidation of graphite by carbon dioxide (discussed in the previous section) and by oxygen arises from the fact that the former is endothermic whereas the latter is strongly exothermic. A 'runaway' condition may therefore occur in large graphite structures when the heat of reaction with oxygen cannot be removed sufficiently quickly. Experimental investigations of this complex situation have been made by ROBINSON and TAYLOR (1959).

For any particular geometrical arrangement of graphite blocks and air-cooled fuel channels there will exist a threshold temperature below which a runaway reaction cannot occur and above which it may occur very rapidly owing to the strong dependence of the rate of reaction upon temperature. The threshold temperature in Robinson and Taylor's rig was 520–530°C, but the quantitative application of their data to systems having different geometry is of doubtful validity.

Further work along both theoretical and practical lines is undoubtedly necessary, and the ideas developed by Dodson and by Robinson and Taylor may subsequently require modification. SCHWEITZER (1960) has pointed out that heat transfer in such systems is very complex and that the heat transfer coefficient used by Robinson and Taylor is probably not appropriate to the range of flow rates which they used. He also considered that under some conditions the CO–oxygen reaction in the gas phase could be a major source of heat.

The actual rates of reaction of graphite with oxygen or air have not been quoted here since they are subject to wide variations. A knowledge of the rate in any particular set of circumstances must be determined from experimental observations on the specific type of graphite proposed. The rate can be affected by the method of manufacture of the graphite, its subsequent history, the amount and distribution of impurities and the level of irradiation to which it may have been taken. According to PRADOS (1961), the rate data over the range 350–750°C for nuclear grades of artificial graphite may be correlated within a factor of six by the expression:

$$k = 7\cdot24 \times 10^9 \exp\left(\frac{-22,000}{T}\right)$$

## Catalysts and inhibitors

Small amounts of certain impurities can lead to large increases in the rate of oxidation of graphite. CURRIE, HAMISTER and MACPHERSON (1955) have shown that 20–40 p.p.m. of sodium, potassium, vanadium or copper, will increase the rate of oxidation by a factor of six at 550°C. Larger quantities lead to even greater oxidation (HENNIG, 1960; NAIRN and WILKINSON, 1960). Mercury vapour may also act as a catalyst in laboratory experiments (SMITH, 1959). An enhancement of the rate of oxidation of samples of graphite removed from the BEPO reactor has been attributed to the introduction of impurities in the coolant air stream (ANDERSON et al., 1960).

Some attention has been paid to the possibility of the inhibition of the reaction. The rate may be reduced by the use of a more impervious graphite (Section 2.1.4), but economical production of this type of material has not yet been achieved on a substantial scale. Alternatively, certain compounds may be added to the gas phase in an emergency, such as a reactor fire, to quench the reaction.

The nitrogen constituent of air is normally regarded as an inert diluent for the oxygen and does not appear to have any other inhibiting action. Chlorine and certain of its volatile compounds (e.g. $CCl_4$, $POCl_3$) do act as inhibitors, probably by chemisorption of chlorine atoms on the active carbon sites preventing the formation of carbon–oxygen surface complexes. Subsequent removal of the chlorine from the oxygen stream allows the original rate of oxidation to be slowly regained (WICKE, 1955; DAY, 1959; DAHL, 1960).

*The effects of irradiation*

Reactor irradiation has been found to have two distinct types of effect upon the oxidation of graphite with oxygen or air.

In the first place, fast neutron bombardment gives rise to appreciable numbers of carbon atoms displaced from their normal positions in the graphite lattice. These not only constitute an additional source of heat (Wigner energy) but they also have an effect upon the subsequent rate of oxidation out of the radiation field. The difficulty of removing Wigner energy from a large graphite stack by thermal annealing was amply illustrated by the accident to the reactor at Windscale in October 1957 (COMMITTEE OF INQUIRY).

It has been shown by KOSIBA, DIENES and GURINSKY (1957) that irradiation of graphite at 25–50°C to a fast neutron dose of $10^{20}$ n cm$^{-2}$ increased by a factor of six the subsequent thermal oxidation at 350°C. The factor is lowered as the temperature of reaction is raised and the activation energy for the oxidation of the irradiated samples was found to be 36·1 kcal mole$^{-1}$ compared with 48·8 kcal mole$^{-1}$ for the unirradiated material. The higher oxidation rate persisted even when 20–25 per cent of the specimen had been oxidized, and it was deduced that the displaced atoms were not being oxidized preferentially but were facilitating in some way the overall reaction. This is the more surprising since SPALARIS (1953) has shown that low temperature irradiation reduces the surface area of graphite and hence would be expected to reduce the rate of oxidation. The surface area of single crystals of *natural* graphite is increased markedly in the early stages of post-irradiation oxidation owing to preferential attack, with the formation of pits, at vacancy sites on the surface (HENNIG, DIENES and KOSIBA, 1958). This causes attack on the basal planes which is additional to the edge attack of the thermal reaction.

The second effect of radiation on the oxidation of graphite with oxygen or air depends upon the products of radiolysis of the gas. STREZNEWSKI and TURKEVICH (1957) have found that carbon films will react with oxygen atoms at temperatures down to 20°C, whereas ozone (another possible product of the irradiation of oxygen) will not react. Other workers, however, have interpreted the enhanced rate of oxidation under irradiation as being due to the presence of ozone. The reaction was studied by DAVIDGE, TOMLINSON and WRIGHT (1959) who found that the rate of carbon dioxide production from graphite at 60–300°C in oxygen under irradiation in BEPO has a complex dependence upon oxygen pressure, flow and volume of the irradiated gas space upstream of the graphite. Although the rate was relatively low, nevertheless it was greater than in corresponding out-of-pile experiments. Experiments at Brookhaven National Laboratory have shown that the rate of in-pile oxidation at 400°C *decreases* with increasing exposure time (HENNIG, DIENES and KOSIBA, 1958).

TOMLINSON (1959) subsequently compared the quantitative results obtained in the Harwell experiments with other work performed under different conditions of geometry and flow in the NRX and Windscale reactors. The gas flow rate had a very large effect on the rate of reaction, and Tomlinson's comparison illustrated the difficulties which may arise from an empirical extension of results from the laboratory scale to a reactor structure.

### 2.3.9 Compatibility with Solid Materials

Graphite may be in contact with a number of different structural metals (which may or may not have surface oxide films according to the environment) in a reactor core. The temperatures of such interfaces will often be low enough to ensure that no reaction can take place, but in some designs of reactor the conditions will be approaching the threshold at which there may be a significant amount of reaction. Normally this will take the form of deterioration of the mechanical or physical properties of the metal by carburization, the graphite remaining relatively unaffected.

The Maritime Gas-Cooled Reactor developed by General Dynamics Corporation requires that a metallic fuel cladding should operate in contact with graphite in a temperature range of 480 to 930°C. The compatibility of graphite with metals of comparatively low neutron absorption cross-section has therefore been investigated in some detail (BOKROS, 1959). The results of another general experimental survey of the problem at 1,000°C at Battelle Memorial Institute have also been published by GERDS and MALLETT (1958). The experiments were performed out of pile; knowledge of the effects of irradiation upon such reactions is meagre. Whilst it is often assumed that the effects will be small, there is no direct evidence that they will not become significant in high flux reactors for systems where the rate of reaction is controlled by diffusion.

Metals on which out-of-pile experimental information is available are listed below in alphabetical order. The reactions between graphite and reactor fuel materials, such as uranium and urania, are discussed in Chapter 4.

#### Aluminium

Graphite does not react with aluminium at temperatures below the softening point of the metal. There may be a reaction between aluminium and the oxidizing impurities evolved from graphite upon heating (CARTER, 1959).

#### Beryllium

Beryllium carbide, $Be_2C$, is formed readily from the elements at 950°C, but no reaction occurs in 200 hours at 600°C (BAIRD et al., 1958).

#### Copper

The solid solubility of carbon in copper is very low and the metal does not form any stable carbides. Gerds and Mallett observed no reaction after 250 hours at 1,000°C. A copper–silver eutectic, with a 12 per cent titanium core, has been used for brazing graphite to metal (STAPLETON, 1959).

#### Magnox alloys

These are compatible with graphite up to 400°C, but no evidence has been published relating to temperatures nearer the melting point, 650°C.

#### Molybdenum

Two carbides, $Mo_2C$ and $MoC$, are stable. Their melting points, and that of the metal itself, are comparatively high, however, and at reactor temperatures about 1,000°C rates of diffusion may be sufficiently low to keep the extent of penetration of carbon into the metal to an acceptable level. Gerds and Mallett observed the formation of a very hard carbide layer at the molybdenum–graphite interface after 250 hours at 1,000°C, but did not observe any attack beyond this layer. Bokros claimed that the penetration of molybdenum by carbon in $10^4$ hours at 700°C would be quite low, but observed relatively rapid penetration at 930°C.

*Nickel*

Like copper, nickel does not form stable carbides, but the solubility of carbon in nickel is higher (0·65 wt. % at the eutectic temperature of 1,318°C). Gerds and Mallet observed only slightly more reaction with nickel than with copper at 1,000°C. Bokros found that the room temperature ductility of nickel was unaffected by carburization at high temperatures, but recommended further work on the kinetics of precipitation of carbon in nickel. He found less penetration of a grain boundary precipitate into monel (70 Ni: 30 Cu) than in nickel after contact with graphite at 930°C.

Alloys of nickel with molybdenum, chromium and iron lose the high-temperature strength conferred by these elements when they are carburized and suffer an appreciable loss of ductility (Bokros, 1959).

*Niobium*

Like molybdenum, this metal also forms two carbides of very high melting point, $Nb_2C$ and $NbC$. Difficulties due to possible carbide formation in contact with graphite are overshadowed, however, by the extremely efficient gettering action of niobium for oxidizing gases. Bokros reported that a partial pressure as little as $2 \times 10^{-4}$ atm $(CO + CO_2)$ in helium would embrittle niobium in less than 500 hours at 815°C. Nitrogen impurity in helium could also embrittle niobium.

*Stainless steels*

The austenitic stainless steels are compatible with graphite up to about 600°C, but above this temperature they are rapidly carburized. Bokros claimed that chromium-plated Type-304 stainless steel resisted carburization at 815°C, but the plating was not effective at 930°C.

Ferritic steels (iron–chromium alloys) resist carburization in contract with graphite up to 815°C according to Bokros.

*Zirconium*

The solubility of carbon in zirconium is very low, but there is a stable carbide: ZrC.

HANDWERK, LIED and SHALEK (1957) found no reaction between graphite and zircaloy-2 after 60 days at 800°C. Solid state diffusion would be expected to produce a zirconium carbide layer at higher temperatures.

An alloy of 48% Ti–48% Zr–4% Be has been found to readily wet graphite and to be very satisfactory for brazing graphite joints (MACPHERSON, 1960).

## 2.4 THE DRAGON REACTOR

There are many similarities of design between the Dragon reactor experiment and the considerably larger reactor to be built at Peach Bottom, U.S.A. (see

*Table 1.1*). Both reactors may become operational at about the same time, although the American plant, being larger and designed to produce useful power, requires a rather more cautious approach: its initial fuel charge may be clad with metal, with a subsequent transition to graphite cladding.

The United Kingdom nuclear power programme has been based primarily upon the gas-cooled reactor concept. Limitations inherent in the first generation of reactors (metal fuel, carbon dioxide coolant, graphite moderator) have been partially overcome in the AGR-type of reactor by the use of ceramic fuel. This has allowed the operating temperatures, and hence the efficiency of the systems, to be increased. Further limitations are set, however, by the oxidizing power of the coolant towards the graphite moderator. The third stage of the development programme has been, therefore, to substitute chemically inert helium in place of carbon dioxide. Ultimately this should make possible temperatures sufficiently high to allow the elimination of heat exchangers and the use of gas turbines driven directly by the coolant gas, but the aims of the Dragon reactor experiment are more modestly set at achieving a very high efficiency steam cycle.

Preliminary papers concerning the design of this type of reactor began to appear at A.E.R.E., Harwell, in 1955. A design for a 10 MW reactor experiment was evolved and was published at the second Geneva Conference (SHEPHERD *et al.*, 1958). In April, 1959, the responsibility for developing and building the reactor experiment at Winfrith Heath was taken over by a joint team from the O.E.E.C. countries.

Dragon is now intended to be a 20 MW helium-cooled system with a maximum coolant temperature of 750°C. The heat output will be rejected to atmosphere and no attempt will be made to produce useful power. The fuel elements will contain a mixture of fissile uranium carbide and fertile thorium carbide in a matrix of graphite. A general description of the reactor has been given by LOCKETT and HUDDLE (1960).

The principal objectives of this reactor experiment are to study the behaviour of the novel graphite fuel element design and the associated fission product purge and clean-up systems. Other areas in which important information will be obtained are fuel cycles and the nuclear and kinetic characteristics of the core as a whole.

Although the original idea for this reactor was that the core should consist of a homogeneous dispersion of uranium and thorium carbides in graphite, the fuel elements ultimately evolved are inhomogeneous and quite complex. The design now incorporates uranium–thorium impregnated graphite fuel pellets, but with a cladding of more impermeable graphite to reduce the possibility of fission products entering the main coolant stream. This cladding material consists of a fine-grained graphite impregnated with furfuryl alcohol to reduce the permeability (HUDDLE, ARRAGON and PRICE, 1960). The difficulty of ensuring uniform impregnation may be illustrated by quoting the dimensions of the required graphite fuel cans: 6 ft. 6 in. long, $3\frac{1}{4}$ in. diameter.

The fuel can is actually the third line of defence against the emission of fission products into the main coolant stream (*Figure 2.16*). The first delay is introduced by diffusion of the fission products from the matrix graphite structure of the fuel ring. The second barrier is the fuel box. The latter serves three primary purposes: firstly to protect the fuel can from irradiation damage by fission fragments, secondly to impose a delay of about one hour upon the escape of volatile fission products and thirdly to act as a barrier to those fission products which move by surface diffusion. The space between the fuel boxes and the inside of the fuel can is purged with helium introduced from the main coolant stream by means of a porous graphite plug, and the gaseous fission products will be swept out of the reactor core into a special auxiliary system in which they will be absorbed on charcoal cooled by liquid nitrogen.

Since the centre graphite temperature will be about 1,700°C and the fuel boxes will be at about 1,500°C, it will be appreciated that the conditions are the most extreme so far encountered in nuclear applications of graphite. Successful operation will require a considerable range of mechanical and physical properties of the graphite to remain relatively unaffected by prolonged and intense irradiation. Moreover the fuel rods must be assembled into clusters to form fuel elements and these intricate components present the graphite manufacturer with some formidable problems, especially since the

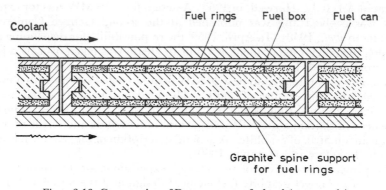

*Figure 2.16.* Cross-section of Dragon reactor fuel rod (not to scale).

graphites are of types not in common use. The fuel elements will have to be degassed at temperatures approaching 2,000°C in vacuum, to remove oxidizing gaseous impurities, and all subsequent handling and loading into the reactor must of necessity be performed in a specially purified atmosphere.

An alternative approach to the same problems of fission product control in a graphite system adopted in several design studies is exemplified in the Krupp–Brown Boverie reactor at Julich in Germany (SCHULTEN, 1960). In this reactor the uranium or thorium-impregnated graphite fuel will be contained in impermeable graphite spheres of several centimetres diameter. The spheres will be randomly packed in the core. Yet another application of the same principle is being studied in several laboratories. This consists of applying a relatively impermeable graphite coating to the individual fuel particles (which may be in the range 50–500 microns diameter) which are then embedded in a dense graphite matrix.

All of these reactors will be extending graphite technology well beyond the limits of established commercial practice.

REFERENCES

ALBAUGH, F. W. (1960). Quoted in *Reactor Core Materials*, **3**, No. 2, 12

ANDERSON, A. R., DAVIDSON, H. W., LIND, R., STRANKS, D. R., TYZACK, C. and WRIGHT, J. (1958). 'Chemical studies of carbon dioxide and graphite under reactor conditions.' *Proc. Second Geneva Conf.*, **7**, 335

ANDERSON, A. R., TAYLOR, N. K., WAITE, R. J. and WRIGHT, J. (1960). 'Measurement of the oxidation rate of BEPO graphite.' (Part of) U.S.A.E.C. Report, TID-7597

ANTILL, J. E. and PEAKALL, K. A. 'Attack of graphite by gaseous impurities in a high temperature helium-cooled graphite-moderated reactor.' *Proc. Third Metallurgy Colloquium: Corrosion, Saclay, June 1959.* North-Holland Publ. Co.

ASHER, R. C., MORETON-SMITH, M., MOUL, A. N. and SHARRATT, E. (1960). Unpublished work at A.E.R.E., Harwell

BACON, G. E. (1958). 'Crystallographic studies of graphites.' U.K.A.E.A. Report, AERE M/R-2702

BACON, G. E. (1960). 'Radiation damage in graphite.' *J. chim. phys.*, **57**, 828

BAIRD, J. D., GEACH, G. A., KNAPTON, A. G. and WEST, K. B. C. (1958). 'Compatibility of beryllium with other materials used in reactors.' *Proc. Second Geneva Conf.*, **5**, 328

BAKER, D. E. (1958). Quoted in 'Information Meeting on Gas-cooled Power Reactors.' U.S.A.E.C. Report, TID-7564

BARRER, R. M. (1936). 'Sorption processes on diamond and graphite, Part I. Reactions with hydrogen.' *J. Chem. Soc. Lond.*, 1256

BARRER, R. M. and RIDEAL, E. K. (1935). 'The interaction of hydrogen with microcrystalline charcoal.' *Proc. Roy. Soc.*, **A149**, 231, 253

BLACKWOOD, J. D. (1959). 'The reaction of carbon with hydrogen at high pressure, *Austr. J. Chem.*, **12**, 14

BLAKELEY, T. H. (1959). 'The gasification of carbon in carbon dioxide and other gases at temperatures above 900°C.' *Proc. Fourth Conf. on Carbon*, p. 95, Pergamon Press

BLOCHER, J. M. and CAMPBELL, I. E. (1958). 'Carbide coatings for graphite.' *Proc. Second Geneva Conf.*, **7**, 374

BOKROS, J. C. (1959). 'Graphite-metal compatibility at high temperatures.' U.S.A.E.C. Report, GA-782. See also *J. Nucl. Materials*, 1961, **3**, 89

BONNER, F. and TURKEVICH, J. (1951). 'Study of the carbon dioxide-carbon reaction using $^{14}C$ as a tracer, *J. Amer. Chem. Soc.*, **73**, 561

BOOCOCK, G. and HOLDSWORTH, S. D. (1958). 'Carbonisation and graphitisation of polymeric and related materials: a survey of the literature.' U.K.A.E.A. Report, AERE CE/M 220

BOYLAND, D. A. (1959). 'The reduction of the permeability of graphite.' *G.E.C. Atomic Energy Review*, **2**, No. 1, 44

BRADSTREET, S. W. (1959). 'Graphite technology.' Wright Air Development Centre Report (U.S.A.), WADC-TR-58-503

BRADSTREET, S. W. (1960). 'Modified graphite technology; quarterly report No. 1.' U.S.A.E.C. Report, ARF-6038-8

BREWER, L., GILLES, P. W. and JENKINS, F. A. (1948). 'The vapour pressure and heat of sublimation of graphite.' *J. Chem. Phys.*, **16**, 797

BROOM, W. E. J. and TRAVERS, M. W. (1932). 'Reaction between carbon and certain gases.' *Proc. Roy. Soc.*, **A135**, 512

BURAS, B. (1955). 'Some experiments concerning pile materials.' *Proc. First Geneva Conf.*, **8**, 478

BURTON, H. H. (1959). Unpublished work at Hanford, quoted in U.S.A.E.C. Report ORNL-2699

CARTER, R. L. (1959). 'Compatibility problems in the use of graphite in nuclear reactors.' *Atompraxis*, **5**, 142

COMMITTEE OF INQUIRY. 'Report on the Accident at Windscale No. 1 Pile on 10th October, 1957.' Her Majesty's Stationery Office, London

CONWAY-JONES, J. M. (1960). 'The new "impermeable" graphite.' *Brit. Power Engng*, **1**, No. 1, 64

COPESTAKE, T. B. and CORNEY, N. S. (1961). 'The reaction between carbon and carbon dioxide under irradiation.' U.S.A.E.C. Report, TID-7597

COPESTAKE, T. B., DAVIDSON, H. W. and TONGE, B. L. (1959). 'A study of the reactions of graphite with carbon dioxide, with reference to gas-cooled nuclear reactors.' *J. Appl. Chem.*, **9**, 75

CORNAULT, P. and DES ROCHETTES, H. 'Problèmes posées par la fabrication du graphite nucléaire.' *Proc. Conf. on Industrial Graphite and Carbon*, London, September 1957

CORNEY, N. S. and THOMAS, R. B. (1958). 'The effect of pile radiation on the reaction between hydrogen and graphite.' U.K.A.E.A. Report, AERE C/R-2502

CORNEY, N. S., MARSH, W. R. and WRIGHT, J. (1960). 'Experimental techniques in the study of the reaction between graphite and carbon dioxide under irradiation.' U.K.A.E.A. Report, AERE-M 667

COWEN, H. and LIND, R. (1960). 'High flux experiments in the system $CO_2/CO/$ graphite.' (Part of) U.S.A.E.C. Report, TID-7597

CROFT, R. C. (1960). 'Lamellar compounds of graphite.' *Quart. Rev.*, **14**, No. 1

CUBICCIOTTI, D. (1952). 'The diffusion of xenon from uranium-carbide impregnated graphite at high temperatures.' U.S.A.E.C. Report, NAA-SR-194

CURRIE, L. M., HAMISTER, V. C. and MacPHERSON, H. G. (1955). 'The production and properties of graphite for reactors.' *Proc. First Geneva Conf.*, **8**, 451

DAHL, R. E. (1960). 'Preliminary evaluation of chlorine for use as a gas-cooled reactor safeguard.' U.S.A.E.C. Report, HW-63902 (Rev)

DARNEY, A. (1957). 'Pitch binder for carbon electrodes.' *Proc. Conf. on Industrial Carbon and Graphite*, London

DAVIDGE, P. C. and MARSH, W. R. (1955). 'The effect of pile radiation on the carbon dioxide–graphite reaction.' U.K.A.E.A. Report, AERE C/R 1374 (Del.)

DAVIDGE, P. C., HODGE, N. and STOCKDALE, G. N. (1960). 'The purification of inert gases by hot uranium.' *Brit. Chem. Eng.*, **5**, 477, 566

DAVIDGE, P. C., TOMLINSON, M. and WRIGHT, J. (1959). 'The oxidation of graphite during irradiation in oxygen.' U.K.A.E.A. Report, AERE C/R-1450

DAVIDSON, H. W. (1958). 'Graphite for nuclear reactors.' *G.E.C. Atomic Energy Review*, **1**, 130

DAVIDSON, H. W. and RYDE, J. W. (1960). 'Improvements in or relating to methods of protecting graphite surfaces.' Brit. Pat. 830,005

DAVIDSON, J. M., WOODRUFF, E. M. and YOSHIKAWA, H. H. (1959). 'High temperature radiation-induced graphite contraction.' U.S.A.E.C. Report, HW-57900

DAWSON, I. M. and FOLLETT, E. A. C. (1959). 'An electron microscope study of synthetic graphite.' *Proc. Roy. Soc.*, **A253**, 390

DAY, R. J. (1959). Quoted by Walker, Rusinko and Austin, *Adv. in Catalysis*, **11**, 134

DIENES, G. J. and VINEYARD, G. H. (1957). *Radiation Effects in Solids*. Interscience Publishers, New York

DODSON, M. H. (1960). 'The depth of oxidation of graphite: a theoretical approach.' U.K.A.E.A. Report, DEG Report 148 (CA)

DOMINEY, D. A. (1961). 'The efficiency of CO as an inhibitor of mass transport from carbon under pile irradiation in the presence of $CO_2$.' U.K.A.E.A. Report, AERE-R. 3481

DOYLE, L. B. (1953). 'High temperature diffusion of individual fission elements from uranium carbide impregnated graphite.' U.S.A.E.C. Report, NAA-SR-255

DUVAL, X. (1961). 'Les réactions du graphite avec l'oxygène.' *J. chim. phys.*, **58**, 3

EATHERLY, W. P. *et al.* (1958). 'Physical properties of graphite materials for special nuclear applications.' *Proc. Second Geneva Conf.*, **7**, 389

EGGLESTON, R. R. *et al.* (1955). 'Graphite outgassing.' U.S.A.E.C. Report, NAA-SR-Memo-1240

ERGUN, S. (1956). 'Kinetics of the reaction of carbon dioxide with carbon.' *J. Phys. Chem.*, **60**, 480

FELDMAN, M. H. (1951). 'A new aspect of radiation damage: changed gas sorption properties of irradiated graphite and metals.' U.S.A.E.C. Report, NAA-SR-124 (Rev.)

FINDLAY, J. R. (1958). Unpublished work, A.E.R.E., Harwell

FINDLAY, J. R. and LAING, T. (1960). Unpublished work, A.E.R.E., Harwell

FINK, C. G. and WROUGHTON, D. M. (1945). 'A study in nitrogen fixation at atmospheric pressures.' *Trans. Electrochem. Soc.*, **88**, 25

FRANKLIN, ROSALIND, E. (1951). 'Structure of graphite carbons.' *Acta Cryst.*, **4**, 253

FRANKLIN, ROSALIND E. (1951b). 'Crystallite growth in graphitising and non-graphitising carbons.' *Proc. Roy. Soc.*, **A209**, 196

GADSBY, J., LONG, F. J., SLEIGHTHOLM, P. and SYKES, K. W. (1948). 'The mechanism of the carbon dioxide–carbon reaction.' *Proc. Roy. Soc.*, **A193**, 357

GERDS, A. F. and MALLETT, M. W. (1958). 'The compatibility of a number of metals and alloys with graphite.' U.S.A.E.C. Report, BMI-1261

GIBERSON, R. C. (1961). 'Reactions of graphite with microwave-activated nitrogen: preliminary report.' U.S.A.E.C. Report HW-68380

GLOCKLER, G. (1954). 'The heat of sublimation of graphite and the composition of carbon vapour.' *J. Chem. Phys.*, **22**, 159

GOW, H. B. F. and MARSH, W. R. (1960). 'Temperature effects on the radiation induced reaction of carbon dioxide with graphite.' U.K.A.E.A. Report, AERE-R 3194

GROTH, W. (1937). 'Photochemische Untersuchungen im Ultraviolet, No. 3.' *Z. phys. Chem.*, **B37**, 307

HANDWERK, J. H., LIED, R. C. and SHALEK, P. D. Quoted in 'Argonne National Laboratory Metallurgy Division Quarterly Report, April–May, 1957.' U.S.A.E.C. Report, ANL-5790

HARTECK, P. and DONDES, S. (1955). 'Decomposition of carbon dioxide by ionising radiation, Part I.' *J. Chem. Phys.*, **23**, 902

HARTECK, P. and DONDES, S. (1957). 'Decomposition of carbon dioxide by ionising radiation, Part II.' *J. Chem. Phys.*, **26**, 1727

HEDLEY, J. A. (1960). 'An electron microscope study of graphite oxidation.' *Nature, Lond.*, **188**, No. 4744, 44

HENNIG, G. R. (1958). 'A chemical model of radiation damage in graphite.' *Nucl. Sci. Engng*, **3**, 514

HENNIG, G. (1960). Quoted in *Reactor Handbook*, Second Edition, Ed. C. R. Tipton, Interscience Publishers

HENNIG, G. R., DIENES, G. J. and KOSIBA, W. (1958). 'Radiation effects on the oxidation rate and on other chemical properties of graphite.' *Proc. Second Geneva Conf.*, **7**, 301

HENNIG, G. R. and HOVE, J. E. (1955). 'Interpretation of radiation damage to graphite.' *Proc. First Geneva Conf.*, **7**, 666

HIRSCHFELDER, J. O. and TAYLOR, H. S. (1938). 'The alpha-particle reactions in carbon monoxide, oxygen and carbon dioxide systems.' *J. Chem. Phys.*, **6**, 783

HORTON, C. C. and ROBERTS, L. E. J. (1958). 'The adsorption of water on pile graphite.' U.K.A.E.A. Report, AERE C/R 2219

HOVE, J. E. 'Thermal properties of graphite.' *Proc. Third Conference on Carbon*, Buffalo, 1957, Pergamon Press

HOVE, J. E. (1958). 'Graphite as a high temperature material.' *Trans. Met. Soc. AIME*, **212**, No. 1, 7

Hove, J. E. (1959). 'Low temperature irradiation and annealing effects in graphite.' *Progr. Nucl. Energy*, Series V, **2**, Pergamon Press

Huddle, R. A. U., Arragon, P. A. P. and Price, M. S. T. (1960). 'Dragon graphite.' *Nuclear Engng*, **5**, 314

Hunter, L. P. (1959). 'Effect of fission fragment recoils on the thermal conductivity of graphites.' *J. Appl. Phys.*, **30**, 1969

Hutcheon, J. M., Longstaff, B. and Warner, R. K. 'The flow of gases through a fine pore graphite.' *Proc. Conf. on Industrial Carbon and Graphite*, London, 1957.

Hutcheon, J. M. and Price, M. S. T. (1960). 'The dependence of the properties of graphite on porosity.' *Proc. Fourth Conf. on Carbon*, Buffalo; Pergamon Press

Iskanderian, H. P. (1960). 'Criticality study on TREAT reactor: cause of excess boron impurity in graphite.' *Nucl. Sci. Engng*, **7**, No. 6, 554

Jain, S. C. and Krishnan, K. S. (1954). 'Distribution of temperature along a thin rod electrically heated *in vacuo*.' *Proc. Roy. Soc.*, **A225**, 1

Juel, L. H. (1952). 'Modifications of the F-process.' U.S.A.E.C. Report, AECD-3758

Juel, L. H., *et al.* 'High density graphite.' Semi-annual report for June through November, 1952. U.S.A.E.C. Report, AECD-3751

Kinchin, G. H. (1959). 'The effects of irradiation on graphite.' Atomic Energy of Canada, Ltd., Report CRNE-539

Kmeto, E. M. *Proc. First and Second Conferences on Carbon*, University of Buffalo, 1956. Edited by Mrozowski and Phillips

Knott, D. M. (1954). 'The graphite-steam reaction.' U.S.A.E.C. Report, HW-30693

Koretzky, J. *et al.* (1959). 'Physical distortion of graphite, progress report.' (Part of) U.S.A.E.C. Report, BMI-1315

Kosiba, W. L., Dienes, G. J. and Gurinsky, D. H. (1957). 'The effect of radiation on the rate of oxidation of graphite.' (Part of) U.S.A.E.C. Report, BNL-489

Langmuir, I. (1915). 'Chemical reactions at low pressures.' *J. Amer. Chem. Soc.*, **37**, 1139

Large, N. R., *et al.* (1961). Unpublished work at A.E.R.E., Harwell

Legendre, A., Gueron, J. and Hering, H. (1958). 'General study of nuclear graphites produced in France.' *Proc. Second Geneva Conf.*, **4**, 243

Leppla, P. W. and Markel, R. F. (1951). 'F-process final report.' U.S.A.E.C. Report, AECD-3759

Lewis, F. A. and Ubbelodhe, A. R. (1960). *Graphite and its crystal compounds*. Clarendon Press; Oxford University Press

Loch, L. D. and Slyh, J. A. (1954). 'The technology and fabrication of graphite.' *Chem. Engng. Progr. Symposium Series*, No. 11, **50**, 39

Lockett, E. E. (1957). 'The use of graphite as a moderator in nuclear reactors.' *Proc. Conf. on Industrial Graphite and Carbon*, London

Lockett, G. E. and Huddle, R. A. U. (1960). 'The Dragon reactor.' *Nuclear Power*, **5**, No. 46, 112

Losty, H. H. W. (1960). 'The effect of impregnation and heat treatment on the physical properties of graphite.' *Proc. Fourth Conf. on Carbon*, Buffalo, Pergamon Press

Lucks, C. F., Deem, H. W. and Wood, W. D. (1960). 'Thermal properties of six glasses and two graphites.' *Amer. Ceram. Soc. Bull.*, **39**, 313

MacPherson, H. G. (1960). Molten salt reactor programme, quarterly progress report for period ending October 31st, 1959. U.S.A.E.C. Report, ORNL-2890

Matuyama, E. (1958). *Tanso*, **7**, 12. Quoted by Steward and Cook, *Nature, Lond.*, **185**, No. 4706 (1960), 78

Mayers, M. A. (1934). 'The rate of oxidation of graphite by steam.' *J. Amer. Chem. Soc.*, **56**, 1879

McNeil, D. and Wood, J. L. (1957). 'The use of coal tar pitch as an electrode binder.' *Proc. Conf. on Industrial Carbon and Graphite*, London

# REFERENCES

Mrozowski, S. (1958). 'Investigation of elastic and thermal properties of carbon-base bodies.' Wright Air Development Center. Report WADC-TR-58-360

Mrozowski, S. (1959). 'Kinetics of graphitisation.' *Kinetics of High Temperature Processes*, ed. by Kingery; Wiley, New York

Nairn, J. S. and Wilkinson, V. J. (1960). 'The prediction of conditions for self-sustaining graphite combustion in air.' U.S.A.E.C. Report, TID-7597 (1960)

Nakai, T., Yajima, S., Shiba, K., Osugi, J. and Shinoda, D. (1960). 'The behaviour of fission products captured in graphite by nuclear recoil, Part II.' *Bull. Chem. Soc. Japan*, **33**, 497

Nathans, M. W. (1954). 'High density graphite-final report.' U.S.A.E.C. Report, COO-202

Nelson, J. B. and Riley, D. P. (1945). 'Thermal expansion of graphite from 15° to 800°C.' *Proc. Phys. Soc.*, **57**, 477

Nightingale, R. E. and Fletcher, J. F. (1957). 'Radiation damage to graphite from 30° to 185°C.' (Part of) U.S.A.E.C. Report, BNL-489

Nightingale, R. E., Davidson, J. M. and Snyder, W. A. (1958). 'Damage effects to graphite irradiated up to 1000°C.' *Proc. Second Geneva Conf.*, **7**, 295

Norton, F. J. and Marshall, A. L. (1944). 'The degassing of metals (and graphite).' *Trans. Amer. Inst. Mining Met. Engrs.*, **156**, 351

O'Driscoll, W. G. and Bell, J. C. (1958). 'Graphite: its properties and behaviour.' *Nucl. Engng*, **3**, No. 32, 479

O'Driscoll, W. G., Dunabin, J. E., Martin, W. H. and Walker, A. (1960). 'The oxidation of graphite by carbon dioxide activated by electrodeless discharge.' U.K.A.E.A. Report, IGR-TN/C-1074

Okada, J. (1960). 'Thermal expansion of pitch-bonded carbons.' *Proc. Fourth Conf. on Carbon*, Buffalo; Pergamon Press

Okada, J. and Ikegawa, T. (1953). 'Combustion rate of artificial graphites from 700–2000°C in air.' *J. Appl. Phys.*, **24**, 1249

Onslow-MacAulay, I. N. and Tomlinson, M. (1960). 'On the possibility of radiation-induced transport of carbon in helium.' U.K.A.E.A. Report, AERE-R 3262

Orth, C. J. (1961). 'Diffusion of lanthanides and actinides from graphite at high temperatures.' *Nucl. Sci. Engng.*, **9**, 417

Overholser, L. G. and Blakely, J. P. (1960). Quoted in Reactor Chemistry Division Annual Progress Report for Period ending January 31, 1960. U.S.A.E.C. Report, ORNL-2931

Pascard, R. and Farbre, R. (1958). Chapter 6—I of *Glove Boxes and Shielded Cells*, Ed. G. N. Walton, Butterworths, London

Perret, R. P. (1959). 'The market for nuclear materials, II. Moderators, A, Graphite.' O.E.E.C. Report to Stresa Conference, May 1959

Petersen, E. E. and Wright, C. C. (1955). 'Reaction of artificial graphite with carbon dioxide.' *Ind. Eng. Chem.*, **47**, 1624, 1629

Powell, R. (1937). 'Thermal and electrical conductivities of a sample of Acheson graphite from 0° to 800°C.' *Proc. Phys. Soc.* **49**, 419

Powell, R. and Schofield, F. H. (1939). 'Thermal and electrical conductivities of carbon and graphite to high temperatures.' *Proc. Phys. Soc.*, **51**, 153

Prados, J. W. (1961). 'Graphite oxidation.' *Nuclear Safety*, **2**, No. 4, 12

Price, M. S. T. (1959). 'The use of furfuryl alcohol as a bonding agent for low permeability graphite.' U.K.A.E.A. Report, AERE L-124, Presented at Dragon Graphite Symposium, Bournemouth

Price, M. S. T. (1959b). 'The development of low permeability graphite.' U.K.A.E.A. report, AERE L-123, Presented at Dragon Graphite Symposium, Bournemouth

RAGONE, D. V. (1960). 'Equilibrium concentrations of several gaseous species (CO, $CO_2$, $CH_4$, $H_2$ and $H_2O$) in contact with graphite at very low hydrogen and oxygen levels.' U.S.A.E.C. Report, GA-1109

RAWSON, H. and BAYNTON, P. L. (1959). 'Improvements in the protection of graphite against gas corrosion at elevated temperatures.' Brit. Pat. 812,740

REDMOND, J. P. and WALKER, P. L. (1960). 'Gas content of graphites.' *Nature, Lond.*, **186**, No. 4718, 72

REDMOND, J. P. and WALKER, P. L. (1960). 'Hydrogen sorption of graphite at elevated temperatures.' *J. Phys. Chem.*, **64**, 1093

RIESZ, C. H. and SUSMAN, S. (1960). 'Synthetic binders for carbon and graphite.' *Proc. Fourth Conf. on Carbon*, Buffalo; Pergamon Press

RILEY, W. C., SUNDERMAN, D. N. and DUNNINGTON, B. W. (1959). 'Release of fission products from fuelled graphite.' *Amer. Inst. Mining, Met., Pet. Engng.*; *Inst. Metals Special Report Ser.* No. 9, 87

ROBINSON, P. J. and TAYLOR, J. C. (1959). 'Thermal instability due to graphite oxidation.' *Nucl. Engng*, **4**, 400

SAWAI, T., *et al.* (1958). 'Some problems of manufacturing reactor graphite.' *Proc. Second Geneva Conf.*, **4**, 257

SCHMIDT, L., BOEHM, H. P. and HOFMANN, U. (1957). 'Red carbon.' *Proc. Third Conf. on Carbon*, 235, Pergamon Press

SCHULTEN, R. (1960). *Proc. Symp. on Gas-cooled Reactors*, sponsored by the Franklin Institute and the American Nuclear Soc., p. 109

SCHWEITZER, D. G. (1960). Comments quoted in U.S.A.E.C. Report, TID-7597

SERMON, G. T. (1948). 'Purification of graphites.' U.S.A.E.C. Report, AECD-3912

SHEA, F. L. (1956). 'Production of coke from petroleum hydrocarbons.' U.S. Patent 2,775,549 (to Great Lakes Carbon Corp.)

SHEPHERD, L. R., LOCKETT, G. E., HUDDLE, R. A. U., STERRY, F., HUSSAIN, L. A. and WORDSWORTH, D. V. (1958). 'The possibilities of achieving high temperatures in a gas-cooled reactor.' *Proc. Second Geneva Conf.*, **9**, 289

SIEGEL, S., CARTER, R. L., BOWMAN, F. E. and HAYWARD, B. R. (1955). 'Basic technology of the sodium graphite reactor.' *Proc. First Geneva Conf.*, **9**, 321

SIMMONS, J. H. W. (1957). 'Irradiation damage in graphite.' Proceedings of U.S./U.K. Graphite Conference, U.S.A.E.C. Report, TID-7565 (Part 1)

SMITH, C. A. and YOUNG, C. T. (1951). 'Diffusion of fission fragments from uranium-impregnated graphite.' U.S.A.E.C. Report, NAA-SR-72.

SMITH, R. N. (1959). 'The chemistry of carbon–oxygen surface compounds.' *Quart. Rev.*, **13**, 287

SPALARIS, C. N. (1953). 'Water adsorbed by graphite at various relative pressures.' U.S.A.E.C. Report, HW-24109

SPALARIS, N. (1953). 'Surface studies of irradiated graphite.' U.S.A.E.C. Report, HW-29082

SPALARIS, C. N., BUPP, L. P. and GILBERT, E. C. (1957). 'Surface properties of irradiated graphite.' *J. Phys. Chem.*, **61**, 350

STAPLETON, B. (1959). 'Brazing graphite to Nilo-K tubes.' U.K.A.E.A. report, IG Report 140(RD/CA)

STEWARD, E. G. and COOK, B. P. (1960). 'X-ray measurement of thermal expansion perpendicular to the layer planes of artificial and natural graphites.' *Nature, Lond.*, **185**, 78

STRAUSS, H. E. (1960). 'Studies of thermal conductivity of polycrystalline graphite at high temperature.' *Proc. Fourth Conf. on Carbon*, Buffalo; Pergamon Press

STREZNEWSKI, J. and TURKEVICH, J. (1957). 'The reaction of carbon with oxygen atoms.' *Proc. Third Conf. on Carbon*, p. 273, Pergamon Press

# REFERENCES

SUTTON, W. H. (1960). 'Apparatus for measuring thermal conductivity of ceramic and metallic materials to 1200°C.' *J. Amer. Ceram. Soc.*, **43**, No. 2, 81

THOMPSON, A. S. (1956). 'Gas cooled nuclear reactor study, final report from Studebaker–Packard Corporation.' U.S.A.E.C. Report, AECU-3559

THORN, R. J. and WINSLOW, G. H. (1957). 'Vaporisation coefficient of graphite and composition of the equilibrium vapour.' *J. Chem. Phys.*, **26**, 186

TOMLINSON, M. (1959). 'Comparison of data on the oxidation of graphite in reactors.' U.K.A.E.A. Report, AERE C/R-2619. *Nuclear Power*, **4**, No. 43, 117

TOMLINSON, M. (1961). Unpublished work at A.E.R.E., Harwell

WALKER, P. L., FORESTI, R. J. and WRIGHT, C. C. (1953). 'Surface area studies of carbon–carbon dioxide reaction.' *Ind. Eng. Chem.*, **45**, 1703

WALKER, P. L., McKINSTRY, H. A. and WRIGHT, C. (1953). 'X-ray diffraction studies of a graphitising carbon: changes in interlayer spacing and binding energy with temperature.' *Ind. Eng. Chem.*, **45**, 1711

WALKER, P. L., RUSINKO, F. and AUSTIN, L. G. (1959). 'Gas reactions of carbon.' *Advances in Catalysis*, **11**, 134

WALTON, G. N. (1962). (Reporting work by Bromley and Large.) 'Migration of fission products in graphite.' *Nucl. Engng*, **7**, No. 70, 97

WATT, W., BICKERDIKE, R. L., BROWN, A. R. G., JOHNSON, W. and HUGHES, G. (1959). 'Production of impermeable graphite.' *Nuclear Power*, **4**, No. 34, 86

WEST, J. M. (1949). 'Purification of graphite.' U.S.A.E.C. Report, HW-12780 (Rev.)

WICKE, E. (1955). *Fifth Symposium on Combustion*, p. 245. Reinhold Publ. Co.

WIRTZ, K. (1955). 'Production and neutron absorption of nuclear graphite.' *Proc. First Geneva Conf.*, **8**, 496

WOODLEY, R. E. (1954). 'Promotion of chemical reaction in gas–graphite systems by gamma radiation.' U.S.A.E.C. Report, HW-31929

WOODLEY, R. E. (1955). 'The promotion of chemical reaction by pile radiation.' U.S.A.E.C. Report, HW-40142

WOODLEY, R. E. (1957). 'A preliminary study of neutron irradiation and oxidation at moderate temperatures on the structural characteristics of CSF graphite.' U.S.A.E.C. Report, HW-52375

WOODRUFF, E. M. (1957). 'Dimensional changes in irradiated graphite.' (Part of) U.S.A.E.C. Report, TID-7565 (Part 1)

WOODS, W. K., BUPP, L. P. and FLETCHER, J. F. (1955). 'Irradiation damage to artificial graphite.' *Proc. First Geneva Conf.*, **7**, 455

WRIGHT, J. (1960). Unpublished work at A.E.R.E., Harwell

WRIGHT, J. (1960b). 'The radiation-induced $CO_2$/graphite reaction: a tentative view of the mechanism.' (Part of) U.S.A.E.C. Report, TID-7597

WYNNE-JONES, W. F. K. (1956). *Reactivity of carbon*. Symposium on the Properties of Carbon, Kings College, Newcastle-upon-Tyne

YOUNG, C. T. (1953). 'High temperature diffusion of individual fission products from small uranium-impregnated graphite samples under deuteron bombardment.' U.S.A.E.C. Report, NAA-SR-247

ZINMAN, W. G. (1960). 'A study of the interaction between carbon and dissociated gases.' *J. Amer. Chem. Soc.*, **82**, 1262

69

# CHAPTER 3

# OXIDATION OF METALS

THE coolant circuits of gas-cooled reactors pose a complex array of compatibility problems. The variety of coolant gases in use or proposed has been indicated in Chapter 1: in many instances an important aspect of compatibility arises from the effect of trace impurities in the gas. There is thus a substantial number of gaseous environments to be considered, and we have had to select for discussion in the present chapter only those of greatest importance for the shorter-term development of power reactors.

Much of the available information is still of a fragmentary nature and it is often difficult to give a rational explanation for the phenomena observed. The compatibility of metals with reactor coolant gases presents a rich field for further investigation: apart from the requirement for a better understanding of the nature of the processes which control the oxidation of the metals in question, the circumstances leading to various forms of localized attack require clarification and the effects of irradiation have been investigated to only a very limited extent.

## 3.1 URANIUM

### 3.1.1 Reaction with Oxygen or Air below 250°C

It is convenient to consider the oxidation of uranium in two regions of temperature, below and above 250°C. In the lower region there is little difference between the reaction with pure oxygen or with dry air. Early results obtained in these media have been summarized by SCHNIZLEIN et al. (1959); they show a very wide scatter, probably as a result of variations in the amounts of moisture impurity in the gas.

A detailed study of the reaction between uranium and dry oxygen has been made at the Argonne National Laboratory by Schnizlein and co-workers. They compared the rate of oxidation at 200°C and a pressure of 1 atmosphere in oxygen, air and 4:1 helium–oxygen mixtures. It was observed that differences as high as a factor of 2 could occur in these more recent experiments, with the lowest long-term rate being in air; such differences are small, however, compared with the scatter shown by the earlier data.

Qualitatively the overall oxidation curve for uranium appears to be as shown in *Figure 3.1*. It is convenient to consider this as composed of three main sections:

OA, a pre-transition region, in which a parabolic or a rectilinear rate law is followed. In view of the gradual acceleration to a higher rate in the region AB, it may be difficult to distinguish between parabolic and rectilinear behaviour.

70

ABC, a post-transition region, with an apparently rectilinear portion at BC which changes in range with changing temperature.

CD, the gradual development of a third, but lower rectilinear rate.

Below 125°C, there is evidence that the oxidation initially follows a parabolic rate law (CUBICCIOTTI, 1952; WABER, 1956; ADDA, 1958):

$$(\text{weight gain})^2 = k \, (\text{time})$$

This phase of the reaction is ultimately succeeded by a considerably increased rate at a time which decreases rapidly with increasing temperature (see also BAGLEY and OLIVER, 1953). According to Waber, for oxidation by dry oxygen at 75°C, the transition takes place at a time of about 600 days and an increase in weight of some 30 $\mu$g cm$^{-2}$; he also obtained some evidence that after about $10^4$ hours exposure the rate transformed to a rectilinear relationship. The transition to higher rates was attributed to cracking of the oxide film on the metal.

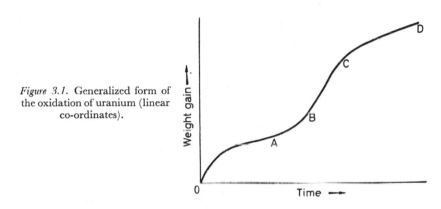

*Figure 3.1.* Generalized form of the oxidation of uranium (linear co-ordinates).

Schnizlein *et al.* claimed that at higher temperatures (125–295°C) the relationship between weight gain and time was linear rather than parabolic over short periods of exposure in oxygen. Furthermore, the linear rate subsequently increased in a manner which depended on temperature as shown in *Figure 3.2*.

The illustration shows that in the region above about 2,000 $\mu$g cm$^{-2}$ of oxygen uptake by the uranium there is a diminution in the rate of oxidation (see also CD of *Figure 3.1*). A similar effect was observed by WABER (1956) for oxidation carried out within the range 185–260°C. He suggested that it might be due to a change in the composition of the film of oxide on the metal.

Information from other sources on the composition of the oxide film is not well defined. Early workers claimed that below about 150–200°C the oxide was mainly $UO_2$, whereas above that temperature it was primarily $U_3O_8$ (WATHEN, 1943; BAGLEY and OLIVER, 1953). Later work at Hanford was in general agreement with this, but the temperature of transition was found to be 300°C (HILLIARD, 1958). The latter deduction was made from the amount of oxygen consumed in the reaction, however, and gave no indication of any possible changes in composition through the thickness of the oxide film.

71

After the initial (parabolic) stage of the reaction, the surface of the uranium begins to acquire nodules of oxide at a rate which differs on different grains, and the nodules spread laterally over the surface (MISHLER *et al.*, 1961). Subsequently the surface becomes covered with a powdery oxide, superimposed on a very thin and more adherent layer. AYLMORE *et al.* (1959) have shown that the thick film formed during the linear oxidation of uranium is porous with respect to the passage of molecular oxygen. X-ray diffraction analysis has indicated that the outer oxide layer has a structure similar to $U_3O_8$, whereas the thin inner layer has a structure similar to $UO_2$ but with some contraction of the unit cell (LORIERS, 1952). An oxide with a tetragonal structure has also been observed (BAGLEY and OLIVER, 1953; WABER, 1956).

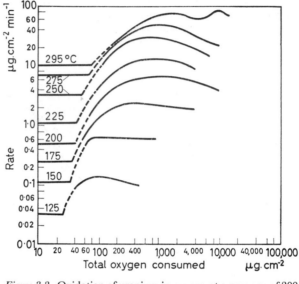

*Figure 3.2.* Oxidation of uranium in oxygen at a pressure of 200 mm (Schnizlein *et al.*, 1959) (by courtesy of Argonne National Laboratory).

In many respects the composite curve shown in *Figure 3.1* is qualitatively very similar to that observed for niobium in oxygen. The latter has been studied and reviewed recently by Cox (1962), who favoured the suggestion of INOUYE (1960) that the transition beyond point A was due to nucleation of nodules of $Nb_2O_5$ in the initially uniform thin film of $NbO/NbO_2$. The transition to the lower linear rate CD was attributed to possible restriction of the flow of oxygen to the inner oxide film by the thickening outer oxide of $Nb_2O_5$. It was necessary to postulate that the porosity of the outer film attained an equilibrium state where it presented a constant restriction to the flow of oxygen.

The nature of the oxidation of uranium might be explained on a similar basis. In the initial stages (OA) the rate of oxidation is controlled by diffusion through a thin uniform film of $UO_2$. SCHNIZLEIN *et al.* (1960) claim to have shown by marker experiments that oxygen ion rather than uranium ion diffusion is predominant: these results were obtained, however, after extensive oxidation into the region BC where additional processes will be taking place.

The transition to the region BC is often explained in the oxidation of other metals as due to continuous cracking of the oxide film leaving a diffusion barrier of constant thickness at the metal–oxide interface. LEIBOWITZ et al. (1961) consider, however, that the results obtained at the Argonne National Laboratory do not substantiate the cracking hypothesis. They have proposed that the rectilinear periods before and after transition at point A may be due to the rate-controlling step taking place at the oxide–gas interface, the increase in rate in the region AB being due to an increase in the surface area undergoing oxidation.

Returning to the comparison with niobium, an alternative hypothesis may be offered. Oxidation curves which are concave upwards and then become straight (ABC of *Figure 3.1*) can be associated with nucleation and lateral growth within the original oxide film (EVANS, 1960). The observation of the formation of nodules on the surface of oxidized uranium has been mentioned above: this may well be the nucleation and growth of a higher oxide from the initial film of $UO_2$. The composition of the new phase would most probably be $U_3O_7$ at temperatures below 200°C. When the growth of this phase has progressed to such an extent that a comparatively thick film is present, the flow to the inner barrier film may become physically restricted, as suggested by Cox (1962), for niobium oxidation.

It would be expected that the dependence of the rate of oxidation upon the pressure of oxygen should be only slight during the early stages of oxidation (region OA) but should be much higher in the region CD. PERKINS (1956) and WABER (1956) observed that the rate of oxidation did increase only slowly with increasing pressure: according to the fifth and the fourth root power of the pressure at 260 and 220°C, respectively. SCHNIZLEIN et al. (1959) found, however, that the pressure dependence in both regions OA and BC was slight at temperatures below 150°C, but was much greater at 250°C. If the influence of pressure was expressed by:

$$\text{Rate} = k_p{}^\alpha$$

the value of $\alpha$ at 250°C was 0·47 for region OA and 0·41 for region BC. The significance of this dependence of $\alpha$ upon temperature is not yet apparent.

Attempts to deduce an energy of activation for the oxidation have shown that this too varies with pressure. The values quoted by SCHNIZLEIN et al. (1959) cover the range 12–19 kcal mole$^{-1}$ for region OA and 17–20 kcal mole$^{-1}$ for region BC, the lower values being at 20 mm and the higher values at 800 mm.

It is evident from the general nature of the curves in *Figures 3.1* and *3.2* that the estimation of rates of oxidation for practical situations must be made with considerable caution. The ambient conditions must be specified precisely, and extrapolation to conditions not covered by the experimental work cannot be made with confidence. A closer study of the topography of uranium surfaces undergoing oxidation will be required in order to gain a better understanding of the processes taking place, especially investigations using the electron microscope and measurements of the change of surface area during oxidation.

*The effect of moisture*

WABER (1956) has reported that small amounts of moisture significantly increase the rate of oxidation of uranium at 75°C in air, but that there is little further increase for moisture contents above about 1 per cent relative humidity. At 200°C, however, SCHNIZLEIN *et al.* (1959) found that additions of up to 1,000 p.p.m. moisture to oxygen (3 per cent relative humidity at room temperature) had little effect on the rate of reaction. The rate in the region BC (*Figure 3.1*) at 30,000 p.p.m. water vapour was about 2·5 times that at 1,000 p.p.m. Such differences suggest that the primary effect of moisture in the ambient gas may not be upon the general corrosion process, but rather a preferential attack upon inclusions of impurities in the metal; these will differ in nature and distribution according to the source of the uranium.

*Uranium alloys*

The long-term ( $> 10^3$ hours) corrosion behaviour of uranium at 75°C in moist air is affected to only a small extent by variations in the normal levels of the common impurities in the metal (WABER, 1958); moreover, the addition of several hundred p.p.m. of iron, nickel, silicon or copper, or 5,600 p.p.m. of carbon, also has little influence (WABER, 1956). Results obtained at the Argonne National Laboratory also show that small additions of molybdenum, copper, ruthenium, aluminium, beryllium, silicon or carbon have only a slightly deleterious effect on the reaction with oxygen at 200°C and 200 mm pressure (SCHNIZLEIN *et al.*, 1959).

WABER (1958) reported that comparatively small additions of titanium ( $< 1$ per cent) to uranium can reduce the extent of attack by about a factor of 10 in air at 75°C and 50 per cent relative humidity. He observed also that additions of less than 6 per cent molybdenum led to undesirable cracking of the specimens during subsequent exposure to moist air at 75°C. Alloys containing 8–10 per cent molybdenum were much more resistant than unalloyed uranium, however, and 6–8 per cent additions of niobium were also beneficial.

A 4·7 per cent addition of niobium to uranium increased the resistance to oxidation by oxygen at 200°C and 200 mm pressure (SCHNIZLEIN *et al.*, 1959). A larger improvement may be obtained with an addition of 1·9 at. % zirconium, and with a ternary alloy U–12·3 at. % Zr–3·7 at. % Nb.

### 3.1.2 Reactions at Temperatures above 250°C

The heat of reaction of uranium with oxygen (or air) to give $U_3O_8$ is comparatively high: 285 kcal per mole of metal. Under suitable conditions, uranium is capable of self-sustained combustion in these gases, and this has given rise to a considerable amount of experimental investigation aimed at understanding the factors controlling the ignition and the burning rate. A brief summary of some early incidents involving the burning of uranium has been given by SMITH (1956).

The ignition temperature of uranium under a particular set of conditions may be defined in a number of different ways. The Argonne Laboratory team (SCHNIZLEIN *et al.*, 1959) have adopted the point at which a sharp increase in temperature occurs when a uranium sample is heated at a constant rate in an oxidizing atmosphere (see also REYNOLDS, 1959). The burning curve is complicated by the absorption of heat during the $\alpha$–$\beta$ and $\beta$–$\gamma$ transformations in the uranium (*Figure 3.3*).

ISAACS and WANKLYN (1960) used an alternative definition: ignition was considered to occur when the rate of supply of oxygen to the metal replaced the kinetics of the surface reaction as the controlling factor in the oxidation. Whichever system is used, the ignition will be dependent not only upon the

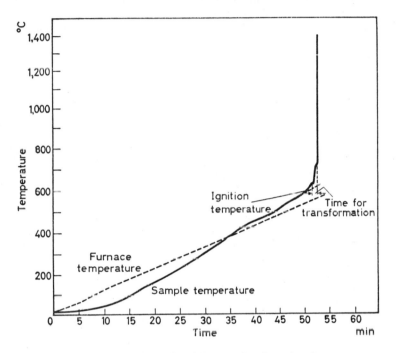

*Figure 3.3*. Ignition behaviour of an 8·5 mm cube of uranium in oxygen at a constant heating rate of 10°C per min (Schnizlein *et al*., 1959) (by courtesy of Argonne National Laboratory).

rate and the nature of the chemical reaction, but also upon the heat transfer properties of the system. It is quite possible for the removal of heat to be so efficient that 'ignition' will not occur even at comparatively high temperatures.

*Oxidation without ignition*

Isaacs and Wanklyn investigated the reaction of uranium with air by a 'shielded ignition' method. Rods of the metal, $\frac{3}{4}$ in. long and $\frac{1}{4}$ in. diameter, were heated in argon, and the temperature of the samples was monitored after the rapid introduction of a flow of air. Over the range 350–800°C, ignition did not occur.

It was observed that the oxide film influenced both the rate of oxidation and the heat transfer from the specimens. The results may be summarized qualitatively as follows:

*300°C*: Linear oxidation rate, but oxide film sufficiently adherent to prevent oscillations of the specimen temperature.

*400–450°C*: Thicker, granular oxide which impedes heat transfer more than oxidation. Specimen temperature oscillates due to discontinuous flaking of the oxide film from the metal.

*450–650°C*: Some sintering within the oxide film, but this remains non-adherent to the metal. No temperature oscillations.

*650–800°C*: More advanced sintering of the oxide to form a complete shell which offers lower resistance to heat transfer than the oxide formed at 400°C. Temperature oscillations observed.

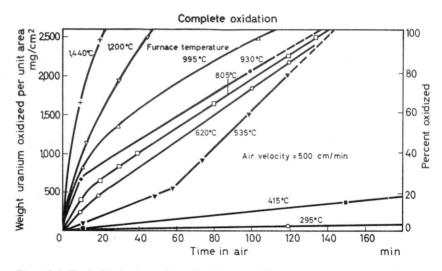

*Figure 3.4.* Typical behaviour of uranium in air at high temperatures (samples 0·75 in. long × 0·25 in. dia.) (Hilliard, 1958) (by courtesy of General Electric Company).

The reaction between uranium and air has also been investigated by HILLIARD (1958) using a similar technique over the temperature range 300–1,440°C with samples of approximately the same surface/mass ratio: the samples were up to 0·5 in. diameter. He found that burning was not sustained when the external heat supply was removed and, in general agreement with Isaacs and Wanklyn, thermal cycling of the samples was observed in the furnace temperature range 400–650°C. The peak metal temperatures were sometimes as high as 500°C above the furnace temperature.

Some typical data obtained by Hilliard for specimens of 0·25 in. diameter are shown in *Figure 3.4*. It is evident that although Isaacs and Wanklyn claimed that the rate of oxidation was linear with time this may have been due to a fortuitous choice of time interval for their measurements. Hilliard's short-term data are summarized in *Figure 3.5* which shows that over the initial ten-minute period the rate of oxidation is not strongly dependent upon the size of the specimen. The dependence of the rate of oxidation on the size of the sample is greater for longer times of oxidation. The usual significance cannot be read into the Arrhenius-type plot of *Figure 3.5* since the temperature is that of the furnace and not that of the uranium sample.

Hilliard found also that the rate of oxidation at 805°C was dependent upon the logarithm of the air velocity past the sample. At higher flow rates there will probably be a different effect due to removal of parts of the oxide layer by high shear stresses at the oxide/gas interface. In stagnant air at 805°C there

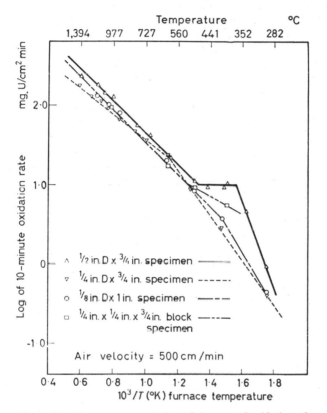

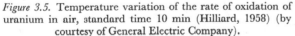

*Figure 3.5.* Temperature variation of the rate of oxidation of uranium in air, standard time 10 min (Hilliard, 1958) (by courtesy of General Electric Company).

was some evidence that the uranium was reacting with atmospheric nitrogen. It had been reported previously (MALLETT and GERDS, 1955) that the rate of reaction of uranium with nitrogen at 900°C was about equal to that with air or oxygen at 350°C.

Although Hilliard found that at all temperatures above 300°C the composition of the oxide produced by the reaction of uranium with air was $U_3O_8$, PARKER *et al.* (1960) concluded that partial oxidation at high temperature gave a considerable proportion of $UO_2$ in the oxide film, especially in the layers adjacent to the metal. SHAW and HINDMARSH (1957) observed mainly

$UO_2$ when the oxygen supply was restricted even at temperatures as high as 900°C.

The use of hot uranium for the purification of inert gases has been summarized by DAVIDGE, HODGE and STOCKDALE (1960) who investigated in detail the reaction with carbon monoxide impurity. They obtained a few results on the reaction between uranium and oxygen impurity in argon: the reaction was found to be first order with respect to oxygen, and the purification factor was high above about 250°C.

*The effect of alloying.* It was found by ISAACS and WANKLYN (1960) that the addition of 10 wt.% molybdenum to uranium resulted in low self-heating and oxidation rates which became lower with increasing time at all temperatures from 450° to 800°C. At 800°C the rate of oxidation was approximately equal to that for unalloyed uranium at 375–500°C. These improvements were attributed to an increase in the plasticity of the oxide in the presence of molybdenum.

The oxidation in oxygen at 200 mm pressure and at 700°C of zirconium–uranium alloys containing up to 4 at.% uranium has been studied by PORTE et al. (1959).

Data on the corrosion of binary alloys containing 40–90 wt.% niobium in air at 300°C have been reported by DEMASTRY, SHOBER and DICKERSON (1959). Above this temperature, the film of corrosion product oxide spalls in comparatively short times of exposure.

*Oxidation with ignition*

DARRAS, BAQUE and LECLERCQ (1959) attempted to overcome ambiguities in their work on uranium oxidation by differentiating qualitatively between 'ignition' and 'inflammation'. In ignition, self-heating could raise the sample to several hundred degrees above the temperature of the gas, but the reaction was retarded if the external source of heat was removed. Inflammation, on the other hand, produced even higher metal temperatures and complete oxidation of the sample within a few seconds. Using this definition, they quoted an ignition temperature of 610°C for samples $20 \times 15 \times 2$ mm, in both dry and moist air; temperature oscillations of the samples were observed at temperatures above 400°C. These results were obtained from experiments in which the temperature of the sample was raised at a constant rate while the oxidizing gas was passed over it.

Schnizlein and his co-workers have obtained a large amount of data using this 'burning curve' technique (see *Figure 3.3*). They found a very complex dependence of the ignition temperature upon both the environmental conditions and the composition, shape and previous history of the samples. The effect of some of these conditions is illustrated in *Figure 3.6*. The ignition temperature of cast or beta-quenched uranium may be considered to vary in a regular manner with the surface area of the samples, although other metallurgical variables in the prior history of the samples can cause marked deviations (the almost vertical line at about 385°C) from the general relationship. Moreover, other forms of the metal, such as bundles of wires or beds of powder, behave quite differently.

The curves shown in *Figure 3.6* cannot be extrapolated satisfactorily to predict the ignition temperature of uranium powder of very high surface area.

A sample with a mean particle diameter of 2·4 microns had an ignition temperature of 125°C: below the extrapolated temperature (SCHNIZLEIN *et al.*, 1959). If the uranium powder is sufficiently dispersed, ignition can even be achieved at room temperature (HARTMANN, 1951).

The extensive work at the Argonne National Laboratory has served to identify the most important factors which may influence the ignition of uranium, but the applicability of the laboratory data to practical cases (e.g. full scale fuel elements) is not yet clear.

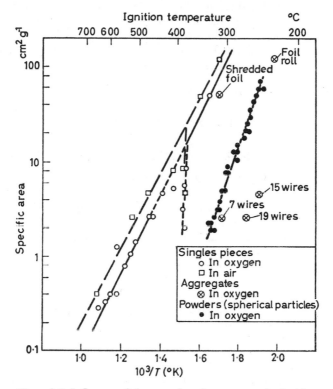

*Figure 3.6.* Influence of shape and surface area on the ignition temperature of uranium in air and oxygen (Schnizlein and Bingle, 1960) (by courtesy of Argonne National Laboratory).

PARKER *et al.* (1960) have investigated the oxidation of irradiated uranium in air. They found that metal which had been irradiated to 0·2 at. % burn-up oxidized considerably faster than unirradiated metal at 800, 1,000 and 1,200°C. On the other hand, SCHNIZLEIN *et al.* (1959) reported that 'fissium' metal (uranium plus inactive metallic fission products in amounts corresponding to typical spent reactor fuel after pyrometallurgical processing) had a much higher ignition temperature than normal uranium. It is possible, therefore, that the effects of radiation damage and of the fission products considered as chemical impurities are very different and may even work in opposition.

### 3.1.3 Reaction with Carbon Dioxide

The primary need to investigate the reaction between metallic uranium and carbon dioxide has arisen from the extensive programme for the construction of reactors cooled by this gas. Under normal conditions of operation the uranium is protected by the fuel cladding of magnesium alloy, but in order to predict the behaviour of the fuel in the event of the cladding becoming defective it is necessary to know the characteristics of the subsequent reaction. To simulate reactor conditions most studies have been made at relatively high temperatures and there has been little incentive to study the reaction. below 200°C. In any case, the reaction at these low temperatures is much slower than the uranium–oxygen reaction.

The overall mechanism of the reaction is more complex than that involving oxygen. It probably occurs in two distinct stages:

$$U + 2CO_2 \rightarrow UO_2 + 2CO \tag{1}$$

$$U + 2CO \rightarrow UO_2 + 2C \tag{2}$$

There may also be additional complications arising from the equilibrium

$$2CO \rightleftharpoons CO_2 + C \tag{3}$$

The relative importance of reactions 1 and 2 will depend upon the ambient conditions. When the flow of gas around the uranium is comparatively unrestricted, the carbon monoxide will be swept away before it can react. Reaction 2 is known to be slower than reaction 1 at low partial pressures of carbon dioxide in an inert carrier gas (DAVIDGE, HODGE and STOCKDALE, 1960).

The reaction of uranium with a fast flowing stream of carbon dioxide at a pressure of one atmosphere has been studied by ANTILL and PEAKALL (1959), and by PAIDASSI et al. (1961). Both investigations showed that after a short initial period the rate of reaction was linear with time in the range 500–800°C for the gas temperature. Antill found that there was marked self-heating of the specimens by the heat of reaction at temperatures above 725°C and that the rate of reaction increased rapidly at about the β–γ transition temperature of the metal (772°C). The latter effect arose from the volume change associated with the transition leading to severe cracking of the oxide film. He also pointed out that the reproducibility of the rates of reaction was not good, partly owing to variations in the impurity content of the metal and the gas, and at higher temperatures due to the self-heating of the metal.

The actual values of the rates of reaction were significantly lower in the experiments of Paidassi than in those of Antill. This may be attributed to the higher purity of the gas used by Paidassi: in both investigations the gas was thoroughly dried, but Antill used gas containing 400 p.p.m. of oxygen whereas Paidassi purified the carbon dioxide to 5 p.p.m. oxygen. In the region below 700°C, where self-heating of the samples is negligible, it may be reasonable to deduce an energy of activation for the process. Paidassi quoted an activation energy of 34·4 kcal mole$^{-1}$ for the range 450–700°C, whereas Antill's value was $26 \pm 10$ kcal mole$^{-1}$. Both authors pointed out the similarity of these values to 30 kcal mole$^{-1}$ which characterizes the diffusion of oxygen ions in non-stoichiometric uranium dioxide (AUSKERN and BELLE, 1961). Thus the diffusion of oxygen ions through a thin protective film of oxide on the metal was postulated as the rate-determining step in the oxidation.

Paidassi, however, also reported the observation of nodules growing on the uniform surface oxide below 600°C. These nodules appeared to form preferentially on polishing striations and on inclusions. This is somewhat similar to the process taking place in the region AB of *Figure 3.1* (uranium–oxygen reaction) but in the present system (U–CO$_2$) it is unlikely that the nodules are due to the formation of a higher oxide since Antill reported only the dioxide as the product of oxidation. The effect in carbon dioxide might be more analogous to the oxidation of zirconium (Volume 2, Chapter 5) where inclusions and grain boundaries offer paths of relatively easy diffusion compared with the bulk of the oxide film.

In view of the sensitivity of the rate of oxidation to the presence of traces of oxygen and water vapour in the carbon dioxide, and the non-uniform nature of the corrosion, the activation energy deduced from the Arrhenius plot may have no precise meaning and it cannot yet be taken that the process is of a simple diffusion-controlled nature. Much more work is desirable on this system in order both to elucidate the nature of the attack and in order to be able to quote reproducible rates. The linear rate of weight increase obtained by Paidassi in very pure carbon dioxide at 500°C was about 0·06 mg cm$^{-2}$ h$^{-1}$, compared with 0·25–1·4 mg cm$^{-2}$ h$^{-1}$ obtained by Antill with gas containing 400 vpm of oxygen.

Antill reported that at 500°C the rate of corrosion was increased by a factor between 8 and 32 when 3 vol. % water vapour was added to the CO$_2$.

For temperatures between 800–1,000°C, Antill found some evidence of a diminution of the rate of oxidation. This may correspond to the region CD of *Figure 3.1* where it was postulated that restriction of the access of gaseous oxidant to the metal/oxide interface by changes in the porous outer oxide film was beginning to influence the overall rate of reaction.

There may also be a change in the mechanism of the reaction below 450°C, the rates observed experimentally being higher than would be anticipated by extrapolation of the data at higher temperatures (cf PAIDASSI *et al.* 1961).

### Defective fuel elements

The conditions in a fuel element comprising metallic uranium clad with magnesium alloy, when there is a defect in the latter which may permit the entry of carbon dioxide, will be very different from those of the experiments discussed above. Reaction 1 may take place rapidly upon the contact of carbon dioxide with the metal; this reaction does not involve a change in volume of the gas, however, and this will at first help to prevent the ingress of more carbon dioxide. Reaction may still proceed at a slower rate between uranium and the carbon dioxide according to equation 2. This does involve a decrease in gas volume and may ultimately reduce the pressure inside the cladding and allow the access of more carbon dioxide through the original defect. No information has been published concerning the possible effects of irradiation on these reactions.

Since there is a large decrease in density in transforming metallic uranium to the dioxide, extensive oxidation could lead to excessive stresses on the cladding and to its subsequent rupture. Normally, however, the diffusion of gaseous fission products (released by the oxidation) through the original defect in the cladding, and their subsequent detection in the main reactor coolant stream, gives sufficient warning and the fuel element is removed from the reactor. Although fuel element failures of this type are potentially important in that they might give rise to the spread of long-lived fission product radioactivity around a nominally inactive coolant circuit, the failure rate in the Calder Hall reactors has been encouragingly low. During the early periods of operation only five elements in each charge of 10,000 elements developed faults during a year of operation (COCKCROFT, 1961). The faults were found to occur in the end welds of the fuel cladding: better inspection techniques and other developments will reduce still further the number of faulty elements.

DAVIDGE, HODGE and STOCKDALE (1960) have shown that for low partial pressures of CO in an inert carrier gas the reaction may be more complex than is implied by equation 2. They found evidence of combined carbon in the products of reaction above 550°C and concluded that the following overall reaction was also possible:

$$3U + 2CO \rightarrow UO_2 + 2UC \qquad (4)$$

Since there is a film of uranium dioxide on the metal, equation 4 would imply the probable diffusion through it of uranium ions as well as oxygen ions. It is not known whether reaction 4 occurs under the conditions of a defective fuel element.

Further improvement may be obtained by increasing the oxidation resistance of the uranium. PAIDASSI et al. (1961) have shown that the uniform oxide film initially formed on uranium is disrupted by the preferential oxidation of inclusions, possibly carbide, in the metal. Recent work in the United Kingdom has shown that high purity uranium has a significantly higher resistance to oxidation by carbon dioxide (GRAINGER, 1961). Thus the adoption of much lower levels of impurity in uranium for fuel elements may therefore be advantageous, but would probably only be achieved at considerably increased fuel production costs.

HUDDLE and SILVESTER (1959) claimed that the resistance to oxidation by $CO_2$ at 500°C could be marginally improved by the addition to uranium of about 1 per cent of any one of the metals V, Ti, Zr, Nb, Ta, Fe, Cu. More recently ANTILL and PEAKALL (1961) found that the addition to the uranium of as much as 5% vanadium, 10% titanium, 10% zirconium, 10% niobium or 15% molybdenum did not significantly improve the resistance to oxidation by carbon dioxide at 500°C. The alloys containing Ti, Mo, Nb or 1 per cent Cu were attacked by carbon dioxide at temperatures between 680–1,000°C to a much less extent than the unalloyed metal, however, The beneficial effect of the copper additions could be explained by a probable increase in plasticity of the oxide film, thus allowing stresses in the film to be relieved by deformation rather than cracking. On the other hand, no ready explanation could be given for the beneficial effects of titanium, molybdenum or niobium. A uranium alloy containing 7·3 per cent silicon was attacked rapidly by carbon dioxide, an effect which could be explained by a reduction in the plasticity of the oxide film.

Uranium will burn in carbon dioxide, but the ignition temperature is much higher than in air. The temperature at which rapid self-heating of the metal occurs is about 725°C (ANTILL and PEAKALL, 1959) at a gas pressure of 1 atmosphere; the ignition temperature increases as the gas pressure is raised, possibly because of higher rates of heat conduction in the gas (DARRAS, BAQUE and LECLERCQ, 1959).

### 3.2 MAGNESIUM

The earliest gas-cooled reactors employed aluminium as cladding for the fuel elements to prevent excessive oxidation of the uranium and the spread of radioactivity in the coolant system. Magnesium, however, has a lower neutron absorption cross-section than aluminium, and is more compatible with uranium. It was realized, therefore, that it might make an attractive substitute for aluminium in later reactors and magnesium alloys have been the subject of considerable investigations in the U.K., France and the U.S.S.R.

TABLE 3.1

APPROXIMATE COMPOSITION OF MAGNOX ALLOYS

| Designation | Alloying elements (%) | | | |
| --- | --- | --- | --- | --- |
| | Al | Be | Mn | Zr |
| Magnox AL80 (formerly A12) | 0·8 | 0·01 | — | — |
| Magnox MN70 (formerly AM.503S) | — | — | 0·7 | — |
| Magnox ZR55 (formerly ZA) | — | — | — | 0·55 |

A review of the properties of magnesium alloys relevant to their application in nuclear reactors has been made by HEAL (1958), and recent experience on their physical metallurgy has been summarized by GRAINGER (1961). It is intended in the present chapter to confine attention to the behaviour of magnesium alloys towards oxidizing gases. The most important alloys arising from the British nuclear power programme are shown in *Table 3.1*. Magnesium–beryllium alloys have also been studied in the U.S.S.R., and magnesium–zinc–zirconium alloys in France.

### 3.2.1 Reaction with Air and Oxygen

The reaction of magnesium with dry oxygen has been studied in detail by GREGG and JEPSON (1958) and by MIKHAIL and GOUDA (1960). Some representative curves obtained by the latter workers are shown in *Figure 3.7* to illustrate the complexity of the reaction.

Below about 450°C, the oxidation of magnesium is very slight and the resultant thin oxide film may be described as protective, i.e. the oxidation is controlled by diffusion (probably of magnesium ions) through a comparatively uniform oxide film, and when the latter is sufficiently thick further diffusion becomes negligible.

In the range 450–550°C, however, a further process occurs in the oxide film.

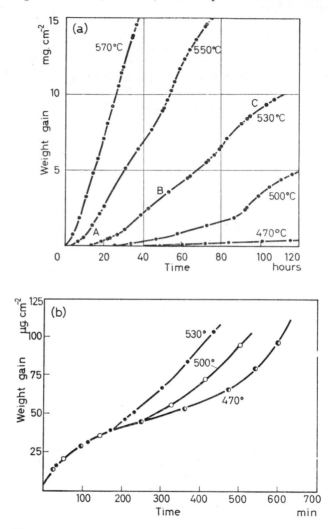

*Figure 3.7.* Representative curves showing the rate of oxidation of magnesium in dry oxygen (Mikhail and Gouda, 1960) (by courtesy of Journal of Applied Chemistry).

A sigmoid curve for the increase in weight against time is observed (*Figure 3.7b*) with transition to a faster rate of oxidation occurring at shorter times as the temperature is raised. During this period nuclei of a more bulky white corrosion product begin to appear on the surface of the uniform thin film.

When lateral growth from the nuclei has covered all of the original surface, the oxidation becomes linear with time (region B of *Figure 3.7a*). Gregg and Jepson suggested that this behaviour was consistent with a stationary state where the rate of film growth is equal to the rate of propagation of cracks in the outer layers of the film, leaving an intact coherent layer of constant thickness next to the metal.

Subsequently a second transition to an even faster rate of oxidation (region C, *Figure 3.7a*) occurs. This was postulated as due to the onset of a more rapid rate of propagation of the cracks, so that the latter extend right down to the metal/oxide interface. The vapour pressure of metallic magnesium above 500°C is comparatively high, and volatilization of the metal may then take place to allow a reaction between magnesium vapour and oxygen. *Figure 3.7* shows that this stage of the reaction becomes eventually stifled, the rate falling away from an initial linear relationship. This may be due to a restriction of the diffusion of metal atoms or of oxygen molecules by the deposition of new oxide from the vapour phase reaction within the cracks in the original oxide.

Gregg and Jepson found that the nature of the original surface has a marked effect upon the subsequent behaviour during oxidation. Chemical polishing with nitric acid conferred the greatest protection against oxidation, whilst the use of abrasives gave the least protection. They suggested that these effects were due to the differing amounts of impurities which remained on the surface after the various treatments.

The behaviour of magnesium in dry air below 400°C is similar to that in oxygen. Above this temperature a linear rate of attack is obtained and the rate is considerably greater than in oxygen. At 500°C the rate of attack in dry air is 0·03 mg cm$^{-2}$ h$^{-1}$ (BOUSSION, GRALL and CAILLAT, 1957). The increase is presumably due to simultaneous reactions with nitrogen and oxygen: STHAPITANONDA and MARGRAVE (1956) have shown that at 460°C the rate of nitridation of magnesium is equal to the rate of oxidation.

Moisture has a very deleterious effect on the oxidation of magnesium by air and oxygen above 350°C. GREGG and JEPSON (1958) have postulated, however, that the attack in the presence of moisture differs only in degree and not in kind from that in dry oxygen. Moisture markedly reduces the induction period of the oxidation curve and increases the linear rate of oxidation. These authors suggest that some of the water is incorporated in the initial oxide film as OH$^-$ ions, and thereby lowers the energy of activation for diffusion of the magnesium ions. The limit of usefulness of magnesium in moist air is about 350°C (BOUSSION et al., 1957); this limit may be raised to about 450°C by the application of a film of magnesium fluoride before exposure to oxidizing conditions. Alternatively, the addition of a small concentration of hydrogen fluoride to the air produces a marked inhibition which has been observed to last for at least several thousand hours (CAILLAT and DARRAS, 1958).

The reaction between magnesium and water vapour in the absence of oxygen has been studied in detail by GIBBS and SVEC (1957).

*The effect of irradiation*

No detailed and systematic investigations of the effect of irradiation on the oxidation of magnesium have been reported. There are several means by which irradiation might be expected to affect the rate of an oxidation which is controlled by processes occurring within an oxide film. For instance:

(a) Where the oxidation is controlled by uniform ionic diffusion, irradiation may increase the total number of defects in the oxide film, leading to an increase in the rate of diffusion.

(b) Irradiation might affect the nucleation step in the oxide film, if one exists.

It has been mentioned above that the propagation of nuclei and their lateral growth over the initially protective thin oxide film does occur in magnesium oxidation and is believed to be the reason for the transition to a higher rate of reaction. A similar process occurs in niobium oxidation and has been studied by CATHCART and YOUNG (1961).

They found that the irradiation of niobium in oxygen at 400°C in a flux of $6 \times 10^{11}$ n cm$^{-2}$ sec$^{-1}$ increased neither the rate of oxidation nor the rate of production of nuclei in the oxide film. Calculation showed that a flux of about $10^{12}$ n cm$^{-2}$ sec$^{-1}$ might significantly affect the rate of production of nuclei: the fact that no change was observed experimentally was taken as evidence that the energy required to initiate a crack in $Nb_2O_5$ film is much larger than that associated with the regions of localized disorder produced by neutron bombardment.

Cathcart and Young also calculated that a flux greater than $10^{15}$ n cm$^{-2}$ sec$^{-1}$ would probably be required to significantly increase the concentration of defects in the oxide film and hence produce a detectable effect on the uniform diffusion process.

Whilst further experiments in higher fast neutron fluxes are desirable, together with an extension to other metal oxidation reactions, these observations give reason to suppose that reactor irradiation may have only a relatively minor effect upon the rates of penetration of constructional metals which oxidize in this way. If the control of the oxidation is by non-uniform diffusion, as in zirconium and possibly uranium, or by electronic conduction, the effect of irradiation may be quite different.

The reactor G-1 at Marcoule employs magnesium fuel cladding operating in air at temperatures up to 300°C. In relation to this reactor CAILLAT and DARRAS (1958) have reported some experiments concerning the effect of irradiation upon magnesium oxidation. They observed that at a neutron flux about $5 \times 10^{11}$ n cm$^{-2}$ sec$^{-1}$ there was no detectable increase in corrosion in moist ($CO_2$-free) air at 350°C for times up to 200 hours. Two results obtained over longer times, however, appear to show a definite increase under irradiation: the weight gains were about 50 per cent higher than in similar out-of-pile experiments.

*Alloys*

The presence of beryllium, even at very small concentrations, has a marked influence upon the rate of oxidation in air at temperatures about 550°C (SINELNIKOV, IVANOV and ZELENSKY, 1958).

An Mg–0·01% Be alloy has a weight gain which increases only according to a logarithmic rate law at 580°C, compared with a much higher linear rate for the unalloyed metal, for times up to several hundred hours. There is subsequently a 'breakaway' to a higher rate; this may be delayed by increasing the beryllium content or by reducing the temperature. These authors suggested that the marked reduction in oxidation due to beryllium additions was due to its effect upon the physical properties of the oxide film (in which its concentration was higher than in the parent metal). This may not be the only reason however (see below).

### 3.2.2. Reaction with Carbon Dioxide

Early work at Harwell, which subsequently led to the adoption of Magnox alloys for use in the British reactors, has been described by HUDDLE and WYATT (1957). Although magnesium of high purity was considered to be a feasible material for use in the Calder Hall reactors, a search was made for alloys which would have better resistance to corrosion under faulty conditions of operation. It was postulated that beryllium additions might affect the rates of diffusion in the oxide film: since the beryllium ion is somewhat smaller than the magnesium ion it might cause an overall contraction in the lattice and a closing-up of the O–O atom distance, thus increasing the resistance to diffusion of the magnesium ions which controls the initial oxidation.

Early tests showed that an alloy containing $0.05\%$ Be, $0.1\%$ Ca and $1\%$ Al had a resistance to oxidation by air at $550$–$615°C$ greatly superior to that of pure magnesium. Further work showed that a minimum addition of $0.02\%$ Be and $0.07\%$ Ca would confer immunity towards breakdown in moist air for 24 hours at $600°C$. The aluminium was added to increase the mechanical strength of the alloys at high temperatures and to facilitate the introduction of beryllium. The calcium addition, although it increased the protective nature of the oxide film, had the undesirable effect of reducing the ease of welding of the alloys, and it was subsequently eliminated from the composition of the alloy used in the Calder Hall reactors (Magnox AL80, formerly known as A12).

Subsequent work showed that the original Magnox series of alloys also had good resistance to oxidation by moist carbon dioxide at atmospheric pressure, but few detailed results have been published.

The nature of the reaction between magnesium and carbon dioxide is intrinsically more complex than the reaction with oxygen. Thus we have the following possibilities:

$$Mg + CO_2 \rightarrow MgO + CO \tag{5}$$

$$Mg + CO \rightarrow MgO + C \tag{6}$$

$$2Mg + CO_2 \rightarrow 2MgO + C \tag{7}$$

$$MgO + CO_2 \rightarrow MgCO_3 \tag{8}$$

At temperatures above $420°C$ and at a pressure of about one atmosphere the product of reaction has been found to be MgO rather than the carbonate. Higher pressures, however, enhance the importance of both reaction 7 and the production of carbonate 8. Carbon monoxide is produced in the coolant stream of an operating nuclear reactor by the reaction of the dioxide with graphite, but no results have been reported concerning the relative importance of reaction 6.

Russian investigators have found that whereas unalloyed magnesium is completely destroyed after 50 hours in carbon dioxide at 580°C and atmospheric pressure, alloys containing greater than 0·1 per cent beryllium (plus

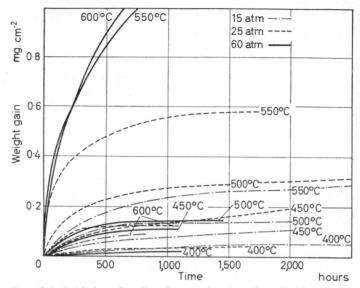

*Figure 3.8.* Oxidation of unalloyed magnesium in carbon dioxide (Darras, Baque and Chevilliard, 1960).

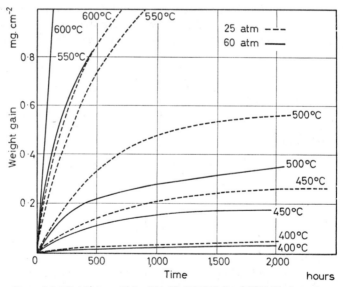

*Figure 3.9.* Oxidation of Mg–1% Al–0·015% Be–0·03% Ca in carbon dioxide (Darras, Baque and Chevilliard, 1960).

aluminium) were very resistant up to 200 hours (SINELNIKOV, IVANOV and ZELENSKY, 1958).

Despite the early promise of alloys of the Magnox AL80 type, however, further work has shown that their oxidation in carbon dioxide at high pressures, although not excessive, is inferior to that of pure magnesium. This observation was made at a pressure of 8 atmospheres by GRAINGER and McINTOSH (1957) and subsequently at pressures up to 60 atmospheres by DARRAS, BAQUE and CHEVILLIARD (1960). The results of the latter authors are shown in *Figures 3.8* and *3.9*. It should be noted that the oxidation of the alloy with composition close to Magnox AL80 remains of a lower order than rectilinear at temperatures up to at least 550°C, i.e. the oxide film is still partially protective.

CAILLAT and DARRAS (1958) have shown that at atmospheric pressure the weight gain of commercially pure magnesium in dry carbon dioxide is much smaller than in air at the same temperature. The curve of weight gain against time is asymptotic rather than linear for times up to 3,000 hours. Samples exposed at 400°C acquired a thin surface layer of $MgCO_3$, those exposed at 500°C had a surface layer consisting primarily of MgO. Small amounts of air in the carbon dioxide did not increase the rate of attack.

### Magnesium–zirconium alloys

Grain growth occurs in unalloyed magnesium at temperatures as low as 350–400°C, and a large grain size, in turn, can lead to cavitational failure

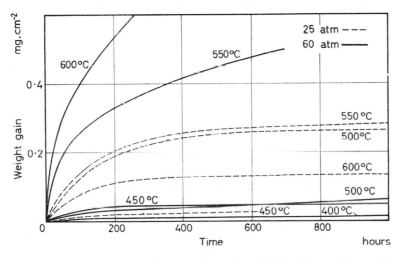

*Figure 3.10.* Oxidation of Mg 0·6% Zr in carbon dioxide (Darras, Baque and Chevilliard, 1960).

under strain. Zirconium additions have been found to produce a much finer-grained material which has more attractive mechanical properties, and the resultant alloys have been subjected to corrosion tests in carbon dioxide. DARRAS, BAQUE and CHEVILLIARD (1960) observed that at pressures up to 60 atmospheres the corrosion resistance of an Mg–0·6% Zr alloy (known as Magnox ZR60 in the U.K.) was much superior to that of the Mg–1% Al–0·015% Be–0·03% Ca shown in *Figure 3.9* (see *Figure 3.10*). They also pointed out that the stability of magnesium carbonate was expected to be greater at the higher pressures, and the protective film may contain significant amounts of carbonate up to 500°C.

### The effect of moisture

Small quantities of moisture in carbon dioxide increase the rate of oxidation of magnesium alloys. The rates of weight gain of Magnox AL80 and Magnox MN70 at 400°C are increased by a factor of about four in the first month of exposure, falling to a factor of two after two months, by 0·15 wt. % moisture (GRAINGER and McINTOSH, 1957). The Magnox ZR60 also shows increased attack in moist carbon dioxide, but according to CAILLAT and DARRAS (1958) the effect is not excessive at 450°C over periods of a few hours.

### The effect of irradiation

CAILLAT and DARRAS (1958) have reported that irradiation at a neutron flux of $5 \times 10^{11}$ n cm$^{-2}$ sec$^{-1}$ of magnesium and a Mg–Zr alloy produced gains in weight of the same order as unirradiated samples after exposures of two months duration in carbon dioxide.

A point of chemical interest which should not be overlooked is that the effect of fission fragment irradiation of an oxide film may be substantially different from that of fast neutrons. Such an effect may be of technological importance should magnesium alloy fuel cladding become defective and allow the access of oxidizing gases to the *inside* surface of the cladding, which has been subjected to intense bombardment by fission fragments from the neighbouring uranium fuel surface. No information is available on this topic.

### 3.2.3 Ignition

As for uranium, discussed earlier in this chapter, some attention must be paid to the possible ignition and burning of magnesium in oxidizing gases. For normal operation in a reactor cooled by carbon dioxide, the maximum temperature of the magnesium alloy fuel cladding is kept by design below about 500°C. At such temperatures the rate of oxidation is low, but fault conditions might lead to higher temperatures and so to ignition.

FASSELL et al. (1951) investigated the ignition of magnesium and its alloys in oxygen and $O_2$–$N_2$ mixtures. The ignition temperature was defined as that at which a sample which was heated at a constant rate of increase of temperature suddenly oxidized very rapidly with the appearance of a visible flame. Unalloyed magnesium had an ignition temperature of 623°C in oxygen at 1 atmosphere pressure. Both increasing and decreasing the oxygen pressure from 1 atmosphere produced higher ignition temperatures, facts which are difficult to explain on the basis of the normal theories of ignition. Many alloying additions were found to decrease the ignition temperature, but calcium in the range 1–5 per cent produced a slight increase. Beryllium and zirconium additions were not investigated.

Contact between the magnesium and carbon steel was found by Fassell et al. not to affect the ignition temperature, but the latter was lowered to 588 and 523°C by contact of the magnesium with nickel and aluminium respectively. This could be due to the localized formation of eutectics with a melting point lower than that of magnesium.

Subsequent work by DARRAS, BAQUE and LECLERCQ (1960) gave the figures shown in *Table 3.2*.

It is evident that in dry carbon dioxide, especially at high pressure, the ignition temperature is substantially higher than in air: moreover, it is considerably higher than the melting point of magnesium under these conditions.

TABLE 3.2

IGNITION TEMPERATURE OF MAGNESIUM ALLOYS (Darras, Baque and Leclercq, 1960)

| Composition | Dry air, 1 atm | Moist air, 1 atm | Dry $CO_2$, 1 atm | Moist $CO_2$, 1 atm | Dry $CO_2$ 15 atm | $CO_2 + 800$ p.p.m. $H_2O$, 15 atm |
|---|---|---|---|---|---|---|
| Mg | 645 | 610 | 880 | 650 | 920 | 780 |
| Mg–0·5% Mn–0·1% Zr | 645 | 615 | 890 | 660 | 940 | 800 |
| Mg–0·8% Al–1% Ca– 0·02% Be | 650 | 625 | 880 | 670 | 945 | 800 |

The presence of moisture in the carbon dioxide drastically reduces the ignition temperature. This could be of importance in the event of a burst tube in the heat exchangers of a carbon dioxide cooled reactor: steam from the secondary circuit may then enter the reactor core. The ignition temperature would not be lowered below the melting point of the fuel cladding, however, and no ignition could take place except in the event of a simultaneous increase in the reactor power above the normal levels of operation.

Although there is no substantial experimental evidence, the presence of pile neutron plus gamma radiation would not be expected to significantly affect the ignition temperatures.

SALESSE (1958) has reported an investigation of the failure of a fuel element clad with unalloyed magnesium in the EL2 reactor. Some of this cladding had melted (650°C) in the $CO_2$-coolant at 10 atmospheres pressure in a flux of $5 \times 10^{12}$ n cm$^{-2}$ sec$^{-1}$, but no significant reaction had occurred.

*Table 3.2* shows that there is little difference between the various alloys considered for use in reactors, the major effects on the ignition temperatures being due to variations in the surrounding gas phase.

It has been reported by DELAVAULT (1945) that the burning of magnesium in air may be extinguished by the addition of about 1 per cent of silicon tetra-fluoride or boron trifluoride to the gas phase.

## 3.3 BERYLLIUM

Although metallic beryllium was first isolated as early as 1828, it has not achieved widespread industrial application. World output of the metal amounts to only a few hundred tons annually, and this is used principally for the precipitation hardening of other metals such as copper and nickel. Beryllium itself has a reputation for having a very low ductility.

In the nuclear field beryllium has some potential advantages which have not yet been fully exploited. The metal has a low neutron capture cross-section coupled with relatively high neutron scattering properties: it is therefore a good moderator. For the United Kingdom reactor programme, however, considerable development has been made towards the use of beryllium as fuel cladding (in AGR-type reactors) rather than as a moderator. The possible advantages over the magnox alloys are the higher melting point, lower neutron absorption and better resistance to oxidizing gases at very high temperatures. The state of knowledge of beryllium oxidation will be reviewed here; other aspects of the use of beryllium in nuclear reactors have been discussed elsewhere (UDY et al., 1953; KAUFMANN and KJELLGREN, 1955; E.N.E.A., 1959).

### 3.3.1 Reaction with Air or Oxygen

Investigations on the oxidation of beryllium have been hampered by irreproducibility in the results which may be at least partly attributed to uncontrolled impurities in the metal. There are two sources of metallic beryllium: that produced by magnesium reduction of beryllium fluoride and that produced by electrolysis of molten beryllium chloride.

The early investigations of GULBRANSEN and ANDREW (1950) were made with magnesium-reduced material of 98·85 per cent purity. They studied the reaction with oxygen in the range 350–950°C and with nitrogen in the range 600–925°C. At a given temperature, the reaction with oxygen was considerably faster than with nitrogen. Gulbransen and Andrew found that for the reaction with oxygen the energy of activation was 8·5 kcal mole$^{-1}$ in the range 350–700°C and 50·3 kcal mole$^{-1}$ in the range 750–950°C. They suggested that their results fitted a parabolic rate law.

Ten years later AYLMORE, GREGG and JEPSON (1960) studied the oxidation of electrolytic flake beryllium with a purity better than 99·5 per cent. Their experiments were also continued for much longer times (300 hours) than those of Gulbransen. They found that in dry oxygen at temperatures up to 650°C the oxide film was protective and the rate of oxidation decreased continuously with time, reaching a value of 0·02–0·04 $\mu$g cm$^{-2}$ h after 300 hours. They found marked deviations from the parabolic rate law and in a later paper (1961) they suggested that the results were consistent with the rate-controlling step being diffusion (of beryllium ions) through a uniform oxide film under the influence of an electrostatic potential gradient. A notable feature of Gregg's results was the appearance of marked short-term discontinuities in the oxidation curves at these temperatures. No fully satisfactory explanation has yet been offered for this effect.

Above 700°C, the rate of oxidation was found to decrease with time initially, but subsequently to increase with time. As with other metals, this is indicative of the transition from a protective oxide film to one which is non-protective. No direct evidence for cracking of the oxide film was obtained, however.

### The effect of moisture

In their later paper (1961) AYLMORE, GREGG and JEPSON also compared the oxidation of beryllium in oxygen and in water vapour. At temperatures up to 600°C, the reaction with moist oxygen and with water vapour follows the same course as that with dry oxygen: the rate becomes very small after 100 hours and shows no signs of increase up to 300 hours. Above 650°C, the oxidation is no longer protective; a breakaway to a high rate of oxidation takes place at a weight gain and a time which decrease with increasing temperature.

The close similarity below 600°C between experiments with and without water vapour suggests that the rate-controlling step in the oxidation remains the same in both cases. This is probably the diffusion of beryllium ions through the thin uniform oxide film.

Beryllium undergoes breakaway during oxidation in water vapour or moist oxygen at a lower film thickness than in dry oxygen: at 750°C breakaway occurs in a film about 5,000 Å thick in dry oxygen but only about 350 Å in water vapour. Aylmore *et al.* suggested that this might be due to an inward diffusion of protons which could accompany the outward diffusion of beryllium ions through the oxide film. The protons would be discharged as gaseous hydrogen upon reaching the metal/oxide interface, and could possibly rupture the oxide film. There is no direct proof of such a mechanism and, moreover, there is not yet any clear explanation of why the post-breakaway oxidation was of a penetrating type, taking place preferentially down grain boundaries in the metal.

### 3.3.2 Reaction with Carbon Dioxide

GREGG, HUSSEY and JEPSON (1960) used a $^{14}C$ radioactive tracer technique to study the system and concluded that the following reactions occur:

$$Be + CO_2 \rightarrow BeO + CO \tag{9}$$

$$2Be + CO_2 \rightarrow 2BeO + C \tag{10}$$

$$Be + CO \rightarrow BeO + C \tag{11}$$

$$2Be + C \rightarrow Be_2C \tag{12}$$

It was also concluded in a further paper (1961a) that the following reactions do *not* occur:

$$4Be + CO_2 \rightarrow 2BeO + Be_2C \tag{13}$$

$$3Be + CO \rightarrow BeO + Be_2C \tag{14}$$

The reaction at low temperatures ($< 500$°C) appears to be solely by equation 9, i.e. no carbon appears in the film of reaction product. Equation 10 becomes significant at higher temperatures and for the first few minutes of exposure even at 500°C (i.e. when the diffusion flux of beryllium ions through the protective film is relatively large).

At temperatures up to 700°C, the rate of attack in dry carbon dioxide decreases continuously with time to reach a very small value (e.g. $0.13 \ \mu g \ cm^{-2} \ h^{-1}$ after 300 hours at 700°C). Gregg and co-workers found that breakaway to a faster rate of oxidation occurred at 750°C. By extending the experiments to longer periods of time, LIVEY and WILLIAMS (1958) observed breakaway at even lower temperatures, occurring after about 400 hours in moist gas at 600° and in dry gas at 650°C. Samples were exposed for as long as 375 days in dry gas at 600°C without achieving breakaway. GREGG *et al.* (1961b) also reported subsequently that the oxidation was non-protective at 650°C in moist carbon dioxide and that a penetrating attack occurred which was similar to that in moist oxygen.

Livey and Williams concluded that the corrosion resistance of beryllium at 600°C would not be likely to place a limit on its life in a reactor cooled by carbon dioxide, provided that the moisture content of the gas remained very low. Further work is required to define more precisely the allowable limit of water vapour in the carbon dioxide as a function of temperature.

Experiments at Oak Ridge have shown that the oxidation of beryllium by carbon dioxide is independent of gas pressure at 600° and 650°C up to 500 hours, as would be expected if the pre-breakaway corrosion were controlled by diffusion through a uniform protective film (GAS-COOLED REACTOR PROJECT, 1960). When the kinetics of the reaction are expressed in the form:

$$\Delta W = kt^{1/n}.$$

($\Delta W$ = weight gain, $\mu$g cm$^{-2}$; $t$ = time, hours), the value of $n$ can vary within the range 1·45–3·1 at temperatures between 600–850°C, i.e. the oxidation is not always strictly parabolic ($n = 2$).

Little work has yet been published on the nature or the rate of the post-breakaway corrosion. The rate can vary widely according to the method of fabrication of the metal and the moisture content of the gas.

If beryllium is to be used in a graphite moderated reactor cooled by carbon dioxide, it must also be capable of withstanding attack by the carbon monoxide which results from the reaction between the coolant and the moderator. GREGG, HUSSEY and JEPSON (1961a) have studied the oxidation of beryllium with carbon monoxide. It is considerably faster in pure CO than in $CO_2$, and above 550°C the film of reaction product is non-protective and spalls from the sample. This presumably arises from the deposition of carbon in the film by equation 11 and its subsequent reaction according to equation 12, thus producing a highly inhomogeneous film. SCOTT (1960) has identified beryllium carbide by electron diffraction as one of the products of the reaction of beryllium with carbon monoxide and carbon dioxide at 700°C.

Fortunately, however, Gregg and co-workers found that the exposure of beryllium at 650°C to $CO$–$CO_2$ mixtures containing up to 7·5% carbon monoxide and at 700°C to a mixture containing 50% carbon monoxide led to reaction primarily with the carbon dioxide. This was attributed to preferential adsorption of carbon dioxide on the oxide surface.

Much more remains to be done in the study of the corrosion of beryllium in oxidizing gases from both a basic and a technological viewpoint. Whilst the application of the metal in carbon dioxide cooled reactors appears promising at temperatures below 600°C, information concerning the upper limit of temperature as a function of such parameters as the composition of the gas, the presence of irradiation, etc., has not been published.

A particularly interesting feature of the irradiation of beryllium is its transmutation by $(n, 2n)$ and $(n, \alpha)$ reactions to helium and smaller amounts of tritium. On annealing irradiated beryllium at a sufficiently high temperature to allow both diffusion of the gas and plastic deformation of the metal to occur, gas bubbles nucleate and grow to produce an apparent decrease in density of the metal. BENNETT *et al.* (1961) have studied the post-irradiation behaviour of beryllium in carbon dioxide. They found that at temperatures where there was a rapid swelling of the metal due to the agglomeration of helium, there was also a considerable increase in the magnitude of the oxidation. Whilst these effects took place above the region of temperature ($>850°C$) normally of interest for reactor operation, the results could be relevant to the behaviour of beryllium-clad fuel elements under fault conditions.

The possibility of improving the resistance to oxidation by the formation of alloys has not yet been investigated systematically; the extent of the possible alloying additions is probably rather limited.

The nature of the breakaway process and of the post-breakaway corrosion of beryllium show some interesting differences from the other metals discussed in this chapter, and it does not seem possible at the present time to draw any close analogies between them. The extension of our understanding of such processes must accordingly await further work upon beryllium itself.

## 3.4 STEEL

Steels of various compositions have a position of great importance in the design of nuclear reactors: they have been used for the construction of the reactor pressure vessels, for cladding the fuel elements and for the heat removal circuits. The quantities of steel required are large and the U.K.A.E.A. has one of the highest consumptions of steel in the United Kingdom (about 17,000 tons of mild steel for its own reactors up to 1960 [OWEN, 1961])

The selection of a particular steel for each application is dependent upon several properties, including resistance to oxidation, creep resistance, weldability and neutron absorption. At the time of construction of the Calder Hall reactors the only steel which had the low transition temperature desirable for on-site welding of thick plate was a mild steel of controlled grain size. The output of the reactors was limited by the maximum allowable gas pressure set by the thickness of steel which could be welded satisfactorily.

The growing experience in the fabrication of the large pressure vessels required for $CO_2$-cooled reactors has led gradually to thicker sections of steel, but the creep resistance sets another limit upon performance. Although the rate of oxidation in carbon dioxide may be quite satisfactory up to higher temperatures, the creep properties do not allow the use of mild steels above about 380°C. The reactor pressure vessels therefore have to be insulated from the main coolant gas stream.

It may be possible to introduce steels of higher strength and better creep resistance into the construction of future power reactors. This may well result in a desire to increase the temperature of operation, and the oxidation properties will then become more important. The heat removal circuit of high temperature gas-cooled reactors of the DRAGON type will certainly be required to withstand temperatures exceeding 500°C. Steel cladding on oxide fuel elements in reactors based on the AGR at Windscale may have to withstand attack by irradiated carbon dioxide at temperatures in the region of 600°C. The knowledge of the reaction of reactor gases with mild and stainless steels in this range of temperature will be reviewed in the following pages.

95

### 3.4.1 Iron and Mild Steel

Mild steel has been specified for the construction of the pressure vessels of the first $CO_2$-cooled power reactors in the United Kingdom. This has been of the low-carbon ($\sim 0.16\%$) type to aid welding, and comparatively high manganese content ($\sim 1.3\%$) to increase the rupture strength. Whilst all the steel has been silicon-killed (Si content $0.13$–$0.2\%$) some applications have also required grain refinement by the addition of about $0.1\%$ of aluminium to react with the nitrogen left after the steel has been deoxidized with the silicon (ROBERTSON and NICHOLS, 1961).

The oxidation of iron by air or oxygen at comparatively low temperatures (less than 350°C) obeys a logarithmic rate law: there is a rapid initial attack which soon attains a rate sufficiently low that the attack may be considered to have stopped. Unfortunately however, the rate of oxidation is higher in carbon dioxide and the reactor designer is often interested in higher temperatures. Above 400°C the oxidation obeys a parabolic rate law for considerable periods of exposure, but this can ultimately change to a rectilinear behaviour (see below). The fact that the progress of oxidation can be expressed by the parabolic relationship may imply that the rate is controlled by diffusion through a protective film. The complex nature of the film has rendered difficult the deduction of the precise nature of the diffusing species. PFEIL (1929) showed that the oxide film formed at high temperatures in air was composed of three distinct layers which became richer in oxygen towards the oxide/gas interface. Each layer itself is also of variable composition, but very approximately they may be represented as:

  (a) Inner layer, wüstite (FeO)
  (b) Middle layer, magnetite, $Fe_3O_4$
  (c) Outer layer, haematite, $Fe_2O_3$

A recent review of the composition of these films has been provided by EVANS (1960). Wüstite is known to decompose to alpha-iron plus magnetite below 570°C: at lower temperatures the oxidation will be controlled by diffusion in $Fe_3O_4$. DAVIES, SIMNAD and BIRCHENALL (1951) found that a graph of the log of the rate of oxidation against the reciprocal of temperature was not straight, i.e. the controlling mechanism could be changing as a function of temperature. There was evidence for a change at about 600°C, and again at about 800°C when a finite thickness of $Fe_2O_3$ appeared in the film.

Wüstite has a cation-deficient structure and grows by cation diffusion. HIMMEL, MEHL and BIRCHENALL (1953) claimed that agreement could be obtained between calculated and measured rates of oxidation if the calculations were based upon cation diffusion in all of the iron oxides. The earlier paper by Davies et al. had shown that diffusion through a magnetite layer would be primarily anionic, however, and this was assumed by MOORE and RAINE (1961) in relation to oxidation by carbon dioxide. The latter authors quoted evidence that both wüstite and $Fe_2O_3$ occur on steel exposed to dry carbon dioxide at 650°C, i.e. the films are similar to those formed in air.

Whilst investigations by SMELTZER (1960) on the oxidation of iron in $CO/CO_2$ mixtures to film thicknesses about $0.05$ mg cm$^{-2}$, and by PETTIT,

YINGER and WAGNER (1960) for film thicknesses about 2 mg cm$^{-2}$, could be interpreted in terms of surface dissociation of $CO_2$ into CO and adsorbed oxygen atoms or ions as the step which controls the rate of oxidation, the conditions of high gas pressure required for reactor purposes still produce an initial parabolic rate law (*Figure 3.11*) which is reasonably attributed to control by diffusion in the film. However, yet another phenomenon has been encountered after very long periods of exposure: an increase in the rate corresponding to the breakaway encountered in the oxidation of other metals is also apparent.

MOORE and RAINE (1961) have reported that the breakaway can be correlated with the appearance of excrescences on the previously uniform oxide film.

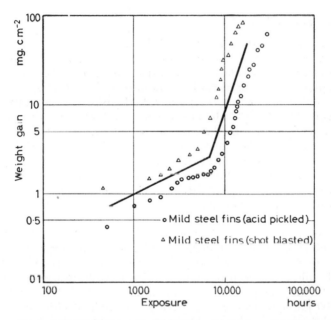

*Figure 3.11*. Oxidation of mild steel in dry carbon dioxide at 400°C, 10 atm pressure (after Moore and Raine, 1961).

Breakaway is found mainly in moist carbon dioxide, but the moisture may not be the causative agent. Since breakaway occurs sooner on a steel surface which is physically rougher, the physical irregularities may act as sites for the relief of stresses in the oxide film which normally grows in compression. It is also possible that preferential oxidation of inclusions in the metal could be the cause.

Determination of the conditions leading to enhanced oxidation, and of the enhanced rates themselves, is of considerable importance for the design of reactor pressure vessels. The implications of the spalling of the oxide include not only a possibly enhanced rate of penetration of the metal, but the transference of particles of oxide around the reactor coolant circuit. These can become activated in the reactor core and upon subsequent transfer to the external circuit they could cause a high background radioactivity which would render maintenance much more difficult.

SCHMELTZER (1960) showed that at a total pressure of 1 atm the initial oxidation of iron in $CO/CO_2$ mixtures was reduced as the partial pressure of CO was increased. The partial pressure of CO in a reactor circuit is unlikely to exceed a few per cent, however, and MOORE and RAINE (1961) state that small amounts of CO have no definite effect on longer-term oxidation at high total pressures. They also state that there is no carburization of the steel underneath the protective oxide film, although some carburization takes place once the film has undergone breakaway. This was postulated to be due to high concentrations of CO localized in the region of the breakaway blisters on the film.

### 3.4.2 Low Alloy Steels

There is a need for the application at higher temperatures of steels which have better resistance to oxidation and higher creep resistance than mild steel. A general survey of the oxidation of alloy steels in carbon dioxide at 600–950°C and high pressures has been made by BOKROS and WALLACE (1960). Their studies included ferritic alloys of the Cr–Mo type. Comparatively rapid oxidation of a $1\frac{1}{4}\%$ Cr–$\frac{1}{2}\%$ Mo alloy occurred at 600°C, the rate of oxidation being lowered by increasing the chromium content.

A wide range of low alloy steels was investigated by LECLERCQ, CHEVILLIARD and DARRAS (1960). For temperatures between 350 and 600°C, a pressure of 25 atm and times up to 4,000 hours they found that an alloy with 2·2% Cr–0·3% Mo–0·5% Al had good resistance to oxidation in static $CO_2$, and within these conditions it did not exhibit deterioration of the protective nature of the oxide film.

Experiments under dynamic flow conditions have been described subsequently by DRAYCOTT and HUBERY (1961). They investigated an alloy with 0·75% Cr–0·35% Mo as representative of comparatively cheap low alloy steels with enhanced creep resistance which have been used extensively in conventional high temperature steam plant. It was found that this alloy had a somewhat lower resistance to oxidation than mild steel in the range 450–525°C and that at gas velocities likely to be encountered in a reactor circuit spalling of the oxide film would ensue (there appeared to be a critical velocity which became lower at higher temperatures). These authors concluded that it was not safe to recommend such a steel for use in $CO_2$-cooled reactors above 450°C.

### 3.4.3 High Alloy Steels

The resistance of steels to oxidation has generally been found to increase as the chromium content is raised. This generalization also applies to oxidation by carbon dioxide. In the range of Cr–Mo steels, BOKROS and WALLACE (1960) have reported that the oxidation resistance of a $2\frac{1}{4}\%$ Cr–1% Mo alloy is much better than that of the 1% Cr–$\frac{1}{2}\%$ Mo alloy in carbon dioxide at 600°C, 1,000 p.s.i. Further improvement was gained by increasing the chromium content to 5%, but an alloy containing 9% Cr was not significantly different from the 5% alloy.

These workers reported also that the composition of the corrosion product on many iron and nickel-base alloys is similar in carbon dioxide to that formed in air or oxygen. A detailed study of oxide films formed on chromium steels and 18 Cr–8 Ni stainless steels in air at 300–700°C has been made by YEARIAN, DERBYSHIRE and RADAVICH (1957). They found that the principal component of the initial film was a solid solution of ferric and chromic oxides preferentially oriented with the (111) plane parallel to the surface. The chromium content of the film increases with time of oxidation. After extensive oxidation the film fails at randomly distributed positions by the rapid growth of nodules consisting largely of alpha-$Fe_2O_3$. It was also observed that the rate of growth after breakdown was reduced by an increase in the chromium content of the alloy and to a lesser extent by small amounts of silicon and manganese.

The most immediate application of stainless steels is likely to be as cladding for the fuel elements in $CO_2$-cooled reactors such as the AGR at Windscale. In such an application the minimization of parasitic neutron absorption in the reactor core is important and the amount of steel must be kept as low as possible. The thickness of the cladding is restricted to the order of $0 \cdot 010$ in.; since the cladding is also required to operate in the region of 600°C for periods between 1–2 years, it is evident that an alloy which is extremely stable towards oxidation is required.

Mild steel or the low-alloy steels will not suffice. Martensitic stainless steels, containing 12–14% chromium or 16–18% chromium with 1–2% nickel are no more suitable as they do not have sufficient resistance to oxidation in carbon dioxide and are also subject to manufacturing and welding difficulties. Whilst the ferritic stainless steels ($> 16\%$ chromium) may have a better resistance to oxidation, fusion welding cannot be carried out satisfactorily since grain growth results in a brittle structure. Such steels, in any case, have low ductility.

The austenitic stainless steels, particularly those of the 18 Cr–8 Ni type, although having a somewhat higher capture cross section for neutrons, overcome the difficulties met in the other steels. Still higher chromium contents may confer increased resistance to oxidation and some attention has been paid to a 25% Cr–20% Ni steel. It should be noted that inclusions in the steel can be deleterious in the thin-walled tubing required, and it is necessary to specify vacuum-melted stock for tube manufacture.

There has been very little detailed information published on the behaviour of austenitic stainless steels in carbon dioxide at high temperatures. DRAYCOTT and SMITH (1960) investigated an 18 Cr–10 Ni titanium-stabilized steel at 550–700°C and pressures of 1–16 atm. They concluded that if the surfaces of the material were work-hardened by vapour-blasting, this steel would be suitable for use as a fuel cladding material in commerically pure $CO_2$ at temperatures up to 675°C at 15 atm and gas velocities up to 100 ft. sec$^{-1}$.

Surface treatment of the steel had a marked effect on its oxidation in carbon dioxide (*Figure 3.12*).

At a pressure of 225 p.s.i. the rate law was found to be approximately parabolic for times up to 1,000 hours, whilst at lower pressures the oxidation could be represented by either a cubic or a logarithmic relationship. The oxide films were very thin ($< 2\mu$) under all conditions, and the increased weight-gains at high temperatures and pressure did not appear to be due to thickening of the uniform film but rather to an increased nucleation of 'warts' of $Fe_2O_3$ on the film. Transition to higher rates did not occur within the conditions investigated, but this may be possible over longer times, BENARD *et al.* (1960) have reported that the oxidation of an 18% Cr–8% N steel in air at 1,050°C undergoes a rapid increase after times sufficient to produce a weight gain of about 1–3 mg $cm^{-2}$. Unlike the oxidation of mild steel, however (see *Figure 3.11*), the rate of increase in weight falls again quite rapidly at a somewhat higher weight gain.

Moisture in the carbon dioxide up to 20,000 p.p.m. has little effect on the oxidation, but the pressure of the $CO_2$ itself is important. Draycott and Smith found that at 575°C the rate of oxidation was approximately proportional to $p^{1/2}$, at 615°C it was directly proportional to pressure, and above

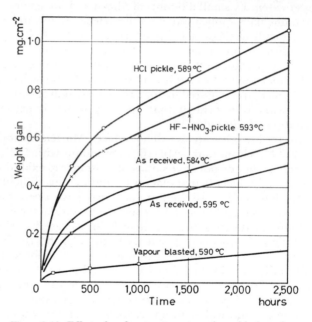

*Figure 3.12.* Effect of surface treatment on the oxidation of an 18% Cr–10% Ni titanium-stabilized stainless steel in carbon dioxide at 10 atm pressure (Draycott and Smith, 1960) (by courtesy of Australian Atomic Energy Commission).

650°C it was proportional to a power of $p$ greater than unity. These effects would not be expected if the rate-determining step were diffusion through the thin uniform film of $Cr_2O_3$.

The rates of oxidation of several austenitic stainless steels and of Inconel have been compared at 100 p.s.i. and 600–750°C by BILLINGTON, STEVENS and DAVIES (1961). They found that on the basis of both weight gain and intergranular penetration an 18% Cr–12% Ni–3% Mo steel was the least resistant of those studied. The most resistant alloy was 25% Cr–20% Ni followed by Inconel, 18% Cr–10% Ni–Ti stabilized and 18% Cr–10% Ni–Nb stabilized steels. Some representative results are shown in *Figure 3.13*. The curves could not be described exactly by any of the normal correlations of weight gain with

time, but the oxide film appeared to be more protective than would be predicted from the parabolic rate law.

Some flaking of oxide was observed from the 25/20 steel at 650 and 750°C, and from the 18 Cr/10 Ni–Ti steel at 750°C after 2,000 hours. The extent of flaking was small, however, and the further observation of intergranular penetration was perhaps of greater technological significance. Inconel

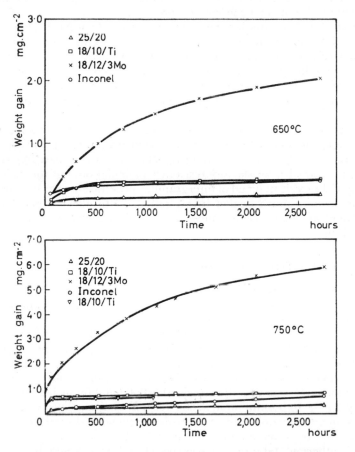

*Figure 3.13.* Oxidation of unpolished alloys in dry carbon dioxide at 100 p.s.i. pressure (Billington, Stevens and Davies, 1961) (by courtesy of the U.K.A.E.A. and the General Electric Co. Ltd.).

suffered particularly severe intergranular penetration at the sheared edges of the samples. The 25 Cr/20 Ni alloy suffered the least intergranular attack. Although the presence of 200 p.p.m. of water vapour in the carbon dioxide did not significantly alter the general oxidation behaviour of any of the alloys for times up to 2,500 hours, it may have enhanced somewhat the intergranular attack.

The relative merits of these alloys were confirmed in similar investigations by MAXWELL (1961). He reported that the poor resistance to oxidation of

18% Cr–12% Ni–3% Mo alloy at pressures up to 100 p.s.i. and temperatures above 565°C rendered it unsuitable for use in carbon dioxide. An 18% Cr–8% Ni titanium-stabilized steel (A.I.S.I. Type 321) showed variable behaviour, but was poor at 630 and 700°C. On the basis of weight gain, an 18% Cr–10% Ni niobium-stabilized steel was satisfactory up to 2,000 hours at 815°C.

An alloy of 7·5% Al, 5% Cr, 3% Nb, 0·5% Zr, balance Fe, had outstanding resistance to oxidation by carbon dioxide. It is difficult to fabricate, however, and is not yet a commercial product.

INOUYE (1960) has studied the behaviour at 760°C of AISI Type-304 steel (18 Cr–10 Ni) in argon containing low partial pressures of carbon dioxide. He reported rates of oxidation which were considerably higher than those observed by Billington *et al.* and by Maxwell. Moreover, when the oxide film on the steel was greater than 0·3 mg cm$^{-2}$ it spalled during thermal cycling; the spalling did not occur in $CO/CO_2$ mixtures containing high proportions of CO.

The rate of oxidation in $CO/CO_2/Ar$ mixtures at 980°C was found to be almost independent of $CO/CO_2$ ratio and concentration in the argon carrier.

In general, steels with greater than 18% Cr and greater than 8% Ni appear to have a reasonably satisfactory resistance to oxidation, but the incidence of spalling of the oxide film and of intergranular penetration over long periods of exposure require much further investigation. Both effects could have considerable technological significance in the performance of thin stainless steel fuel cladding.

### 3.4.4 Carburization and Other Effects

In the design of advanced reactors cooled by carbon dioxide and moderated by graphite it is necessary to take into account increasing amounts of carbon monoxide in the coolant. There may also be significant partial pressures of reducing gases such as CO, $H_2$ and $CH_4$ in helium-cooled reactor circuits. The presence of the reducing carbonaceous gases can give rise to special effects on some types of steel.

The formation of volatile iron carbonyl is possible from the reaction of carbon monoxide with low-alloy steels. Loss of metal by such a mechanism is unlikely to be important in nuclear reactor systems, however, since the presence of an oxidizing species ($CO_2$) is beneficial and the rate of attack is characterized by a maximum at about 200°C: above that temperature the decreasing thermal stability of iron carbonyl leads to a rapid fall of the rate to negligible proportions. The reaction with CO also becomes much less extensive with higher alloy steels and the peak in the rate at 200°C does not exist for the 25 Cr/20 Ni alloy (ROSSUM, 1953).

Some steels have been found to undergo excessive corrosion of a different form when subjected to reducing conditions. Thus at high temperatures stainless steels exposed to gas mixtures rich in CO and hydrogen at temperatures above 400°C are reported to show pitting attack (HOYT and CAUGHEY, 1959). Such conditions will not arise in $CO_2$-cooled reactor systems, but the possibility of this type of attack should not be overlooked in helium-cooled reactors where reducing impurities will predominate over oxidizing impurities owing to the presence of the large mass of graphite moderator. To explain the attack, Hoyt and Caughey favoured the hypothesis that certain points on the surface of the metal could catalyse the reaction:

$$2\ CO \rightarrow CO_2 + C$$

The resultant carbon assumes the form of thin filaments which readily disengage from the surface of the metal but in the process of doing so they may also remove small particles of metallic carbide.

Finally, there may be a process of carburization or decarburization of the steel, both effects being detrimental to the mechanical properties. Carburization most probably occurs by the reaction:

$$3Fe + 2CO \rightarrow Fe_3C + CO_2$$

and in stainless steels this can be followed by:

$$Fe_3C + 4Cr \rightarrow Cr_4C + 3Fe$$

Evidently a mixture of CO and $CO_2$ can be in equilibrium with a definite amount of carbon in the steel. Dovey and Jenkins (1949) have pointed out that for unalloyed steels the carburizing effect is masked by the comparatively rapid rate of oxidation by the $CO_2$, but that the effect becomes of greater importance in the heat-resisting steels where the rate of oxidation is much lower. Since at a given temperature an alloy containing chromium will only be able to maintain a limited amount of carbon in solution, there will be a special value of the ratio $(CO)^2/(CO_2)$ in the gas phase above which the conditions will lead to carburization of the metal and below which decarburization may take place (the rate at which these processes take place may be retarded by oxide film formation). The variation of the equilibrium constant and of that for carburization of steel by methane:

$$3Fe + CH_4 \rightleftharpoons Fe_3C + 2H_2$$

has been given graphically by Austin (1948).

These equilibria apply also to $CO/CO_2$ mixtures at low concentrations in an inert carrier gas. For instance, the carburization of A.I.S.I. Type 304 steel has been shown experimentally to be controlled by the relative concentrations of the gases in argon carrier gas at about 1,000°C (ORNL Staff, 1960).

Nickel-chromium alloys are particularly susceptible to attack by carburization and subsequent internal oxidation: a process known industrially as 'green rot'. Carbide precipitation leads to a reduction in the effective concentration of chromium in the matrix metal. Oxygen is then believed to diffuse inwards at a more rapid rate through the chromium-depleted material and to oxidize preferentially the precipitated chromium carbide. Since much of the latter is present on grain boundaries, rapid intergranular penetration of the metal can occur. Spooner, Thomas and Thomassen (1953) have reported that an alloy of 90% Ni–10% Cr deteriorates very rapidly above 800°C when heated in air with a restricted supply of oxygen. Whilst these authors considered that the effect they observed was another example of green rot, it seems likely that it is a different type of penetrating attack. They showed that the attack was caused when the oxygen supply to the metal surface was restricted sufficiently to oxidize the chromium without oxidizing the nickel. The effect was less in $CO/CO_2$ mixtures than in air.

Fortunately, the addition of iron to nickel–chromium alloys has been reported to decrease their susceptibility to green rot (BUCKNALL and PRICE, 1948; DOVEY and JENKINS, 1949). The presence of silicon in the alloy is also beneficial in this respect. In the present fragmentary state of knowledge it is difficult to generalize, however. For instance, an iron–chromium alloy (16% Cr) is rapidly carburized at about 925°C in a mixture of (CO and $CO_2$) at a partial pressure of $2 \times 10^{-4}$ atm in helium (BOKROS et al., 1959).

There is some evidence that stress can greatly enhance the carburization of stainless steels in CO at 925°C (ORNL STAFF, 1959).

In summary, these special effects are unlikely to be encountered in current reactors cooled by carbon dioxide where the maximum gas temperature is less than 600°C. Reactors cooled by nominally pure helium may give cause for concern, however, since the helium may contain significant proportions of reducing and carbonizing gases. For those helium-cooled reactors in which it is intended to employ steel cladding of the fuel elements, the operating temperatures of the steel may extend into the region where carburization could become comparatively rapid. Attempts to increase the exit gas temperature to obtain an efficient gas turbine cycle could also give rise to a similar problem in the containment steel of the external coolant circuit (see, for instance, BOKROS and SHOEMAKER, 1961). The selection of materials for the construction of such reactors will prove difficult since their reliability over long terms of operation must be much higher than is normally required in other industrial applications.

### REFERENCES

*Uranium*

ADDA, Y. (1958). 'Kinetic study of oxidation, nitriding and hydrogenation of uranium.' French CEA Report 757. Also, U.S.A.E.C. Report, AEC-TR-3749

ANTILL, J. E. and PEAKALL, K. A. (1959). 'Kinetics of the oxidation of uranium by carbon dioxide.' *J. Less Common Metals*, **1**, 227

ANTILL, J. E. and PEAKALL, K. A. (1961). 'Oxidation of uranium alloys in carbon dioxide and air.' *J. Less Common Metals*, **3**, 239

AUSKERN, A. B. and BELLE, J. (1961). 'Self-diffusion of oxygen in uranium dioxide.' *J. Nuclear Mat.*, **3**, 267

AYLMORE, D. W., GREGG, S. J. and JEPSON, W. B. (1959). 'The formation of porous oxides on metals.' *J. Electrochem. Soc.*, **106**, 1010

BAGLEY, K. Q., and OLIVER, D. S. (1953). 'The oxidation of uranium in air.' U.K.A.E.A. Report, R. & D.B. (C) TN-32

COCKCROFT, SIR JOHN (1961). 'British experience in the technical development of power reactors.' *Atom*, No. 52, 16

COX, B. (1962). 'The oxidation of niobium.' *Trans. Met. Soc. A.I.M.E.*, in the press

CUBICCIOTTI, D. (1952). 'The reaction between uranium and oxygen.' *J. Amer. Chem. Soc.*, **74**, 1079

DARRAS, R., BAQUE, P. and LECLERCQ, D. 'Magnesium and uranium ignition in different gaseous atmospheres.' *Third Metallurgy Symposium on Corrosion, Saclay*, 1959. North Holland Publ. Co., Amsterdam

DAVIDGE, P. C., HODGE, N. and STOCKDALE, G. N. (1960). 'The purification of inert gases by hot uranium.' *Brit. Chem. Eng.*, **5**, 477

## REFERENCES

DEMASTRY, J. A., SHOBER, F. R. and DICKERSON, R. F. (1959). 'Metallurgical studies of niobium–uranium alloys.' U.S.A.E.C. Report, BMI-1400

EVANS, U. R. (1960). *The corrosion and oxidation of metals.* Edward Arnold Ltd., London

GRAINGER, L. (1961). 'Fuel elements for civil reactors.' *Nucl. Engng,* **6**, 102

HARTMANN, I. (1951). 'The explosivity of Ti, Zr, Th, U and their hydrides.' U.S.A.E.C. Report, NYO-1562

HILLIARD, R. K. (1958). 'Oxidation of uranium in air at high temperatures.' U.S.A.E.C. Report, HW-58022

HUDDLE, R. A. U. and SILVESTER, D. R. V. Brit. Pat. 823,392; filed 1956, complete specification published 1959. (To U.K.A.E.A.)

INOUYE, H. (1960). Paper presented at the *Columbium Metallurgy Symposium,* Lake George, New York

ISAACS, J. W. and WANKLYN, J. N. (1960). 'The reaction of uranium with air at high temperatures.' U.K.A.E.A. Report, AERE-R. 3559

LEIBOWITZ, L., SCHNIZLEIN, J. G., BINGLE, J. D. and VOGEL, R. C. (1961). 'The kinetics of the oxidation of uranium between 125° and 250°C.' *J. Electrochem. Soc.,* **108**, 1155

LORIERS, J. (1952). 'Oxidation of metallic uranium.' *Compt. rendus,* **234**, 91. Also U.S.A.E.C. Report, HW-61493

MALLETT, M. W. and GERDS, A. F. (1955). 'Reaction of nitrogen with uranium.' *J. Electrochem. Soc.,* **102**, 292

MISHLER, L., LEIBOWITZ, L., SCHNIZLEIN, J. G. and VOGEL, R. C. (1961). 'A microscopic study of oxide films on uranium.' *J. Electrochem. Soc.,* **108**, 1153.

PAIDASSI, J., POINTUD, M. L., CAILLAT, R. and DARRAS, R. (1961). 'Contribution to the study of the oxidation of uranium in carbon dioxide.' *J. Nucl. Materials,* **3**, 162

PARKER, G. W., CREEK, G. E., MARTIN, W. J. and BARTON, C. J. (1960). 'Fuel element catastrophe studies: hazards of fission product release from irradiated uranium.' U.S.A.E.C. Reports, ORNL-CF-60-6-24, ORNL-2983

PERKINS, K. T. (1956). Quoted in U.S.A.E.C. Report, LA-2035

PORTE, H. A., SCHNIZLEIN, J. G., VOGEL, R. C. and FISCHER, D. F. (1959). 'Oxidation of zirconium and zirconium alloys.' U.S.A.E.C. Report, ANL-6046

REYNOLDS, W. C. (1959). 'Investigation of ignition temperatures of solid metals.' American National Aeronautics and Space Administration Report, NASA-TN-D 182

SCHNIZLEIN, J. G. and BINGLE, J. D. (1960). (Part of) Chemical Engineering Division Summary Report, July–September, 1960. U.S.A.E.C. Report, ANL-6231.

SCHNIZLEIN, J. G., PIZZOLATO, P. J., PORTE, H. A., BINGLE, J. D., FISCHER, D. F., MISHLER, L. W. and VOGEL, R. C. (1959). 'Ignition behaviour and kinetics of oxidation of uranium, zirconium, plutonium and thorium, and binary alloys of each. A status report.' U.S.A.E.C. Report, ANL-5974

SCHNIZLEIN, J. G., WOODS, J. D., BINGLE, J. D. and VOGEL, R. C. (1960). 'Identification of the diffusing species in uranium oxidation.' *J. Electrochem. Soc.,* **107**, 783

SHAW, D. and HINDMARSH, P. (1957). 'The oxidation of uranium in argon containing traces of oxygen.' U.K.A.E.A. Report, IGR-TN/W517

SMITH, R. B. (1956). 'The fire properties of uranium.' U.S.A.E.C. Report, TID-8011

WABER, J. T. (1956). 'A review of the corrosion behaviour of uranium.' U.S.A.E.C. Report, LA-2035

WABER, J. T. (1958). 'The corrosion behaviour of uranium and plutonium.' *Proc. Second Geneva Conference,* **6**, 204

WATHEN, T. (1943). 'The corrosion of uranium metal in air and steam at various temperatures.' British Report, BR223A

*Magnesium*

BOUSSION, M. L., GRALL, L. and CAILLAT, R. (1957). 'Oxidation of magnesium by air between 350–500°C.' *Rev. Met.*, **54**, 185

CAILLAT, R. and DARRAS, R. (1958). 'Corrosion of magnesium and some of its alloys in gas-cooled reactors.' *Proc. Second Geneva Conf.*, **5**, 220

CATHCART, J. V. and YOUNG, F. W. (1961). 'Influence of reactor radiation on the oxidation of niobium.' *Corrosion*, **17**, No. 2, 77

DARRAS, R., BAQUE, P. and CHEVILLIARD, C. (1960). 'Compatibility of magnesium alloys with pressurised carbon dioxide.' French Report, CEA-1702. See also, *Rev. met.*, **56** (1959), 61

DARRAS, R., BAQUE, P. and LECLERCQ, D. (1960). 'Inflammability of magnesium and uranium in air and carbon dioxide.' *Proc. Third Metallurgy Colloquium on Corrosion, Saclay*, p. 53, North Holland Publ. Co.

DELAVAULT, R. (1945). 'The inhibition of the combustion of magnesium and its alloys.' *Compt. rend.*, **221**, 498

FASSELL, W. M., GULBRANSEN, L. B., LEWIS, J. R. and HAMILTON, J. H. (1951). 'Ignition temperatures of magnesium and magnesium alloys.' *J. Metals*, **3**, 522

HEAL, T. J. (1958). 'Magnesium and its alloys: applications in nuclear engineering.' *Nucl. Engng.*, **3**, No. 23, 52

HUDDLE, R. A. U. and WYATT, L. M. (1957). 'Early metallurgical problems (relating to Calder Hall).' *J. Brit. Nucl. Energy Conf.*, 110, April

GIBBS, D. S. and SVEC, H. J. (1957). 'Kinetics of the reaction between magnesium and water vapour.' *J. Electrochem. Soc.*, **104**, 434

GRAINGER, L. (1961). 'Fuel elements for civil reactors.' *Nucl. Engng.*, **6**, 102

GRAINGER, L. and McINTOSH, A. B. (1959). 'Metallurgical developments (towards Calder Hall).' *J. Brit. Nucl. Energy Conf.*, 121, April

GREGG, S. J. and JEPSON, W. B. (1958–9). 'The high temperature oxidation of magnesium in dry and moist oxygen.' *J. Inst. Metals*, **87**, 187

MIKHAIL, R. SH. and GOUDA, V. K. (1960). 'Rate of oxidation of magnesium metal in dry oxygen.' *J. Appl. Chem.*, **10**, 384

SALESSE, M. (1958). 'Safety of magnesium canning for $CO_2$-cooled reactors.' *Nucleonics*, **16**, 123

SINELNIKOV, K. D., IVANOV, V. E. and ZELENSKY, V. F. (1958). 'Magnesium–beryllium alloys as materials for nuclear reactors.' *Proc. Second Geneva Conf.*, **5**, 234

STHAPITANONDA, P. and MARGRAVE, J. L. (1956). 'Kinetics of nitridation of magnesium and aluminium.' *J. Phys. Chem.*, **60**, 1628


*Beryllium*

AYLMORE, D. W., GREGG, S. J. and JEPSON, W. B. (1960). 'The high temperature oxidation of beryllium, Part I. In dry oxygen.' *J. Nucl. Materials*, **2**, No. 2, 169

AYLMORE, D. W., GREGG, S. J. and JEPSON, W. B. (1961). 'The high temperature oxidation of beryllium, Part IV. In water vapour and in moist oxygen.' *J. Nucl. Materials*, **3**, No. 2, 190

BENNETT, M. J., CRICK, N. W., BLYTHE, P. C. and ANTILL, J. E. (1961). 'The oxidation of irradiated beryllium in carbon monoxide.' U.K.A.E.A. Report, AERE-R. 3873

E.N.E.A. (1959). 'Market for nuclear materials—II—Moderators. Beryllium.' Stresa Conference, May 1959

GAS-COOLED REACTOR PROJECT (1960). Quarterly report for period ending September 30, 1960. U.S.A.E.C. Report, ORNL-3015

GREGG, S. J., HUSSEY, R. J. and JEPSON, W. B. (1960). 'The higher temperature oxidation of beryllium. Part II. The reaction with carbon dioxide and with carbon monoxide.' *J. Nucl. Materials*, **2**, 225

# REFERENCES

GREGG, S. J., HUSSEY, R. J. and JEPSON, W. B. (1961a). 'The high temperature oxidation of beryllium, Part III. In carbon dioxide, carbon monoxide and carbon monoxide–dioxide mixtures.' *J. Nucl. Materials*, **3**, 175

GREGG, S. J., HUSSEY, R. J. and JEPSON, W. B. (1961b). 'The high temperature oxidation of beryllium, Part V. In moist carbon dioxide and moist carbon monoxide.' *J. Nucl. Materials*, **4**, No. 1, 46

GULBRANSEN, E. A. and ANDREW, K. F. (1950). 'The kinetics of the reactions of beryllium with oxygen and nitrogen, and the effect of oxide and nitride films on its vapour pressure.' *J. Electrochem. Soc.*, **97**, 383

KAUFMANN, A. R. and KJELLGREN, B. R. F. (1955). 'Status of beryllium technology in the U.S.A.' *Proc. First Geneva Conference*, **8**, 590

LIVEY, D. T. and WILLIAMS, J. (1958). 'Some aspects of the fabrication technology of beryllium and beryllia.' *Proc. Second Geneva Conf.*, **5**, 311

SCOTT, V. D. (1960). 'Formation of beryllium carbide during the corrosion of beryllium in carbon monoxide and in carbon dioxide gas.' *Nature, Lond.*, **186**, No. 4723, 466

UDY, M. C., SHAW, H. L. and BOULGER, F. W. (1953). 'Properties of beryllium.' *Nucleonics*, **11**, No. 5, 52


*Steel*

AUSTIN, J. B. (1948). Quoted in *Corrosion Handbook*, Ed. H. H. Uhlig, John Wiley & Sons, New York

BENARD, J., HERTZ, J., JEANNIN, Y. and MOREAU, J. (1960). 'Sur le mécanisme d'oxydation aux températures élevées de l'acier austénitique 18% Cr–8% Ni.' *Mem. Sci. Rev. Met.*, **57**, 389

BILLINGTON, S. R., STEVENS, C. G. and DAVIES, M. W. (1961). 'The oxidation of four austenitic stainless steels and Inconel in carbon dioxide.' (Part of) U.S.A.E.C. Report, TID-7597

BOKROS, J. C. and SHOEMAKER, H. E. (1961). 'Reactor materials compatibility with impurities in helium.' U.S.A.E.C. Report, GA-1508

BOKROS, J. C., SHOEMAKER, H. E. and EARLE, R. (1959). Quoted in MGCR Programme Quarterly Progress Report, June 30, 1959. U.S.A.E.C. Report, GA-1099

BOKROS, J. C. and WALLACE, W. P. (1960). 'High temperature, high pressure oxidation of alloys caused by carbon dioxide.' *Corrosion*, **16**, No. 2, 117

BUCKNALL, E. H. and PRICE, L. E. (1948). 'Etude de l'attaque des atmospheres controlées sur les resistors et autres parties des fours en alliages nickel–chrome.' *Rev. met.*, **45**, 129

DAVIES, M. H., SIMNAD, M. T. and BIRCHENALL, C. E. (1951). 'On the mechanism and kinetics of the scaling of iron.' *Trans. Met. Soc. A.I.M.E.*, **191**, 889

DOVEY, D. M. and JENKINS, I. (1949–50). 'The behaviour of nickel–chromium–iron alloys in carbon-bearing gases in the range 900–1000°C.' *J. Inst. Metals*, **76**, 581

DRAYCOTT, A. and HUBERY, R. W. (1961). 'Oxidation of 1% Cr, 0·5% Mo steel in carbon dioxide.' Australian Atomic Energy Comm. Report, AAEC-E71

DRAYCOTT, A. and SMITH, R. (1960). 'Initial results on the compatibility of austenitic stainless steel with carbon dioxide.' Australian Atomic Energy Comm. Report, AAEC-E.52

EVANS, U. R. (1960). *The corrosion and oxidation of metals.* Edward Arnold Ltd., London

HIMMEL, L., MEHL, R. F. and BIRCHENALL, C. E. (1953). 'Self-diffusion of iron in iron oxides, and the Wagner theory of oxidation.' *Trans. Met. Soc. A.I.M.E.*, **197**, 827

HOYT, W. B. and CAUGHEY, R. H. (1959). 'High temperature metal deterioration in atmospheres containing carbon monoxide and hydrogen.' *Corrosion*, **15**, 627

INOUYE, H. (1960). (Part of) U.S.A.E.C. Reports, ORNL-2988, 3049

Leclercq, D., Chevilliard, C. and Darras, R. (1960). 'Oxydation d'aciers ordinaires ou alliés chauffés dans le gaz carbonique sous pression.' French CEA Report, CEA-1407

Maxwell, W. A. (1961). 'Studies on the compatibility of high temperature carbon dioxide with stainless steels and other materials.' (Part of) U.S.A.E.C. Report, TID-7597

Moore, C. and Raine, T. (1961). 'The oxidation of reactor steels in carbon dioxide.' Special report No. 69, The Iron and Steel Institute

ORNL Staff (1959). 'Gas-cooled reactor project quarterly progress report, period ending Dec. 31st, 1959.' U.S.A.E.C. Report, ORNL-2888

ORNL Staff (1960). 'Gas-cooled reactor project quarterly progress report, period ending June 30, 1960.' U.S.A.E.C. Report, ORNL-2964

Owen, Sir Leonard (1961). 'Steel and nuclear power.' Special report No. 69, The Iron and Steel Institute

Pettit, F., Yinger, R. and Wagner, J. B. (1960). 'The mechanism of oxidation of iron in carbon monoxide–carbon dioxide mixtures.' *Acta Met.*, **8**, 617

Pfeil, L. B. (1929). 'The oxidation of iron and steel at high temperatures.' *J. Iron and Steel Inst.*, **119**, 501

Robertson, J. M. and Nichols, R. W. (1961). 'High temperature mechanical properties of steels used in gas-cooled reactor pressure vessels.' Special Report No. 69, The Iron and Steel Institute

Rossum, O. Van (1953). 'Werkstoff-Fragen bei den Hochdrucksynthesen.' *Chem.-Ing.-Tech.*, **25**, 481

Smeltzer, W. W. (1960). 'The oxidation of iron in carbon dioxide–carbon monoxide mixtures.' *Trans. Met. Soc. A.I.M.E.*, **218**, 674

Spooner, N., Thomas, J. M. and Thomassen, L. (1953). 'High temperature corrosion of nickel–chromium alloys.' *J. Metals*, **5**, 844

Yearian, H. J., Derbyshire, W. D. and Radavich, J. F. (1957). 'The formation of oxide films on chromium and 18 Cr–8 Ni steels.' *Corrosion*, **13**, No. 9, 597t

# Chapter 4

# CERAMIC FUELS

THE need to increase the operating temperature of nuclear power reactors—one of the most effective ways of improving the economics of electrical power generation from a given system—has revealed the limitations of metallic fuel elements. For example, if a reactor fuelled by uranium metal were operated at a fuel temperature exceeding 670°C, the uranium would be cycled through the alpha–beta transition point, and serious dimensional changes would be encountered. An equally important consideration lies in the magnitude of the burn-up, which would be severely limited by the swelling of the metal at 500–800°C brought about by the internal pressure of gaseous fission products. This problem could be alleviated either by enclosing the fuel element in a strong retaining can, or by suitably alloying the metal (for example with molybdenum) to increase its creep strength. Both of these solutions are limited in scope, however, and in a thermal reactor would result in increased neutron wastage. A more radical and satisfactory approach lies in the development of non-metallic fuel elements.

TABLE 4.1

NON-METALLIC FUELS

| Type | Composition | Theoretical density (g cm$^{-3}$) | Melting point (°C) |
|---|---|---|---|
| Oxides | $UO_2$ | 10·97 | 2,800 |
| | $ThO_2$ | 10·00 | ~3,300 |
| | $PuO_2$ | 11·46 | ~2,400 (in $O_2$) |
| Carbides | UC | 13·63 | ~2,400 |
| | $U_2C_3$ | 12·88 | — (Dec. 1,800) |
| | $UC_2$ | 11·68 | 2,470 |
| | ThC | 10·67 | 2,620 |
| | $ThC_2$ | — | 2,650 |
| | PuC | 14·00 | 1,650 |
| | $Pu_2C_3$ | 12·70 | 2,050 |
| Nitrides | UN | 14·32 | ~2,550 |
| | ThN | — | 2,630 |
| | PuN | 13·30 | — |
| Silicides | $U_3Si_2$ | 12·20 | 1,665 |
| | USi | 10·40 | 1,575 |
| | $Th_3Si_2$ | 9·75 | 1,850 |
| | ThSi | 8·92 | >1,900 |

Some fissile and fertile compounds which have been considered as fuel materials are summarized in *Table 4.1*, together with their theoretical densities and melting points.

109

For many years an extensive effort has been devoted to the development of ceramic bodies of uranium dioxide, both in the pure state, and containing additions of other fissile and non-fissile oxides. The first investigations on uranium dioxide fuel elements were conducted for application in pressurized water reactors; here the motive in using ceramic fuel was not the need for high temperatures, but for a material less reactive to water than the metal. Using carefully developed techniques to densify the powder, bodies of up to 97 per cent theoretical density can now readily be prepared, and uranium dioxide bodies have already shown outstanding advantages over the metal as fuel. Up to the melting point of 2,800°C, no phase change is encountered, and dimensional changes are negligible at burn-ups of up to 30,000 MWd tonne$^{-1}$. The most serious disadvantages appear to be (i) a low thermal conductivity, which decreases with increasing temperature; (ii) a lack of physical strength which must therefore be supplied by the fuel cladding; (iii) a tendency to release fission product gases, which must be retained by the can. The low physical strength is probably a characteristic of all brittle ceramic fuels, and one which must inevitably be allowed for in fuel element design. Low thermal conductivity can be serious in a highly rated system such as a fast reactor, and has provided an incentive to investigate alternative ceramic materials which may have superior characteristics, such as carbides and possibly nitrides and silicides. Fission product gas release is an overriding criterion governing the suitability of a ceramic fuel (Chapter 5): the need to minimize release provides an important incentive to fabricate ceramic bodies having a density as close to theoretical as possible—more important even than the economic desire to achieve the maximum density of fissile fuel.

Solids of theoretical density can be prepared by melting and casting techniques, but in the case of refractory compounds such a procedure would be difficult and expensive on a production scale. A more promising approach lies in the compaction of powders, followed by a sintering (or 'firing') procedure which induces densification at a temperature considerably below the melting point. The variations in the procedure are in most cases associated with the preparation of the 'green' body (the powder compact prior to sintering). Available methods of densification may be summarized broadly as follows:

### (i) Cold die compaction and sintering

Cold compaction of the powder may be carried out in a suitable die either dry, or admixed with a binder and a lubricant. The green body is then heated if necessary to remove additives, and finally sintered.

### (ii) Hydrostatic pressing and sintering

Under some circumstances the die compaction technique can produce density gradients at the green stage which result in dimensional distortion during subsequent sintering. Such gradients can be minimized by employing an alternative cold compacting technique known as hydrostatic pressing, in which the powder is enclosed in a flexible mould and subjected to pressure transmitted through a suitable liquid. This technique ensures the production of a more uniform compact than can be obtained with a die, but the procedure is more expensive.

110

### (iii) *Slip casting and sintering*

An alternative method of minimizing pressure gradients is to employ slip casting. A suspension of the powder dispersed in a suitable liquid medium is poured into a mould of an absorbent material, such as plaster of Paris. The liquid is absorbed by the mould, and the powder forms a green body in the shape of the mould cavity. This technique is most suitable where hollow bodies are required. For solid fuel element rods it would be tedious, and there has been little attempt to develop it as a production method.

### (iv) *Extrusion and sintering*

In this method, the powder is mixed with a suitable fluidizing matrix, such as an organic resin, and extruded through a die. The technique is particularly applicable where long thin rods are required.

### (v) *Hot pressing*

The technique of hot pressing (e.g. MURRAY *et al.*, 1952; SCOTT and WILLIAMS, 1957) involves the simultaneous application of heat and pressure, and is advantageous in that the temperatures required to achieve densification are considerably lower than those needed when pressure and heat are applied separately (e.g. for $UO_2$, 800°C for hot pressing, 1,600°C for sintering of a cold compact). The main disadvantage appears to lie in expense and in the choice of a suitable material for the hot die (which must be inert to the ceramic compound).

Numerous variations of the above methods are available. Some workers have sought to eliminate the process of sintering entirely, and have concentrated on the development of techniques, such as swaging or vibratory packing, designed to pack the fuel powder as efficiently as possible in suitable cans (e.g. PATERSON and CHALDER, 1959; WEBB, 1959; HAUTH, 1959, 1961; CERAMIC FUELS STAFF, HANFORD, 1960). A procedure such as this, however, while undoubtedly leading to lower fabrication costs, may well produce a serious aggravation of the problem of fission gas release.

Most ceramic fuel development, of oxides, carbides and more recently nitrides, appears to have concentrated on the method of cold compaction followed by sintering. This technique has been adopted by the nuclear power industry with a fair measure of success, particularly in the case of uranium dioxide.

Research and development work in many laboratories has attempted to supply, in the case of fuel element materials, a scientific foundation for the art of manufacturing ceramic bodies. The effort has so far met with limited success, and although we are now in a position to specify broadly what powder characteristics are favourable to sintering, and what preparative techniques will yield the most suitable powders, much work remains to be carried out on the mechanism of sintering and on the relationship between the properties of a powder and those of the ceramic body prepared from it.

In this chapter, we shall present a general review of fabrication work performed on the preparation and densification of refractory fissile compounds, chiefly oxides, carbides and nitrides. The original publications referred to are of necessity selective, since much of the technological effort in this field is obviously outside the scope of reactor chemistry. Studies of chemical compatibility and irradiation behaviour will also be reviewed for each of the systems considered.

### 4.1 URANIUM DIOXIDE

#### 4.1.1 Phase Relationships and Chemical Properties

*Phase relationships*

The complexities of the uranium–oxygen system appear to be unparalleled by those of any other metal–oxygen combination. The system is based upon four major phases: $UO_2$, $U_4O_9$, $U_3O_8$ and $UO_3$. There is a scarcity of information in the range of composition between $U_3O_8$ and $UO_3$, but the region from

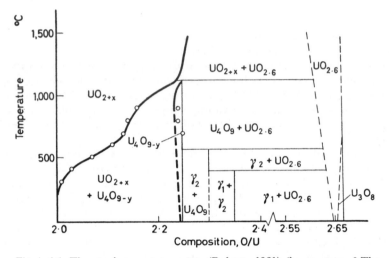

*Figure 4.1.* The uranium–oxygen system (Roberts, 1961) (by courtesy of The Chemical Society).

$UO_2$ to $U_3O_8$ has been subjected to intensive study (GRONVOLD, 1955; BLACKBURN, 1955; ARONSON and BELLE, 1958; SCHANER, 1960; ROBERTS and WALTER, 1960). A phase diagram recently constructed on the basis of these data by ROBERTS (1961) is reproduced in *Figure 4.1*. Roberts has presented an excellent overall review of the phase relationships, and we shall therefore confine discussion of fundamental properties to the oxidation and thermal stability of $UO_2$.

*Oxidation*

The phases $UO_{2+x}$ and $U_4O_{9-y}$ are both cubic; the excess oxygen can be considered to be incorporated as an interstitial solution of oxygen ions in the $UO_2$ fluorite lattice. If oxidation of $UO_2$ is carried out below 300°C, GRONVOLD (1955) showed that a tetragonal $U_3O_7$ phase can be produced. This appears to be a non-equilibrium structure since it transforms slowly to a mixture of $UO_2$ and $U_4O_9$ on heating above 140°C for long periods (PERIO, 1953).

Data on the equilibrium pressure of oxygen over uranium oxides up to $UO_{2.6}$ have been reported by a number of workers (ACKERMAN *et al.* 1956; BLACKBURN, 1955; ARONSON and BELLE, 1958; ROBERTS and WALTER, 1960) and the curves are summarized in *Figure 4.2*. In air at atmospheric pressure, $UO_2$ is thermodynamically unstable with respect to $U_3O_8$ but the degree of oxidation is greatly dependent upon temperature and upon the state of subdivision of the oxide.

The oxidation of uranium dioxide powder over the temperature ranges $-130$ to $+50°C$ and $130$ to $180°C$ was studied by ANDERSON *et al.* (1955), who established that the process took place by two distinct mechanisms. The first

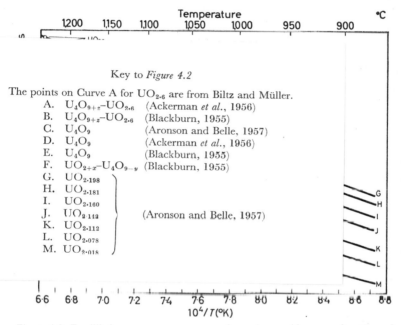

Key to *Figure 4.2*

The points on Curve A for $UO_{2.6}$ are from Biltz and Müller.

A. $U_4O_{9+z}$–$UO_{2.6}$ (Ackerman *et al.*, 1956)
B. $U_4O_{9+z}$–$UO_{2.6}$ (Blackburn, 1955)
C. $U_4O_9$ (Aronson and Belle, 1957)
D. $U_4O_9$ (Ackerman *et al.*, 1956)
E. $U_4O_9$ (Blackburn, 1955)
F. $UO_{2+x}$–$U_4O_{9-y}$ (Blackburn, 1955)
G. $UO_{2.198}$
H. $UO_{2.181}$
I. $UO_{2.160}$
J. $UO_{2.143}$ (Aronson and Belle, 1957)
K. $UO_{2.112}$
L. $UO_{2.078}$
M. $UO_{2.018}$

*Figure 4.2.* Equilibrium oxygen pressures of uranium oxides as a function of temperature (Belle, 1958) (by courtesy of United Nations).

mechanism was operative between $-130$ and $50°C$, where the oxygen absorbed increased as the logarithm of the time: the data were interpreted in terms of preliminary chemisorption of oxygen, followed by its diffusion into interstitial positions in the $UO_2$ lattice. The degree of total oxidation effected by this mechanism is dependent upon the surface area of the oxide, and diffusion of oxygen into individual crystallites therefore appears to be limited to the formation of an inhomogeneous 'oxidized skin' about 40 Å in thickness which prevents further oxidation. It is this phenomenon which explains the variable oxygen content of $UO_2$ samples prepared by different routes: whereas low surface area powder may retain an oxygen/uranium ratio close to $2·0$, powder of high surface area undergoes oxidation on storage in air at room temperature to overall compositions approaching a ratio of $2·25$, depending upon the magnitude of the surface area. If the latter exceeds a value of about $10 \text{ m}^2 \text{ g}^{-1}$, the material may be pyrophoric, since exothermic oxidation takes place so rapidly that a conversion to $U_3O_8$ is effected. It has been shown, however (BEL and CARTERET, 1958), that even high surface area powder can be oxidized in a controlled fashion in air without the formation of $U_3O_8$: material of surface area 17 $m^2$ $g^{-1}$, for example, was oxidized to a composition $UO_{2.25}$. The importance of 'non-stoichiometric' oxygen as an aid to sintering is discussed in Section 4.1.3.

Over the temperature range 130 to 180°C, Anderson *et al.* found that the oxidation continued beyond that corresponding to surface skin oxidation, and obeyed kinetics which could be interpreted in terms of a diffusion of interstitial oxygen into the crystallites, up to a composition approximating to $U_4O_9$. This work was later extended by ARONSON and BELLE (1957) who studied the oxidation of $UO_2$ to $U_3O_8$ in dry air and in oxygen over the temperature range 160–350°C. These workers found that the reaction proceeded in two stages: the first stage consisted of the formation of the tetragonal phase $U_3O_7$, a process which was controlled by the diffusion of oxygen through the $UO_2$ lattice with a diffusion coefficient corresponding to

$$D = 5 \cdot 5 \times 10^{-3} \exp \frac{-26,300 \pm 1,500}{RT}$$

Below 260°C, oxidation ceased with complete conversion to $U_3O_7$. Above this temperature, however, a second-stage oxidation to $U_3O_8$ took place, with kinetics which were indicative of a process of nucleation and growth. These findings were substantially confirmed by BLACKBURN *et al.* (1958) and by DEMARCO *et al.* (1959), though the latter authors did not observe the onset of nucleation to give $U_3O_8$ below 300°C. This limiting temperature has technical importance in that green pellets of $UO_2$ can be heated in air to below 300°C to remove binder or lubricant without the danger of $U_3O_8$ formation (WILLIAMS, WHEATLEY and LLOYD, 1959). Detailed work on the low temperature oxidation of $UO_2$ to the tetragonal phase has been reported recently by HOEKSTRA *et al.* (1961) and BELBEOCH *et al.* (1961).

*Thermal stability*

The thermal stability of uranium dioxide under non-oxidizing conditions has important implications both on high temperature fabrication processes and on behaviour in a reactor, where, because of the low thermal conductivity, the temperature at the centre of a fuel element may approach the melting point. Evidence for the thermal decomposition of non-stoichiometric uranium dioxide (probably to $UO_2$ and $UO_3$) has been obtained during sintering experiments (Section 4.1.3) and irradiation testing of fuel compacts (Section 4.1.6).

Tests on the thermal stability of stoichiometric uranium dioxide were reported by WISNYI and PIJANOWSKI (1957), who claimed that no decomposition occurred on melting. However, more recent work by ANDERSON *et al.* (1960) has provided firm evidence that uranium dioxide decomposes at its melting point. The fusion of samples in an argon arc furnace at $2,800 \pm 100$°C, resulted in lustrous grey solids with a metallic appearance, having the gross analytical composition $UO_{2-n}$, where $0 \cdot 15 > n > 0$. The extent of deficiency in oxygen increased with the time a sample was held in the molten state, but the composition seemed to approach a limit of about $UO_{1.86}$ after prolonged fusion. The product consisted of substoichiometric $UO_2$ (O/U ratio 1·96–1·97) with inclusions of metastable beta-uranium metal.

Subsequent work by ROTHWELL (1961) has not only confirmed instability at the melting point, but has shown also that inclusions of metallic uranium appear on annealing pellets of $UO_2$ in an inert atmosphere or *in vacuo* above 1,800°C: the precipitation of metal at 2,000°C has likewise been observed by MACEWAN (1961). These findings may have important implications both on the practicability of fabricating $UO_2$ fuel elements by melting and casting, and on the behaviour of fuel if centre melting should take place.

### 4.1.2 Physical Properties

#### Melting point

Two of the recent values of the melting point, those of LAMBERTSON and MUELLER (1953) (2,880 ± 20°C) and EHLERT (1958) (2,880 ± 50°C) are in excellent agreement. The value obtained by WISNYI and PIJANOWSKI (1956) is slightly lower (2,760 ± 30°C), and it seems prudent to accept the limits set by ANDERSON et al. (1960) of 2,800 ± 100°C.

#### Thermal conductivity

Values of the thermal conductivity of $UO_2$ over the range 0–1,600°C obtained by various authors are plotted in *Figure 4.3.** The data have been corrected to theoretical density by applying the simplified relationship of LOEB (1954) which relates the measured thermal conductivity $k_m$ to that of theoretically dense material, $k_t$ by

$$k_m = k_t(1-f)$$

where $f$ is the fractional pore volume. Ross (1959), in carrying out studies on materials of different density, found that less dense samples had considerably lower conductivity than that predicted by the Loeb equation because of the existence of irregular or anisometric pores at the grain boundaries which are more effective obstacles than spherical pores to flow of heat. This may possibly account for the scatter in the data of *Figure 4.3*. The discrepancies must be resolved before temperature distributions in bulk material can be predicted accurately. For analysing the results of irradiation experiments, a parameter which may be termed 'integrated thermal conductivity' ($\int kd\theta$) promises to be very useful. This will be discussed in Section 4.1.6.

Earlier evidence for a pronounced fall in the thermal conductivity of $UO_2$ brought about by irradiation has since been discredited. For example EICHENBERG (1958) obtained evidence that pile irradiation reduces the thermal conductivity by a factor of 2·3 up to about 400°C, but this observation appears to have been due in part to a large diametral clearance between can and specimen during the measurements: later experiments with an essentially zero clearance resulted in figures close to the out-of-pile data of Deem

* It should be noted that a recent prediction by BATES (1961) that the thermal conductivity should rise again at higher temperatures is not borne out by the data of REISWIG (1961), which extend to 2,100°C.

(*Figure 4.3*) over the range 100–800°C. Ross (1960) has carried out post-irradiation conductivity measurements at 60°C on $UO_2$ samples which had been irradiated in NRX to various burn-ups at temperatures up to 500°C. It was found that after a thermal neutron dose of $2 \times 10^{17}$ nvt, the conductivity of the irradiated samples was about 26 per cent lower than that of unirradiated samples but that longer irradiations up to $6.8 \times 10^{19}$ nvt brought about no further decrease. Annealing experiments at 1,000°C revealed that the thermal conductivity could be partially restored, but the degree of restoration decreased with the irradiation time. This point is worthy of fundamental study.

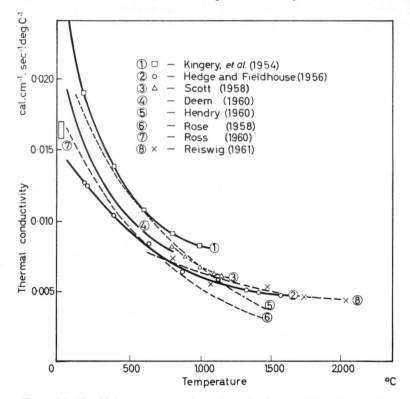

*Figure 4.3.* The high-temperature thermal conductivity of $UO_2$ (corrected to theoretical density).

From the technological viewpoint, it seems safe to assume that the effects of irradiation on thermal conductivity will be small, and that any decrease will lie within the uncertainty in $k$ deduced from *Figure 4.3*.

There is firm evidence that an increase in the O/U ratio brings about a marked decrease in the thermal conductivity of uranium dioxide (BELLE, 1958; NICHOLLS, 1958; ROSS, 1960). The data for samples with O/U ratio varying from 2·00 to 2·66 are plotted in *Figure 4.4*. It is uncertain whether a similar effect would be encountered at higher temperatures, though data for hot-pressed $UO_{2.13}$ over the temperature range 100–600°C (MURRAY and LIVEY, 1956) are essentially identical with those of Kingery for $UO_{2.00}$ over the same range, and might be regarded as evidence for a decrease in the effect of excess oxygen at higher temperatures.

Preliminary data reported from the laboratories of the Sylvania-Corning Nuclear Corporation (SHAPIRO and POWERS, 1959; CAVALLARO *et al.*, 1960) indicated that the incorporation of other oxides, notably $Y_2O_3$, could promote a significant improvement in the thermal conductivity of uranium dioxide. However, these data are now known to be erroneous (POWERS, 1960). Moreover ROBERTSON *et al.* (1960) have concluded from post-irradiation examination of pellets that the addition of 4 mole per cent $Y_2O_3$ does not significantly improve the thermal conductivity of $UO_2$ over the temperature range 350 to 2,800°C.

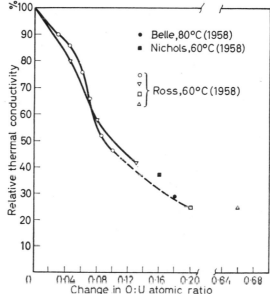

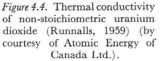

*Figure 4.4.* Thermal conductivity of non-stoichiometric uranium dioxide (Runnalls, 1959) (by courtesy of Atomic Energy of Canada Ltd.).

It is possible that some advantage could be gained by incorporating metal wires in $UO_2$ bodies. KANE (1960) has described work on the fabrication by swaging of $UO_2$ compacts containing molybdenum fibres, and has found that 15 vol. % of fibre produces a 30 per cent increase in thermal conductivity at 100°C; presumably, by comparison with work on thoria (p. 160), the increase at higher temperatures would be considerably greater. However the penalties of higher enrichment and poorer neutron economy incurred by this technique are heavy, and the mechanical strength of the fibre impregnated compacts is relatively poor.

*Specific heat*

The specific heat of stoichiometric $UO_2$ over the temperature range 298–1,500°K is expressed by the equation

$$C_p = 0{\cdot}071 + 6 \times 10^{-6}\,T - 1{,}466\,T^{-2}\,\mathrm{cal\,g^{-1}\,deg^{-1}\,K}$$

(KELLY, 1949).

## Coefficient of expansion

Values for the coefficient of thermal expansion reported by several authors are in good agreement (*Table 4.2*), despite the variations in density and stoichiometry of the samples employed.

TABLE 4.2

THE COEFFICIENT OF LINEAR THERMAL EXPANSION OF $UO_2$ (Seddon, 1960)

| Material | Temp. (°C) | Mean coefficient of linear expansion (c.g.s. units × $10^6$) | Reference |
|---|---|---|---|
| $UO_{2 \cdot 1}$ (density 7·2), argon atmos. | 400–900 | 10 | a |
| $UO_{2 \cdot 13}$ (density 8·5), argon atmos. | 400–900 | 10 | |
| $UO_{2 \cdot 0}$ (from x-ray data) | 20–946 | 10·8 | |
| | 20–720 | 11·5 | b |
| | 27–400 | 9 | |
| $UO_{2 \cdot 0}$ (density 9·9) | 400–800 | 11 | c |
| | 800–1,260 | 13 | |

a. Murray and Thackray (1952).
b. Gronvold (1955).
c. Burdick and Parker (1956).

A useful summary of other physical properties of uranium dioxide has been published by SEDDON (1960). Data on the plastic properties will be discussed later in relation to the mechanism of sintering (Section 4.1.3).

### 4.1.3 Factors Affecting Densification

Numerous factors, both chemical and physical, affect the ease with which $UO_2$ powders can be sintered to bodies of high density, and the interplay of these factors makes it very difficult to predict the sintering behaviour of a powder in terms of its other properties. Furthermore, the adjective 'sinterable', though often used in the ceramics literature, is nebulous, and has no absolute meaning when applied to a powder except in relation to a set schedule of compaction and firing. Despite these difficulties, many useful qualitative effects of powder characteristics have been observed. Some have been investigated under controlled conditions, using a quasi-fundamental approach; most have emerged from technological programmes, whose primary aim has been to provide bodies of a density acceptable for reactor application. In this section we shall summarize the evidence of the effect upon sinterability of oxygen/uranium ratio, powder physical properties, pressing and sintering treatment and additives.

### Oxygen/Uranium ratio

The ease of inclusion of excess oxygen in the cubic lattice of $UO_2$ to give a non-stoichiometric oxide of composition $UO_{2+x}$ ($x = 0$–$0 \cdot 25$) was mentioned in Section 4.1.1. The importance of excess oxygen in aiding the sintering of compacted $UO_2$ powders was first indicated by the work of THACKRAY and

MURRAY (1950) who showed that material of composition $UO_{2.13}$ and $UO_{2.17}$ could be sintered to a density greater than 9·5 g cm$^{-3}$ at a temperature several hundred degrees lower than that required for material having a value of $x$ approaching zero. The effect observed by Thackray and Murray was

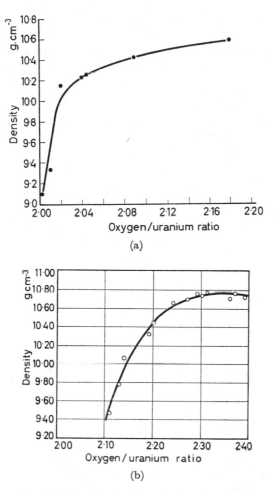

*Figure 4.5.* Density *vs.* oxygen content for uranium dioxide sintered in argon: (a) at 1,450°C for 2 hours (Murray and Williams, 1958) (by courtesy of United Nations); (b) at 1,300°C for 2 hours (Langrod, 1960) (by courtesy of The American Ceramic Society).

ambiguous, however, for it is known that the value of $x$ following exposure to air increases with the surface area of the powder, and it was not clear whether enhanced sintering was due to excess oxygen, a higher surface area, or a combination of both. One variable parameter was later eliminated by preparing stoichiometric powder of a high specific surface, and allowing $x$ to increase gradually by exposure of successive batches to air: samples of different

119

oxygen content were then cold compacted and sintered for 2 hours at 1,450°C in argon (MURRAY and WILLIAMS, 1958). The plot obtained of density against oxygen composition is shown in *Figure 4.5*(a): the final sintered density increases with oxygen content up to a composition of $UO_{2\cdot18}$, but the most pronounced effect is shown over the range $UO_{2\cdot00}$–$UO_{2\cdot02}$. Quite a marked difference in the effects of excess oxygen has been reported by LANGROD (1960), who studied the sintering of ADU-derived oxide at 1,300°C (*Figure 4.5*(b)). At this lower temperature, a steep rise in the curve takes place up to an O/U ratio of about 2·30, when a sintered density of up to 10·8 g cm$^{-3}$ is obtained. The curves in *Figures 4.5* (a) and (b) may not be directly comparable, however, since Langrod's powders were prepared under conditions which may have given rise to changes in physical characteristics as well as of O/U ratio. Also the ratios plotted in both diagrams refer to the initial composition of the powders, and it is known (WILLIAMS *et al.*, 1959) that loss of oxygen takes place during sintering in argon.

If advantage is to be taken of the improved sinterability of non-stoichiometric material, it is essential to avoid a reducing atmosphere during sintering. The effects of atmosphere will be discussed in detail below.

Some attempt has been made to relate the sinterability of uranium dioxide indirectly to its oxidation properties by the use of differential thermal analysis (DTA). The exothermic phase changes involved in conversion of $UO_2$ to $U_3O_8$ result in a DTA curve which shows distinct maxima in the rates of evolution of heat, and it was hoped to relate the temperature separation of these maxima to the varying sintering properties of different samples (MURRAY and LIVEY, 1956). However, lack of quantitative agreement between the data of different laboratories has diminished confidence in this technique of assessing powder behaviour (MURRAY and WILLIAMS, 1958).

*Surface area*

The effect of surface area in isolation from oxygen/uranium ratio may strictly be assessed only by testing powders which have not been exposed to oxygen after preparation. However, if sintering is carried out in a hydrogen atmosphere the removal of non-stoichiometric oxygen is in most cases essentially complete before sintering takes place, and therefore causes no complication.

Generalizing from the available data, it appears that variations in surface area over the range of approximately 1–6 m$^2$ g$^{-1}$ exert no important effect on the sintering properties of a powder, though the exact range varies between different sets of conditions, and is affected by other physical properties. The data of CHALDER *et al.* (1958) on the sintering of $UO_2$ in hydrogen at 1,650°C indicate that below about 2 m$^2$ g$^{-1}$, there is a pronounced decrease in sintered density with surface area. (*Figure 4.6*.) Similar results were obtained by BEL and CARTERET (1958), VAUGHAN *et al.* (1957) have found no effect of the mean crystallite size of a powder on sinterability in hydrogen over the range 200–2,000 Å (corresponding to a range of surface area of about 4–0·4 m$^2$ g$^{-1}$). The data of STENQUIST and ANICETTI (*Figure 4.7*) show an appreciable fall in sintered density (hydrogen, 1,750°C, 8 hours) with surface area below about 1·5 m$^2$ g$^{-1}$, and a similar effect has been observed by WRINKLE (1959) in sintering tests with extruded rods. The data of these authors also illustrate a fall in green density with surface area, with a corresponding increase in shrinkage on sintering.

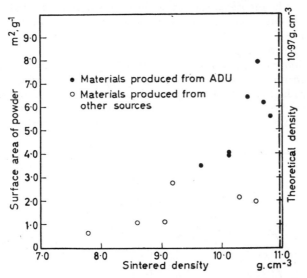

*Figure 4.6.* The relation between surface area and sintered density for a number of $UO_2$ samples (Chalder *et al.*, 1958) (by courtesy of United Nations).

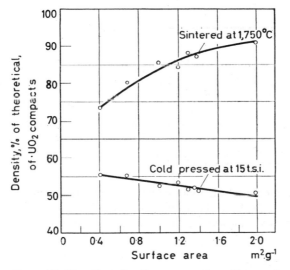

*Figure 4.7.* The effect of surface area on the cold pressed and sintered density of $UO_2$ compacts pressed at 15 t.s.i. (Material from denitration of UNH.) (Stenquist and Anicetti, 1957) (by courtesy of U.S.A.E.C.).

The effect of high surface areas on sintering behaviour has been reported by BEL *et al.* (1959, 1959a). These workers prepared oxide powders of high surface area (up to $\sim 20$ m² g⁻¹) by reducing precipitates of either uranyl

121

peroxide or ammonium diuranate at low temperature: some oxides were allowed to oxidize in air under controlled conditions to give a non-stoichiometric product before densification, while others were prevented from oxidizing by carrying out operations in an inert atmosphere. Plots of the final sintered density attained by several powders after pressing at 4–5 ton in.$^{-2}$ and sintering for 3–5 hours at temperature are shown in *Figure 4.8*. Whereas for material (both stoichiometric and non-stoichiometric) having a surface area less than 6 m$^2$ g$^{-1}$ the final density tended to increase with sintering temperature, powders with higher surface area not only achieved a higher density at lower temperatures, but also exhibited a maximum in the temperature-density curve. The optimum density tended to decrease with increasing surface area:

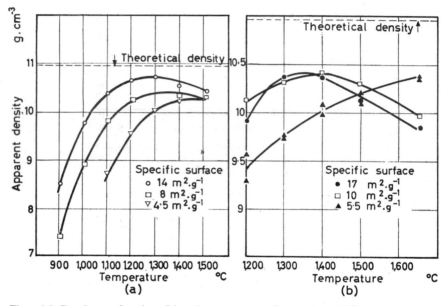

*Figure 4.8.* Density as a function of sintering temperature for powders of different surface area (Bel *et al.*, 1959). (by courtesy of Compte Rendus de l'Académie des Sciences, Paris).

(a) Stoichiometric powder
(b) Non-stoichiometric powder } Both obtained from peroxides

for stoichiometric material, a value of 10·7 g cm$^{-3}$ was attained at a sintering temperature of 1,300°C. This effect is one of considerable importance in affording a means of lowering the sintering temperature, and is worthy of further investigation.

*Agglomerate size distribution*

Crystallites of a powder are joined together into agglomerates which have a fair degree of physical strength. The agglomerate size distribution can exert an effect on the densification properties of $UO_2$ quite apart from the effect of the surface area (which is often closely related to crystallite size).

Systematic experiments using fused $UO_2$ (thereby minimizing effects of surface roughness) were carried out by BURDICK and PARKER (1956). The fused oxide was ground and separated into fractions having particles in the ranges 0–5, 5–10, 10–15 and 15–20 microns respectively. Sintered bodies were

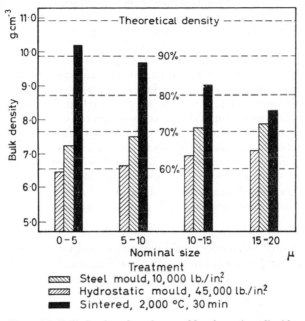

*Figure 4.9.* Bulk density of specimens of fused uranium dioxide (Burdick and Parker, 1956) (by courtesy of the American Ceramic Society).

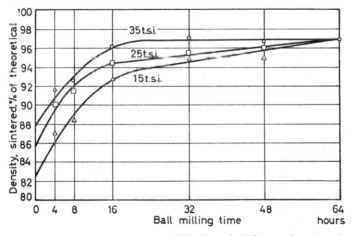

*Figure 4.10.* The sintered density of PWR-grade $UO_2$ as a function of compacting pressure and ball milling time; sintering 8 hours in $H_2$ at 1,750°C (Stenquist and Annicetti, 1957) (by courtesy of U.S.A.E.C.).

obtained by pressing at 10,000–45,000 p.s.i. and firing in argon at 2,000°C. *Figure 4.9* shows the densities obtained for the various size fractions, and illustrates the fall in sintered density with increased particle size. Flexural and compressive strength tests revealed also that the smallest size fraction gave the strongest sintered compact.

A similar effect of agglomerate size seems to obtain with $UO_2$ powders of small crystallite size which can be sintered to comparable densities at temperatures much lower than that of fused $UO_2$: in general, it appears that the presence of a high proportion of large agglomerates tends to lower the final sintered density (EVANS *et al.*, 1957; ALLISON and DUCKWORTH, 1955; LAMBERTSON and HANDWERK, 1956; BELLE, 1958; WRINKLE, 1959; CLAYTON and BERRIN, 1960). *Figure 4.10* contains data of STENQUIST and ANICETTI (1957) concerning the effect of ball milling on the final sintered density of $UO_2$. More detailed examination of the powders by these authors revealed that not only was a high proportion of small agglomerates important to ensure good sinterability, but it was also desirable to obtain a high ratio of surface area/ average agglomerate diameter, i.e. a high 'roughness factor'. This was qualitatively confirmed by the observation of RUNFORS *et al.* (1958), who found that high surface area material of mean agglomerate size $> 37\mu$ sintered better than low surface area material of mean agglomerate size $< 37\mu$.

*Powder bulk density*

The bulk density of a powder may depend upon other properties in addition to surface area and agglomerate size distribution, and there appears to be no

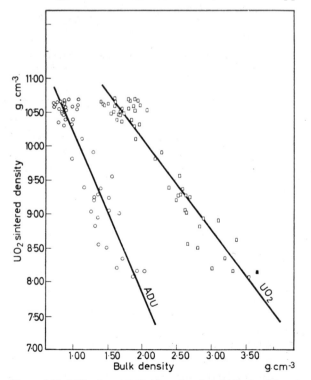

*Figure 4.11.* $UO_2$ sintered density related to bulk densities of ADU and $UO_2$ (Yatabe and Watson, 1958) (by courtesy of Atomic Energy of Canada Ltd.).

reason why bulk density should give an accurate guide to sintering behaviour. However, both Canadian and Swedish workers report an inverse relationship between powder bulk density and final sintered density for $UO_2$ obtained from ADU (YATABE and WATSON, 1958; RUNFORS et al., 1958). The data of Yatabe and Watson are reproduced in *Figure 4.11*, and indicate that a similar inverse relationship exists for the bulk density of the ADU (obtained by continuous coprecipitation) from which the $UO_2$ was derived. This relationship may be useful for crude assessment of powder on a plant production scale, but it does not appear to apply generally to material produced by other routes (CLAYTON and BERRIN, 1960). In any case, the scatter in the region of sintered density from 10·0 to 10·7 is considerable, and application of bulk density to fine control therefore seems to be impracticable.

*Pressing*

The different methods by which a green body can be formed have been outlined in the beginning of the chapter. The most widely used technique consists of end-pressing in a suitable die (stainless steel, case hardened if necessary) to cylindrical pellets. This method can result in non-uniform stresses, but the latter can be minimized by combining double-ended pressing with the use of a lubricant (e.g. an oil or fatty acid compound) intimately mixed with the oxide. To give strength to the green pellet, it may also be desirable to add a 'binding agent' (a wax-type compound dissolved in a suitable organic solvent), and commercial preparations are available which include both a binder and a lubricant. The comparative effectiveness of a wide range of commercial binder-lubricant additives for use with uranium dioxide has been summarized by MIZZAN and CHALDER (1958). A study of the effect of lubricant additives on the sintering of $UO_2$ has been reported by CARRASCO et al. (1959).

Before sintering the green pellet, it is necessary to remove the binder-lubricant by heating at a relatively low temperature. The decomposition of organic compounds can result in a residual deposit of carbon, which may lead in turn to carbide impurities in the pellet, or at least to the removal of non-stoichiometric oxygen which would otherwise lower the sintering temperature (e.g. LANGROD, 1960; BEL et al., 1959a; WILLIAMS, 1960) Such contingencies must be allowed for when an organic additive is employed: for example a procedure successfully developed in the United Kingdom by WILLIAMS, WHEAT-LEY and LLOYD (1959) for removal of the commercial binder-lubricant 'Cranco' (polybutyl methacrylate and dibutyl phthalate dissolved in a ketone) involves heating the pellets in air at 200–250°C. Oxidation to about $UO_{2·35}$ takes place without any disintegration of the pellet and on raising the temperature still further in an argon atmosphere, the excess oxygen is sufficient both to oxidize any residual carbon and to aid the sintering process at 1,450°C. The same workers have also illustrated the dangers of removing the binder-lubricant too quickly: on raising the temperature directly to 1,450°C, it was found that a crazed cracking of the pellets took place.

The precise dependence of the sintered density upon the cold compacting pressure seems to vary with the nature of the powder and the pre-pressing

treatment. However, for several types of powder having good sintering characteristics, a gradual rise in density with increasing pressure flattens out at
around 10–20 ton in.$^{-2}$ (EVANS *et al.*, 1957; CHALDER *et al.*, 1958; SCHÖNBERG
*et al.*, 1958; CHALDER, 1959; LANGROD, 1960). Similar behaviour was reported
by SCHANER (1959) for hammer-milled powders obtained from denitration of
uranyl nitrate. In contrast, unmilled powders containing large agglomerates
not only sintered to a much lower density, but showed an increase in density
with compacting pressure up to 130 ton in.$^{-2}$, an effect undoubtedly associated
with the crushing of the agglomerates. Similar observations have been
reported by BELLE and LUSTMAN (1957).

There is some evidence in the literature for an inverse relationship between
green density and sintered density for $UO_2$ compacts (STENQUIST and ANICETTI,
1957 (*Figure 4.7*); YATABE and WATSON, 1958; BANCROFT and WATSON,
1958), but other authors have reported a direct relationship (EVANS *et al.*, 1957;
SCHÖNBERG *et al.*, 1958; WINCHELL, 1958). It must be concluded that the
relative magnitude of the two densities is greatly dependent upon the physical
properties of the powder employed.

*Sintering temperature and atmosphere*

As a general rule, the sintered density achieved in a given time increases
with the sintering temperature, but the detailed density-temperature relationship is greatly dependent upon the atmosphere in which sintering is carried
out. The exceptional behaviour of powders with high specific surface (*Figure
4.8*), which exhibit a maximum in the sintered density-temperature curve has
already been discussed. A careful study of the sintering behaviour of oxides
obtained from ADU, with particular reference to the effects of sintering temperature and atmosphere, has been reported by WILLIAMS *et al.* (1959).
Dilatometric data on the densification of a powder of composition $UO_{2\cdot18}$
(surface area 6 m$^2$ g$^{-1}$) cold-pressed at 10 ton in.$^{-2}$ and sintered in various
atmospheres are shown in *Figure 4.12*. In argon or nitrogen the density begins
to rise steeply above 800°C, and levels out under isothermal conditions to a
value depending upon the final temperature: at 1,300°C, the final value is
about 10·2 g cm$^{-3}$.

Quite different behaviour is shown in a hydrogen atmosphere, where a
considerably slower rate of density increase begins at 1,000°C and levels out
to a much lower value at 1,300°C. A carbon monoxide atmosphere has a
deleterious effect similar to that of hydrogen: the general conclusion may be
drawn that reducing atmospheres which tend to remove non-stoichiometric
oxygen from the pellet will lower the rate of sintering.

The behaviour of the $UO_{2\cdot18}$ powder after cold-pressing at 10 ton in.$^{-2}$ and
sintering for 2 hours at constant temperature is illustrated in *Figure 4.13*. It
may be concluded that a sintering temperature some 400°C higher is required
to achieve comparable densities when a reducing atmosphere is employed
instead of a neutral atmosphere. Since for highest thermal conductivity and
optimum irradiation behaviour a final O/U ratio of 2·00 is desirable (Section
4.1.6), the advantages of low temperature sintering in an inert atmosphere
are somewhat offset by the need to change to a hydrogen atmosphere after

sintering.* There is also clear evidence that, on heating above about 1,000°C in an inert atmosphere or *in vacuo*, non-stoichiometric uranium dioxide loses oxygen due to volatilization of $UO_3$, which is deposited on cooler parts of the sintering furnace.

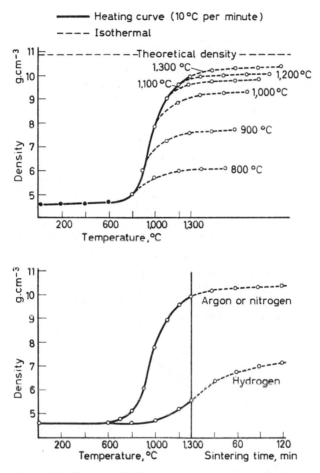

*Figure 4.12.* Sintering of $UO_{2\cdot18}$ in argon, nitrogen and hydrogen (Williams *et al.*, 1959) (by courtesy of North Holland Publishing Co.).

Williams *et al.* are careful to point out that although their work underlines the importance of atmosphere in its effect on O/U ratio, physical characteristics of the powder can exert an equally profound influence on sinterability. Thus a powder of low specific surface would show sintering behaviour inferior to the one tested in *Figure 4.13*, while the presence of large agglomerates in a powder of reasonably high surface area (such as might be obtained from thermal denitration of uranyl nitrate) would also have a deleterious effect.

* BRIGGS and SCOTT (1958) have found that, to avoid the possibility of crazing, the sintered pellet must be reduced at a temperature above 1,400°C.

It has been shown that sintering in an atmosphere of steam can promote the rate of densification, even when the initial O/U ratio of the powder is close to 2·00. At 1,400°C, oxidation to a composition $UO_{2.20}$ takes place in agreement

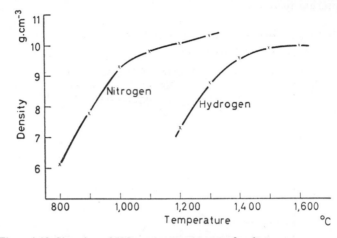

*Figure 4.13.* Sintering of $UO_{2.18}$ (surface area $6 \, m^2 \, g^{-1}$) in nitrogen and hydrogen (2 hours at temperature) (Williams *et al.*, 1958) (by courtesy of North Holland Publishing Co.).

with predictions from thermodynamic data (BELLE and LUSTMAN, 1957); reduction to $UO_{2.00}$ can be effected by changing the atmosphere to one of hydrogen. The presence of water vapour in hydrogen can also decrease the rate of removal of oxygen from a non-stoichiometric powder, with benefit to

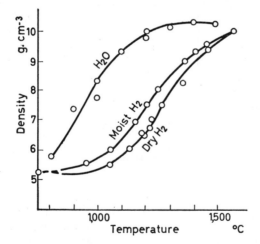

*Figure 4.14.* Comparison of densities obtained by sintering $UO_2$ in different atmospheres at varying temperatures (Runfors *et al.*, 1958) (by courtesy of United Nations).

the sintering behaviour (WILLIAMS *et al.*, 1959; RUNFORS *et al.*, 1958; ARENBERG and JAHN, 1958).

The densification at various temperatures of a powder of composition about $UO_{2.10}$ in steam, hydrogen and hydrogen saturated with water vapour at room temperature (water content *ca.* 10 g m$^{-3}$) is shown in *Figure 4.14*.

128

The influence of non-stoichiometric oxygen on the ease of sintering of $UO_2$ is scientifically one of the most interesting phenomena to emerge from ceramic fuel preparation studies, and as a means of lowering the sintering temperature it was at first considered to be of great economic value. Its technological importance has since diminished, however, since a change of furnace atmosphere after sintering is not easily adapted to high throughput processes (probably involving continuous operation) which a large power programme will demand. At the time of writing most development teams tend to sinter in a hydrogen atmosphere at 1,600–1,750°C. However, fundamental data on the effects of O/U ratio promise to be of considerable value in arriving at an understanding of the mechanism by which sintering takes place.

*The mechanism of sintering*

The sintering of a powder at elevated temperature to form a dense body may involve a combination of processes, usually classified under viscous plastic flow, evaporation-condensation processes, volume diffusion and surface diffusion (e.g. RYSHKEWITCH, 1960). Even in the case of elemental metals, the details of the sintering mechanism are generally a matter of debate; it is not surprising, therefore, that our understanding of the processes involved in the densification of $UO_2$ is by no means complete.

A careful study of the flow properties of uranium oxides has been made by HALL, SCOTT and WILLIAMS (1958), who measured the effect of temperature and oxygen/uranium ratio on the plastic deformation of $UO_2$ rods (prepared by hydrostatic pressing and sintering in nitrogen to a density greater than 95 per cent of theoretical). They found that oxide with an O/U ratio greater than $UO_{2.06}$ could be deformed at 800°C, whereas oxide of stoichiometric composition became plastic only above a temperature of about 1,600°C. Values of the Newtonian viscosity $\eta_d$ (obtained from the initial linear portion of the strain rate–stress curves) are plotted against the reciprocal of the absolute temperature in *Figure 4.15*. The fact that the viscosity of $UO_{2.00}$ becomes comparable with that of $UO_{2.06}$ only at a temperature some 350°C higher is strikingly parallel to the relative sintering behaviour of the oxides discussed earlier: it indicates strongly that the influence of excess oxygen on sintering may be attributed to its effect on the plastic flow behaviour at elevated temperatures.

It is not yet clear how this relationship may be interpreted further in terms of movement of ions within the lattice. The activation energy of $\geqslant 95$ kcal mole$^{-1}$ derived from *Figure 4.15* for the flow of the stoichiometric material is close to the value of 87 kcal mole$^{-1}$ quoted for the self diffusion of $U^{4+}$ ions in $UO_{2.00}$ (AUSKERN and BELLE, 1961) but the activation energies of flow for $UO_{2.06}$ (72 kcal) and $UO_{2.16}$ (65 kcal) are far removed from those for the self-diffusion of oxygen in $UO_{2.004}$ and $UO_{2.06}$ (30 kcal) (AUSKERN and BELLE, 1961a); the change in flow properties cannot therefore be interpreted simply in terms of a mechanism involving replacement of diffusion of uranium ions by that of diffusion of oxygen ions as the rate determining step.

Further evidence discounting the role of oxygen diffusion has been obtained by CHRISTIE and WILLIAMS (1961) who found that small additions of yttria (0·5–1 wt. %), which introduce anionic defects into the $UO_2$ lattice, had no effect on the plastic deformation of fully reduced samples at 940°C.

129

Undoubtedly, however, the presence of excess oxygen reduces the binding energy of the lattice, as is demonstrated by the values of Young's modulus found by HALL *et al.* (1958). A tentative hypothesis based on the effects of a high oxygen/uranium ratio on the mechanical properties of the crystals has been advanced by MURRAY and WILLIAMS (1958), who advocate further studies of the self-diffusion of uranium and oxygen ions in non-stoichiometric oxides as an aid to interpretation of the flow behaviour.

The effects of powder physical properties are amenable to a general qualitative interpretation. Powder of high surface area would be expected to have a lower effective lattice energy on account of a high crystallite surface energy, and possibly the existence of strain. Increase of the surface area above a certain minimum may have little effect on the flow properties owing to

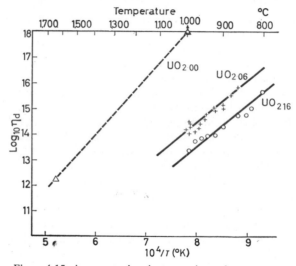

*Figure 4.15.* Apparent viscosity *vs.* reciprocal temperature for uranium oxides (Hall *et al.*, 1958) (by courtesy of U.K.A.E.A. and North Holland Publishing Co. (Scott *et al.* (1959) Journal of Nuclear Materials, **1**, 39)).

presintering of crystallites as the temperature is raised. At very high surface areas, however, this presintering may involve the formation of pores due to the internal shrinkage of agglomerates of crystallites. This may explain the behaviour observed by Bel *et al.* (*Figure 4.8*); it is also consistent with the lower densities obtained by these workers for non-stoichiometric material (assuming that enhanced presintering induced by excess oxygen competes effectively with the reduction by hydrogen). The deleterious effects of the presence of large agglomerates in all powders can also be understood qualitatively in terms of local sintering and the formation of permanent pores.

It is clear that, if presintering and shrinkage within agglomerates is accepted to have a marked effect on the bulk density of the sintered body, the precise thermal history of the sintering cycle is of vital importance. Unfortunately many authors do not quote these details, which may well be responsible for lack of agreement between the data of different laboratories. If a more quantitative understanding of the sintering process and the factors which influence it is to emerge, it is essential that all authors give precise details of the pressing and sintering schedule, as well as of surface area, agglomerate size distribution and O/U ratio of the powder.

*The effect of additives and impurities*

While the mechanism of the sintering of $UO_2$ remains obscure, it is difficult to predict what additives would be most likely to aid the process. Moreover, if the fuel is required for thermal reactors, the character and amount of additives will be limited by considerations of neutron economy. Experiments on the effects of addition of other oxides on the sintering of $UO_2$ have in general shown only small improvements in the fuel density (CHALDER *et al.*, 1958; WEBSTER and BRIGHT, 1957; BOURNS and WATSON, 1958; ARENBERG and JAHN, 1958; SOWMAN and PLOETZ, 1956).

Results obtained with titanium dioxide and niobium pentoxide (added to the $UO_2$ by mixing) are summarized in *Figure 4.16*. The highest density is

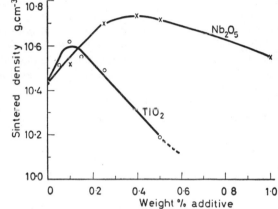

*Figure 4.16.* The effect of additions of $TiO_2$ and $Nb_2O_5$ on the sintered density of $UO_2$ (fired for 30 min in $H_2$ at 1,700°C) (Chalder *et al.*, 1958) (by courtesy of United Nations).

obtained by adding 0·4 wt.% of $Nb_2O_5$, when some 3 per cent improvement over pure $UO_2$ is achieved. A more beneficial effect of $TiO_2$ is claimed by WATSON and WILDER (1960), who increased both the sintering rate and the final sintered density of a $UO_2$ powder (from 8·2 to 10·3 g cm$^{-3}$ after 3 hours at 1,500°C) on adding 0·1 wt. % $TiO_2$. It is not possible to assess generally whether these improvements would outweigh the disadvantages involved; however, it seems desirable to avoid the addition of other elements whenever possible, and to seek increases in density by modifying methods of production and physical treatment of powder. The addition of fissile or breeder oxides to $UO_2$ constitutes a special case, which will be dealt with in detail in subsequent sections.

No systematic examination of the effect of metal ion impurities on the sinterability of $UO_2$ powder has been reported, and neutron economy is therefore the only known criterion which sets the levels which can be tolerated.

The effect of carbon on the sintering behaviour has been studied in some detail by BRIGHT *et al.* (1957). Elemental carbon may be introduced, for example, from organic binders, or from graphite components of the sintering furnace. It reacts with $UO_2$ at elevated temperatures, and if present in sufficient quantity will not only remove the non-stoichiometric oxygen, but will also produce UC and $UC_2$ (Section 4.4.2); the resulting CO will cause bloating of the pellet. Illustrations of these deleterious effects have been provided by Bright *et al.*, who carried out sintering experiments in a hydrogen atmosphere with $UO_2$ powders containing synthetic additions of graphite. The authors conclude from their data that the carbon content of a green pellet before sintering should be less than 200 p.p.m. To ensure that this level is not exceeded, it is desirable to avoid the use of graphite in the sintering furnace, and to ensure that organic binders are removed from the green pellet with the minimum of decomposition to elemental carbon.

The maximum permissible level of carbon advocated by Bright *et al.* is probably conservatively low if densification is carried out by sintering of non-stoichiometric $UO_2$ in an inert atmosphere. The removal of non-stoichiometric oxygen by carbon appears to take place rapidly below 1,000°C (AINSLEY and SOWDEN, 1961), and since most of the sintering will take place above this temperature, expulsion of the CO might well have little effect on the final sintered density. If this hypothesis is correct, about 4,000 p.p.m. of carbon might be tolerated in a powder of composition $UO_{2.10}$: the rate of heating of the green pellet must obviously be slow, however, and experiments complementary to those of Bright *et al.* are desirable to relate the maximum permissible level of carbon to the $UO_2$ composition and the firing schedule.

### 4.1.4 Production Routes for Ceramic $UO_2$

The generalizations which have emerged from Section 4.1.3 provide a guide to the type of powder which is required for ceramic fuel element manufacture. The powder must have a reasonably high surface area (greater than about $2–3 \text{ m}^2 \text{ g}^{-1}$), and it must contain the minimum of large agglomerates (greater than, say, 10–20 microns in diameter). Examination of various production routes has rarely been carried out with these generalizations firmly in mind; indeed, the generalizations themselves have emerged slowly from experience with a wide variety of powders. It will nevertheless be instructive to review broadly the various methods of production which are available, and to compare their relative ability to produce a powder of good sintering quality.

The two main starting products for the manufacture of $UO_2$ are uranyl nitrate and uranium hexafluoride. It may appear unfortunate at first sight that most experimental work has been carried out with material obtained from uranyl nitrate, since for isotopically enriched $UO_2$ the hexafluoride is at present most likely to be the starting material. However the precipitation routes leading to uranium dioxide have much in common for the two starting materials.

An outline scheme of the principal methods of preparing uranium dioxide is shown in *Figure 4.17*. From uranyl nitrate, two main routes to $UO_3$ are available; either direct denitration, or precipitation from solution of a solid such as ammonium diuranate (ADU) which can be calcined to $UO_3$. The higher oxide can then be reduced to $UO_2$ either directly or by way of $U_3O_8$. Similar processes can be employed with uranyl fluoride solution obtained by hydrolysis of $UF_6$. If a good decontamination of the product from fluoride ion is important, it may be advisable to dissolve the precipitate obtained from

132

$UO_2F_2$ in nitric acid, and to remove fluoride by a cycle of solvent extraction and reprecipitation. An alternative and more direct method of proceeding from $UF_6$ to $UO_2$ involves the hydrolysis to solid uranyl fluoride with steam, followed by hydrolytic reduction to uranium dioxide.

Characteristic sintering behaviour of the powders prepared by these various routes is summarized in *Table 4.3*.

The route chosen for preparing $UO_2$ powder can have a significant influence upon its crystallite size and agglomerate size distribution. Furthermore, crystallite size and surface area are affected not only by the nature of the intermediates themselves, but also by the details of the final reduction step.

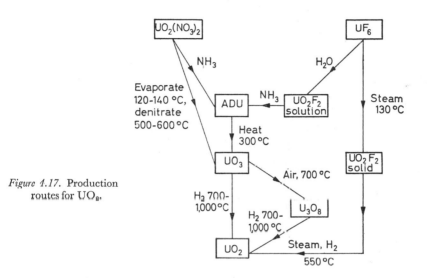

*Figure 4.17*. Production routes for $UO_2$.

Generally speaking, larger crystallites (and a lower specific surface) are obtained both by reducing at higher temperatures and by proceeding through $U_3O_8$ as an intermediate (ANDERSON *et al.*, 1952; CLAYTON and ARONSON, 1958).

### Direct denitration of uranyl nitrate

Production of uranium dioxide by thermal denitration became established in the United States as a stage in the process of metal production (HARRINGTON and RUEHLE, 1958, 1959), and it was natural that the same method should be used to prepare oxide for use as blanket material for the Shippingport Pressurized Water Reactor. In retrospect, the choice seems to have been rather an unfortunate one. Direct denitration followed by reduction at about 800°C with cracked ammonia tends to produce a powder with a low surface area containing large agglomerates, and early sintering experience with the material was very bad (e.g. data in *Table 4.3*). It was eventually established, however, that attrition of the powder by ball-milling produced a great improvement in sintering behaviour. A particularly effective process is to wet-mill the $UO_3$ prior to reduction with hydrogen: the resulting hydration can bring about a significant increase in surface area and roughness factor of the

TABLE 4.3

SINTERING BEHAVIOUR OF $UO_2$ POWDERS PREPARED BY VARIOUS METHODS

| Method of Preparation | Surface area $m^2\,g^{-1}$ | O/U ratio | Pelleting pressure ton $in.^{-2}$ | Sintering temperature °C (in $H_2$) | Range of sintered density $g\,cm^{-3}$ | Reference |
|---|---|---|---|---|---|---|
| Direct denitration of $UO_2(NO_3)_2$; reduction with $H_2$, 800°C | 0·62–2·75 | 2·02–2·06 | 18 | 1,700 (30 min) | 7·8–9·2 | (a) |
| Hydration of $UO_3$ from direct denitration by wet ball-milling; reduction with $H_2$, 800°C | 1·9–7·9 | 2·04–2·16 | 18 | 1,700 (30 min) | 10·4–10·8 | (a) |
| Batch pptn. of ADU; reduction with $H_2$, 900°C | 3–8 | Up to 2·28 | 18 | 1,600–1,650 (60–90 min) | 9·5–10·8 (mostly above 10·2) | (b) |
| Continuous pptn. of ADU; reduction with $H_2$, 900°C | 1–8 | — | 18 | 1,600–1,650 (60–90 min) | 8·1–10·7 (depending mainly upon pH of pptn.) | (c) |
| Homogeneous pptn. of ADU; reduction with $H_2$, 700°C | — | — | 25–30 | 1,600 (5 hours, moist $H_2$) | > 10·2 | (d) |
| Peroxide pptn. dilute soln; reduction with $H_2$ | — | — | 5·3 | 1,750 (45 min) | 10·7 | (e) |
| Hydrolysis of $UF_6$ with steam at 130°C and with $H_2$/steam at 150°C | — | — | 20 | 1,600 (4 hours) | Up to 10·8 | (f) |

(a) Chalder et al. (1958).
(b) Bourns and Watson (1958).
(c) Yatabe and Watson (1958).
(d) Schönberg et al. (1958); Ainscough (1961).
(e) Wirths and Ziehl (1958).
(f) D'Eye and Blundell (1960).

134

$UO_2$ finally produced. It appears also that the sintering characteristics of both untreated and wet or dry-milled powder obtained from denitration are affected by the thermal and mechanical history of the denitration process (VAUGHAN *et al.*, 1957), but further experimental work (particularly a complete physical and chemical characterization of the powders) is necessary before the detailed effects can be understood even qualitatively.

### Precipitation from nitrate or fluoride solution

*Ammonia precipitation.* Addition of ammonia to a nitrate or fluoride solution yields a precipitate of 'ammonium diuranate' (ADU). The formula $(NH_4)_2U_2O_7$ often ascribed to this substance is undoubtedly incorrect. Structural studies carried out in the United Kingdom by DEANE (1960) and ELLIS *et al.* (1960) have shown that the material is more accurately represented by the formula $UO_2(OH)_2.xH_2O.yNH_3$, where the values of $x$ and $y$ depend upon the mode of precipitation and the drying treatment. ADU decomposes to $UO_3$ at about 300°C in air, and the product can be reduced in either hydrogen or carbon monoxide to yield a uranium dioxide powder of high surface area containing agglomerates which can be broken down readily either by the cold pressing procedure used to form green pellets or by a light ball-milling operation prior to pressing. The quality of the powder varies with the method of precipitation and reduction, but in general it is much easier to prepare a readily sinterable $UO_2$ powder by the ADU route than by direct denitration.

The effect of variations in the conditions of ADU precipitation and reduction upon the quality of the $UO_2$ powder produced has been studied carefully by workers at Chalk River. BOURNS and WATSON (1958) report that powder which sinters to a density of $10\cdot2$–$10\cdot7$ can be produced by hydrogen reduction (900°C) of ADU precipitated batchwise under a wide variety of conditions. The sintering tests were carried out by pressing the powder to 40 ton in.$^{-2}$ using a paraffin wax (20 per cent in carbon tetrachloride) binder; the binder was removed by heating at 500°C in flowing hydrogen, and the pellets were then heated at 100–200°C h$^{-1}$ to 1,600–1,650°C, held at this temperature for 1 hour and cooled at a rate not greater than 400°C h$^{-1}$. Good powders were obtained using both aqueous and gaseous ammonia, though in the latter case it was found that a slower rate of cooling was required to prevent the pellets from cracking. The main factors which apparently lead to a decrease in the sinterability of the powder are the use of dilute solutions of reagents and/or slow addition, and digestion of the precipitate at a low pH: it may be supposed that these treatments promote the formation of an agglomerated precipitate the structure of which is retained by the reduced powder. The optimum conditions leading to a high density $UO_2$ recommended by Bourns and Watson are high reagent concentrations (uranium 100–200 g l.$^{-1}$; aqueous ammonia 13 N), fast mixing at 60°C and a final pH of 9–9·3.

It is unfortunate that these conditions lead also to a fine, bulky precipitate which settles and filters slowly. A similar generalization emerges from the work of Yatabe and Watson, who studied the production of ADU by continuous precipitation from nitrate solution with ammonia: the relationship between the settled bed density of the ADU after 30 min and the sintered

135

density of the $UO_2$ after reduction and densification is shown in *Figure 4.18*. Apart from this disadvantage, powders with good sintering properties could be prepared (by reduction in $H_2$ at 900°C) from ADU precipitated continuously, but the value of the pH at which the precipitation was conducted had a profound effect on the sinterability of the resulting $UO_2$ (*Figure 4.19*). Between values of pH of 4·5 (where precipitation was essentially complete) and 6·5 the sintered density rises from about 75 to 97 per cent of theoretical. Operation at still higher pH has no further effect on the sintered density, but leads to a precipitate of poorer filtration and settling characteristics. Yatabe and Watson recommend an optimum working pH of 7·0–7·5: variations in reagent concentrations and flow rates and in precipitation temperature do not appear to be critical.

Similar observations to those of the Canadian workers were made in the United Kingdom by BROOKS (1961), who studied the continuous precipitation of ADU from uranyl fluoride solution prepared by hydrolysis of $UF_6$, and PLACEK and NORTH (1960) have also reported the production of

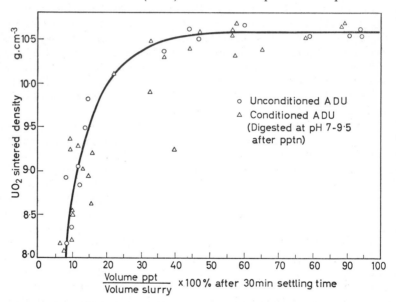

*Figure 4.18.* Relationship between settled bed density of ADU (continuously precipitated) and sintered density of resulting $UO_2$ (Yatabe and Watson, 1958) (by courtesy of Atomic Energy of Canada Ltd.)

ceramic grade $UO_2$ in the United States by this technique. The permissible level of fluoride in the final pellet cannot be stated with certainty, but it can be reduced either by dissolution, solvent extraction and reprecipitation, or by treating $U_3O_8$ produced from the ADU with steam prior to the final reduction. The Mallinkrodt Chemical Company, however, claims that unwashed ADU containing 3–4 per cent of fluoride reduces to a uniform $UO_2$ powder of high bulk density and improved sintering properties (MALLINKRODT, 1960).

The effect of reduction conditions upon three samples of ADU precipitated batchwise from nitrate solution has been reported by BANCROFT and WATSON

(1958). A reducing temperature of between 750 and 1,000°C brought about no significant change in the sintering quality of the uranium dioxide from ADU prepared under optimum conditions, and variations in the heating rate and time at maximum temperature (1–6 hours) were likewise without effect. This is in accord with the lack of sensitivity of sintered density to surface area over a fairly wide range. Prior conversion of the ADU to $U_3O_8$ at 600–700°C and heating at this temperature for a period before final reduction to $UO_2$ results in a decrease in surface area, and eventually of sinterability. The insertion of a $U_3O_8$ stage is beneficial, however, in the reduction of fine precipitates such as are obtained by continuous precipitation with ammonia: if reduction to $UO_2$ is carried out directly at 700–900°C, a $UO_2$ powder having a surface

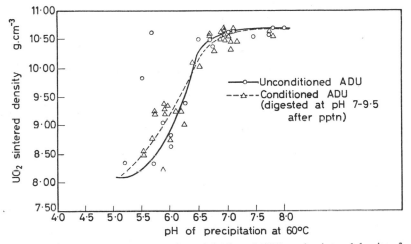

*Figure 4.19.* The effect of the pH of precipitation of ADU on the sintered density of the resulting $UO_2$ (after Yatabe and Watson, 1958) (by courtesy of Atomic Energy of Canada Ltd.).

area of the order of 10 m² g⁻¹ can be produced, with a marked tendency towards pyrophoricity. The surface area is reduced by 30–40 per cent by first converting the ADU to $U_3O_8$ in air (700°C, 1 hour) before reducing with hydrogen (SOWDEN *et al.*, 1962).

Bancroft and Watson also examined the effect of depth of the ADU bed during reduction upon the sintering quality of the uranium dioxide They found that material in the lower layers of a deep bed sintered to lower densities than that in the upper layers, perhaps due to crystallite growth of $UO_3$ before reduction took place. This fact must be borne in mind during the design of high throughput reduction units: a ready access of the reducing gas is important, and must be ensured by the use of shallow beds or adoption of a mixing or fluidizing technique.

The above work on production of uranium dioxide by way of ADU precipitation has sought to lay down conditions leading to a $UO_2$ powder which can undergo densification readily without post-reduction treatment. Even a lower quality powder, however, can be improved by ball-milling (preferably by a wet process), though it is obviously desirable to avoid this stage if possible.

Overall, the ADU precipitation process appears much more versatile than the denitration process, and apart from problems of filtration (q.v.) can be confidently recommended as a means of producing ceramic grade oxide.

RUNFORS et al. (1958) and SCHÖNBERG et al. (1958) have used homogeneous precipitation from nitrate solution by hydrolysis of urea as a first step in the production of loosely aggregated $UO_2$ powder which sinters to a density of up to 10·5 in moist hydrogen at 1,575°C: similar densities on sintering in dry hydrogen have been obtained by AINSCOUGH (1961). The precipitate is much easier to filter than material produced by direct mixing of nitrate solution and ammonia, but the homogeneous method is not easily adapted to large scale production.

WARREN (1960) has developed a method of reducing ADU of varying quality so as to produce $UO_2$ powders of controlled surface area and sintering characteristics. ADU in aqueous suspension is treated with carbon dioxide, hydrogen and anthraquinone under pressure (ca. 1,000 p.s.i.) in the presence of a platinum catalyst: reduction takes place first to $U_3O_8$ by way of a uranyl carbonate intermediate, and thence to $UO_2$ by further reduction with hydranthraquinone, which is regenerated. It is claimed that the quality of the product is determined by the reduction parameters, and careful control at the precipitation stage is thereby rendered unnecessary. However, the method would appear to be an expensive one to scale up to a production level.

*Other precipitation processes.* Precipitation using ammonia has the advantage of cheapness, but normally produces a solid which is very difficult to filter; moreover the product is virtually impossible to separate using a process of settling and decantation, particularly if continuous precipitation is employed.

The only other process employed on a production scale is the precipitation of $UO_4$ with hydrogen peroxide (WIRTHS and ZIEHL, 1958), which can be reduced to yield a $UO_2$ powder sintering to 10·7 g cm$^{-3}$ after 45 min at 1,750°C in hydrogen. The conditions used by Wirths and Ziehl for preparing the powder, however (involving the growth of coarse particles from seed crystals during precipitation from dilute solution), appear to constitute a rather lengthy and expensive process, and it is probable that acceptable $UO_2$ can be prepared by the peroxide method under conditions which are more readily adapted to production at high throughput (e.g. BEL and CARTERET, 1958; WHETSEL and DEAN, 1960).

A comparative study of the filtration and settling characteristics of ADU and U(IV) oxalate, precipitated by a variety of methods, has been described by SOWDEN and STOCKDALE (1961). It was found that the oxalate precipitates in general exhibited better handling characteristics than ADU, the differences being particularly marked when continuous precipitation was employed. The oxalate precipitation technique has particular attractions in the production of $(U, Pu)O_2$ powders, and will be discussed from this aspect later (Section 4.3.2).

### 'Dry' production from $UF_6$

Preliminary work on a method of converting $UF_6$ to $UO_2$ which eliminates all solution stages has been carried out by D'EYE and BLUNDELL (1960), who established that uranium hexafluoride reacts with steam at 130°C to yield unhydrated uranyl fluoride. This can in turn be converted to $UO_2$ by reaction with hydrogen and steam in the ratio of about $2:1$ at $550°C$ to yield a powder which sinters in hydrogen at $1,600°C$ to a density of $10·6–10·8$. It has been found that too high a rate of hydrolysis of $UF_6$ can result in a $UO_2F_2$ powder of low specific surface, which in turn can lead to a $UO_2$ powder of poor sintering quality. Carrying out the steam-hydrogen reduction at temperatures above $550°C$ can have similar results.

*Steam oxidation of metallic uranium*

Some work has been devoted to the preparation of $UO_2$ powders by the oxidation of uranium metal foil or powders with steam at $140–450°C$ (CLAYTON and ARONSON, 1958; BELLE, 1958; HARRINGTON, 1957). The product has a low specific surface, often contains unreacted metallic uranium, and is of poor sintering quality. It is most unlikely that large quantities of material will ever be prepared by so uncertain and expensive a method.

*Recycling of reject pellets*

If $UO_2$ is prepared by a 'wet precipitation' route, an obvious method of recycling reject pellets is to dissolve them in acid and repeat the precipitation, reduction and fabrication processes. If a 'dry' route such as the $UF_6$ hydrolytic conversion is employed, however, it is desirable to recycle by a dry technique. Sintered pellets are difficult to break up mechanically; the powder produced is invariably of relatively low specific surface, and as such is unsuitable for resintering. An alternative method is that of 'chemical pulverization', involving oxidation of the pellets to $U_3O_8$ powder, which is then reconverted to $UO_2$.

STRAUSBERG and LUEBBEN (1959) and STRAUSBERG, LUEBBEN and REED (1960) have investigated this technique, both as a method of recycling reject pellets and as a means of chemical reprocessing of irradiated fuel when partial decontamination from fission products is acceptable. Oxidation of pellets of 90–93 per cent theoretical density was carried out at $400°C$ in flowing air (3 hours), followed by reduction at $600–700°C$ in flowing hydrogen (6 hours). Tests of the sinterability of the $UO_2$ produced were carried out both at this stage, and following repeated oxidation-reduction cycles on the powder. For both pure $UO_2$ and $UO_2$ impregnated with 1 per cent of artificial fission product oxides, the sintered density improved over the first three oxidation-reduction cycles, and thereafter remained essentially constant despite a continued reduction in mean particle size.

Similar observations have been made by ALLEN and SAUM (1961), who favour the same oxidation temperature as Strausberg *et al.*, but a lower reduction temperature ($500°C$). The surface areas of powders obtained from a batch of $UO_2$ pellets of density $10·5$ g $cm^{-3}$ following successive oxidation-reduction cycles are listed in *Table 4.4*.

The $UO_2$ obtained after the third reduction cycle could be sintered in hydrogen at $1,600°C$ (4 hours) to a density of $10·5$ g $cm^{-3}$.

The technique of controlled oxidation to $U_3O_8$ is capable of development as a means of removing dense $UO_2$ from metallic cladding. HANSON (1959) gives an account of experiments in which fuel was removed by this method from the zircaloy cladding of irradiated PWR fuel elements. The resulting $U_3O_8$ powder was only slightly contaminated with $ZrO_2$, and could be refabricated following a suitable series of oxidation-reduction cycles. Similar work with

TABLE 4.4

EFFECT OF OXIDATION-REDUCTION CYCLES ON SURFACE AREA OF $UO_2$
(Allen and Saum, 1961)

| | Surface area of $U_3O_8$ (m² g⁻¹) | Surface area of $UO_2$ (m² g⁻¹) |
|---|---|---|
| First Cycle | 1·37 | 1·29 |
| Second Cycle | 2·38 | 2·51 |
| Third Cycle | 3·3 | 3·9 |
| Fourth Cycle | 4·4 | 4·3 |

stainless steel-clad $UO_2$ fuel elements has been described by GROCE and SULLIVAN (1960).

### 4.1.5 The Chemical Reactivity of Dense $UO_2$ Bodies

Information on the chemical compatibility of $UO_2$ with likely coolant or cladding materials, even in the absence of irradiation, is relatively sparse. Except where otherwise stated, the data reviewed in this section refer to reactivity under out-of-pile conditions: the deposition of energy by fast neutrons and/or fission fragments may promote reaction, and until satisfactory irradiation tests have been carried out, the out-of-pile information should be treated with reserve when applied to reactor situations.

*Reactions with fluids*

In the event of a cladding defect in the fuel element arising during reactor operation, oxidation of uranium dioxide fuel by the coolant fluid could have serious consequences. If the oxidation were sufficiently extensive to involve nucleation of $U_3O_8$, which is 30 per cent less dense, the resulting volume expansion could enlarge the can defect, and a cumulative deterioration might take place. It is therefore important to obtain estimates of the stability of $UO_2$ in the presence of coolant fluids. Most experimental investigations have been confined to compatibility with water and with carbon dioxide: attack on $UO_2$ by a liquid metal coolant such as sodium or sodium potassium alloy is inconceivable on thermodynamic grounds up to the boiling point of the metal* (although reaction could occur with oxygen if it were present as an impurity, and disruption of a $UO_2$ compact might take place in the absence of oxygen if the surface were wetted).

*Air.* The access of oxygen to bare $UO_2$ fuel would produce the worst possible conditions for oxidative attack. A study of the oxidation of $UO_2$ pellets (density 10·5 g cm⁻³) in air over the temperature range 350–1,000°C has been reported by PEAKALL and ANTILL (1960). The rate at which a pellet gains weight in air at various temperatures (measured on a thermal balance) is shown in *Figure 4.20*. Below 350°C, the rate of oxidation is very low. At 350–600°C, the reaction exhibits an induction period, the length of which decreases

---

* LAMBERTSON and HANDWERK (1956) found that $UO_2$ compacts were unchanged after contact with Na/K alloy for 72 hours at 600°C.

with the temperature but is unaffected by the surface condition of the specimen: at the end of this period, the oxidation rate accelerates to a constant value, and $U_3O_8$ falls away from the surface as a fine powder. At 650–850°C, the $U_3O_8$ appeared to form a protective shell, but breakaway and resumption of a linear rate followed after a time which increased as the temperature was raised. Above 900°C, the protective shell appeared to be stronger, and no breakaway occurred during complete oxidation (though the protective shell

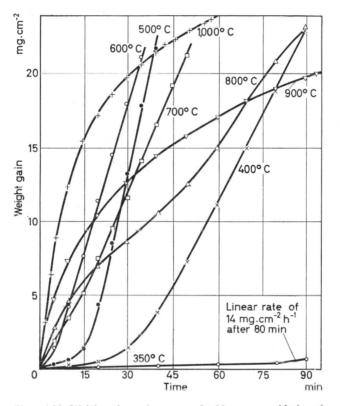

*Figure 4.20.* Weight gain *vs.* time curves for 30 per cent oxidation of $UO_2$ pellets to $U_3O_8$ in air at 350–1,000°C (Peakall and Antill, 1960) (by courtesy of North Holland Publishing Co.).

could be broken down on thermal cycling): the final product had the composition $UO_{2.65}$. The authors consider that the induction period corresponds to the nucleation and growth of $U_3O_8$, and that the rate following the induction period is controlled by the diffusion of oxygen ions through the $U_3O_8$ layer. Subsequent experiments by the same workers on the oxidation of $UO_2$ contained in defected beryllium and stainless steel fuel cans have confirmed that serious cladding failures can be brought about by volume expansion.

Detailed studies of the oxidation of $OU_2$ in oxygen over a lower range of temperature (up to 450°C but with most experiments carried out below

141

350°C) have been reported by SMITH (1960). With high density pellets, an induction period similar to that of Peakall and Antill was observed, but with lower density pellets the induction period was absent. The composition of the powder which broke away from the surface was not established with certainty but appeared to consist of both $U_3O_8$ and a cubic $UO_{2+x}$ phase. The mechanism of oxidation at these lower temperatures (where nucleation of $U_3O_8$ takes place slowly) can be interpreted in terms of three major processes (a) chemisorption of oxygen on the $UO_2$ surface, followed by adsorption of oxygen on the chemisorbed layer; (b) formation of a thin layer (ca. 200 Å) of $U_3O_7$ or $U_4O_9$, and diffusion of oxygen through this layer; (c) formation of $U_3O_8$ at the grain boundaries, which causes the surface layer (of uncertain composition) to break away.

Stabilization of the fluorite lattice of $UO_2$ during oxidation by incorporation of cations of lower valency ($La_2O_3$, $Y_2O_3$, $Y_2O_3$–CaO) has been demonstrated by WILSON (1959) and WILSON and GERDS (1960). It is unlikely that this practice would be adopted, however, on account of the inevitable decrease in fuel density and deterioration in neutron economy which would result.

*Carbon dioxide.* Thermodynamic equilibrium data for the reaction

$$2CO_2 \rightleftharpoons 2CO + O_2$$

have been combined with the equilibrium data for $UO_{2+x}$–$O_2$ from *Figure 4.2* to estimate the conditions under which $UO_2$ will be oxidized by carbon dioxide (ROBERTS *et al.*, 1958). The conclusion was drawn that, in the absence of radiation, at a fuel surface temperature of about 600°C (likely to be encountered in a gas-cooled reactor) oxidation would not be serious if the CO content of the $CO_2$ was greater than 10 p.p.m., and $U_3O_8$ would not be formed unless the CO content fell below 0·1 p.p.m. In a graphite moderated reactor CO formed by oxidation of the graphite (Chapter 2) would exceed the higher of the two levels.

However, preliminary experiments by YOUNG (1958) have indicated that oxidation of $UO_2$ by $CO_2$ is significantly enhanced by reactor irradiation at 80°C. The process appears to be complex, and the mechanism is as yet uncertain. Further experimental effort is needed before the technological significance of this effect can be fully assessed, though present information indicates that the rate of the radiation-induced reaction following a can defect in a $CO_2$ cooled reactor will not be serious.

*Water and steam.* Thermodynamic data predict that no reaction should take place between $UO_2$ and liquid water up to the critical point, and it has been confirmed that $UO_2$ compacts were stable in outgassed water for more than 300 hours at 330°C (BELLE and LUSTMAN, 1957). If oxygen is present in the water, however, experiments with $UO_2$ and $U_3O_8$ slurries have shown that oxidation takes place above a temperature of about 150°C to yield hydrated $UO_3$ ( GILLIES, 1946; see Volume 2, Chapter 4). The kinetics of the oxidation of $UO_2$ powder by oxygen in water have been qualitatively examined at the Bettis laboratories (BELLE and LUSTMAN, 1958; ARONSON, 1958): the reaction appears to proceed to $UO_3$, 0·8 $H_2O$ with a low activation energy (5–10 kcal mole$^{-1}$), but the mechanism is unknown. Studies of the corrosion of bare $UO_2$ fuel pellets in oxygenated water at temperatures up to 315°C have indicated that the rate of oxidation depends on the pH of the water, being greatest at values between 9·5 and 10.5 (LOJEK *et al.*, 1958).

The disintegration in outgassed water of $UO_2$ pellets containing carbon as an impurity has been reported by KIESSLING and RUNFORS (1957); presumably this was due to hydrolysis of UC or $UC_2$ formed at the grain boundaries. The observation is a reminder of the importance which must be attached to the complete removal of organic binders added at the cold pressing stage during fuel fabrication.

In steam, it has been computed that oxidation of $UO_2$ beyond $UO_{2.10}$ can be prevented by the presence of gaseous hydrogen at the following levels (HARDER and SOWDEN, 1960):

| Temperature (°C) | 700 | 850 | 1,100 |
| --- | --- | --- | --- |
| Level of $H_2$ (p.p.m.) | 10 | 100 | 1,000 |

In the presence of irradiation, however, although the $G$ value for molecular oxygen production will be low (Volume 2, Chapter 2), it is conceivable that enhanced oxidation could be brought about by interaction of an activated $UO_2$ surface with energized intermediates such as OH radicals or excited water molecules. To obtain information on this point, Harder and Sowden irradiated $UO_2$ and $U_3O_8$ powders in contact with steam under reactor irradiation: their data, although limited to a temperature of about 80°C and pressures of water vapour less than one atmosphere, indicate that oxidation is brought about mainly by oxygen produced during radiolytic decomposition of the water vapour. Estimates based upon extremely pessimistic assumptions indicate that the rate of oxidation of $UO_2$ pellets in defected cans of a steam-cooled reactor would be extremely low.

A preliminary account of experiments with defective $UO_2$ fuel elements under reactor irradiation has been presented by SPALARIS (1961), who carried out tests in boiling water (290°C, 1,000 p.s.i.) and steam (450°C, 950 p.s.i.) for a period of several weeks. Signs of slight oxidation of $UO_2$ were apparent only in samples exposed to boiling water, where liquid had penetrated the cladding. These experiments were insufficiently controlled, however, for any general conclusions to be drawn.

*Organic coolants.* Although no chemical reaction between $UO_2$ and organic coolants is to be expected, difficulties can arise from decomposition of the coolant on a hot $UO_2$ surface. KINZER and MELLOT (1960) have conducted out-of-pile tests on pefected fuel elements of $UO_2$ clad in stainless steel, immersed in Santowax-R at a maximum surface temperature of 460°C and centre temperatures of up to 1,100°C. During thermal cycling, penetration of the pellets took place with formation of carbon which eventually led to rupture of both pellet and cladding. No in-pile confirmatory tests have yet been reported.

*Compatibility with metals and metal oxides*

A number of conditions can be envisaged under which $UO_2$ fuel will be brought into physical contact with structural metals. In the case of plate-type fuel elements or cermets the components are, of course, in intimate contact by design. On the other hand, when the fuel element is made up of pellets of $UO_2$ stacked in a metallic sheath, contact can in principle be minimized by the existence of a gas-filled gap between fuel and metal. Even in this design, however, contact cannot be avoided entirely, particularly as the pellets will fracture during thermal cycling (Section 4.1.7). It is important, therefore, to know the likelihood and extent of reaction between $UO_2$ and metals which may be employed either as matrix or canning materials. Reaction between $UO_2$ and other oxides may also be important, particularly non-fissile oxides which may be employed in a fuel element.

If the reaction between $UO_2$ and a metal can be considered to take place by a mechanism of simple oxygen displacement

$$\frac{y}{2}UO_2 + xM \rightarrow M_xO_y + \frac{y}{2}U$$

a fair estimate of the possibility of reaction can be made from thermodynamic data alone. This simple approach may be invalidated, however, by the formation of stable intermetallic compounds, coupled with solution of oxygen in the metal. Thus, although the deduction of a large positive value of $\Delta G$ on the basis of the oxygen displacement equation may be safely assumed to indicate lack of reactivity (e.g. of $UO_2$ with sodium or potassium up to the boiling point of the metals), borderline cases are unreliable and require experimental investigation. Such cases unfortunately include several metals of low neutron capture cross-section such as aluminium, zirconium, beryllium and magnesium, all of which form oxides having a stability comparable with that of $UO_2$ over a wide range of temperature.

*Zirconium.* The reaction between $UO_2$ and zirconium has received detailed attention (MALLETT *et al.*, 1955, 1957). Studies were carried out with zirconium cylinders containing $UO_2$ powder, compacted mixtures of the powders and 'sandwiches' of compacted $UO_2$ and zirconium plates: results from the last technique were found to be most amenable to quantitative interpretation.

Above about 500°C, a reaction takes place involving diffusion of uranium and oxygen into the body of the zirconium. Over the range 700–1,000°C, three layers could be observed on sectioning: next to the $UO_2$ was a zirconium-rich layer containing α-uranium, after this a uranium-rich layer consisting of the epsilon intermetallic compound of uranium and zirconium + α-uranium, and finally a layer of zirconium containing dissolved oxygen. The composition of the uranium-rich layer was dependent upon temperature; after treatment at 1,100°C, the uranium content was higher than 80 per cent, but after prolonged treatment below 700°C, it was essentially zero, and the layer was undetectable. Following thermal treatments over a range of temperatures, sections were taken across the layers and analysed for oxygen and uranium: typical distributions as a function of distance from the $UO_2$–Zr boundary are shown in *Figure 4.21*. The weight $W$ of $UO_2$ reacting per cm² of contact area could be expressed by the equation

$$\log_{10} Wt^{-1/2} = 2 \cdot 118 - \frac{5,110}{T}$$

with $t$ in hours and $T$ in deg K. Penetration equations were also obtained for oxygen and uranium: the extent of oxygen penetration into zirconium (assuming an oxygen content of 0·25 wt. % as the boundary) was given by

$$\log_{10}(dt^{-1/2}) = 1\cdot22 - 4{,}040T^{-1}$$

where $d$ is the distance from the interface in cm. The thickness of the zirconium-rich layer was given by

$$\log_{10}(dt^{1/2}) = 0\cdot20 - 3{,}680T^{-1} \quad (T = 1{,}000\text{–}1{,}400°\text{K})$$

or by $\quad \log_{10}(dt^{1/2}) = 4\cdot81 - 8{,}200T^{-1} \quad (T = 900\text{–}1{,}000°\text{K})$

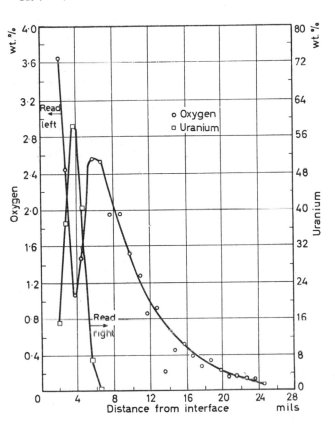

Figure 4.21. Composition of zirconium sample after heating in contact with $UO_2$ at 870°C for 95 hours (Mallett et al., 1957) (by courtesy of U.S.A.E.C.).

These equations may be used to estimate degrees of reaction and penetration only where good contact is maintained, and since the products of the reaction have a lower density than the reactants, penetration can be arrested upon loss of contact between phases due to shrinkage. Nevertheless the equations may be useful in obtaining firm upper limits. For example, Mallet et al. have applied their data to estimate that a zirconium cladding of thickness 0·030 in. in intimate contact with $UO_2$ would have a useful life of about 300 days at

700°C. A few experiments showed that zircaloy-2 reacted more slowly than zirconium, but no quantitative data were obtained.

*Aluminium.* The occurrence of a reaction between aluminium and uranium dioxide was first established during the preparation of plate-type fuel elements for the swimming-pool reactor built by the U.S.A.E.C. for the First Geneva Conference (PICKLESIMER, 1956; WAUGH and CUNNINGHAM, 1956; EISS, 1958). It was found that uranium metal tended to migrate into the aluminium at temperatures around 600°C, with the formation of intermetallic compounds, accompanied by swelling and distortion. Qualitative metallographic examination of specimens produced by hot rolling of powders revealed that the reaction was very slow below 500°C, and that the rate at 600°C was greatly dependent upon the method of manufacture of the $UO_2$, decreasing as the crystallite size of the material increased. Further semiquantitative rate data have been published by WAUGH (1959), who has identified products which include $Al_2O_3$, $UAl_2$, $UAl_3$ and $UAl_4$, the intermetallic phases present depending upon the conditions of the reaction. No diffusion data have yet been published, and it is clear that the mechanism of this reaction is inadequately understood. It may be concluded at this stage, however, that $Al-UO_2$ fuels are unlikely to find application in power reactors.

*Beryllium.* According to available thermodynamic data (SMITHELLS, 1949), beryllium is capable of reducing uranium dioxide to uranium at all temperatures. BAIRD and WEST (1959) have shown that, in pressed powder mixtures of $UO_2$ and beryllium, extensive reaction takes place during one month at 700–800°C, with the formation of $UBe_{13}$ and, presumably, beryllium oxide. Subsequent tests carried out by KNAPTON and FINCH (1961), using clamped specimens of $UO_2$ pellets and beryllium sheet, have shown that a slow reaction can be detected at a temperature as low as 600°C, but no quantitative data are available.

*Stainless steel.* Unpublished work at the Culcheth Laboratories of the U.K.A.E.A. indicates good compatibility between $UO_2$ and stainless steel at high temperature. No reaction was detected between stoichiometric $UO_2$ and stainless steel after 1,000 hours in contact at 800°C and 24 hours in contact at 1,550°C. Preliminary tests indicate however that reaction is promoted by the presence of non-stoichiometric oxygen.

*Other metals.* Tests of compatibility with refractory metals have been carried out, principally to examine their suitability as high temperature thermocouple and container materials. GANGLER et al. (1960) report that $UO_2$ is completely inert towards tungsten, tantalum, molybdenum and niobium up to the melting point of the metal or the oxide, whichever is lower. BYERLY (1960) found that slight adherence to molybdenum, tantalum and niobium took place at 2,660°C, but without detectable attack after one hour. Tungsten and rhenium exhibited no evidence even of adherence.

*Metal oxides.* No evidence of compound or solid solution formation has been detected between $UO_2$ and the oxides of beryllium and aluminium up to 1,800°C (LANG et al., 1956; BUDNIKOR et al., 1958). Above this temperature some penetration of an $Al_2O_3$ matrix by $UO_2$ has been reported (WATSON and BAIRD, 1961).

Magnesium oxide dissolves in stoichiometric $UO_2$ to the extent of not more than a few mole per cent at high temperature, forming a fluorite structure with

146

anion vacancies. This defect structure takes up oxygen readily however, and the solubility of MgO thereupon rises: ANDERSON and JOHNSON (1953) on heating a mixture of the oxides at 1,100°C obtained a solution which retained the $UO_2$ cubic lattice and contained 25–30% of MgO, while BUDNIKOR et al. (1958) obtained an MgO content as high as 37 per cent on heating a mixture at 1,700°C. The latter workers also found that extensive solid solution formation took place under non-oxidizing conditions above 1,700°C if MgO was present in excess; presumably under these conditions oxygen from dissociation of MgO enters the defect fluorite lattice and promotes further dissolution.

Some observations on the behaviour of sintered bodies of $UO_2$ and MgO irradiated in contact have been made by MYLES and SAYERS (1961). The two oxides appear to be compatible up to 1,600°C, but above this temperature interpenetration takes place, again possibly by a mechanism involving decomposition of magnesium.

Zirconium dioxide forms a limited range of solid solution with $UO_2$. Up to 1,300°C, MUMPTON and ROY (1960) report that a maximum of 8 mole per cent of $ZrO_2$ will dissolve in $UO_2$, and a maximum of 4 mole per cent of $UO_2$ will dissolve in $ZrO_2$. These values are significantly lower than the earlier data of LAMBERTSON and MUELLER (1953). Sintered bodies of $UO_2$ and $ZrO_2$ have been found to react only above a temperature of 1,500°C (WATSON and BAIRD, 1961).

The behaviour of binary mixtures of $UO_2$ and oxides of metals having little or no interest as canning materials is summarized by LANG et al. (1956). Higher oxides may undergo reduction on heating with $UO_2$, as is the case with vanadium pentoxide which is reduced to the dioxide.

*Other compounds*

Tests of the compatibility of $UO_2$ with a series of refractory carbides, borides and nitrides over the temperature range 1,900–2,700°C have been reported by GANGLER et al. (1960). The experiments, which were carried out by heating bulk specimens of $UO_2$ and the respective compounds *in vacuo* or argon for 10 min, were of a qualitative nature only, designed to give preliminary information on the suitability of the compounds as matrices and burnable poisons in high temperature dispersion fuels containing $UO_2$.

Of the carbides tested, only hafnium carbide was completely inert to $UO_2$ up to 2,800°C. The carbides of tantalum, tungsten, niobium, zirconium, molybdenum, vanadium and silicon all reacted to form carbides of uranium at temperatures ranging from 2,000 to 2,500°C. The borides of tantalum, tungsten, niobium, thorium, hafnium and zirconium all underwent slow reaction at temperatures ranging from 2,200 to 2,500°C: it is claimed that uranium monoxide was formed, but the evidence for this is not conclusive. The nitrides of tantalum, zirconium, hafnium and titanium exhibited blistering at temperatures not far above 2,000°C.

### 4.1.6 Effects of Irradiation

Technological interest in the effects of reactor irradiation on bulk uranium dioxide may be conveniently considered under three main headings:

(i) The behaviour of fission products, particularly the mode and extent of their release from the solid.

(ii) The effect of heavy particle bombardment on the crystal structure of uranium dioxide.

(iii) The effect of temperature gradients in the fuel, particularly in relation to grain growth and centre melting, which can seriously affect item (i).

The degree of release of fission products is a problem of vital importance to the safe operation of a reactor, and as such will be considered in some detail in Chapter 5. The effects of heavy particle irradiation on the structure of crystalline solids in general is a subject which is imperfectly understood (e.g. CLARKE, 1960), and until comparatively recently no data were available on uranium dioxide. A valuable technique has been developed at A.E.R.E. Harwell (WAIT, 1962) which allows structural changes induced in single crystals by fission fragment bombardment to be studied by x-ray techniques. Preliminary results with uranium dioxide up to burn-ups of 1,000 MWd/T have shown that, at a temperature of 50°C, the effect is limited to a small dilation of the cubic lattice with no crystal fragmentation (cf. results with uranium monocarbide, Section 4.4): on heat-treating at higher temperatures (500–600°C), the bulk of the damage can be annealed out, and only very small changes have been observed in samples irradiated at 400 and 600°C respectively. Experiments similar to those of Wait were reported earlier by BOYKO et al. (1958). These workers irradiated $UO_2$ powders up to 100 MWd/T at 90–135°C and observed line broadening which they attributed to the appearance of radiation-induced strain in the lattice. The broadening could equally have been due, however, to oxidation by traces of oxygen in the helium-filled zircaloy-2 capsules which were used to contain the powders: Wait, who used helium-filled silica capsules and took special care to remove all traces of oxygen, detected no line broadening up to burn-ups of 1,000 MWd/T. Furthermore the structural stability of $UO_2$ incorporating other oxides ($ZrO_2$, $Al_2O_3$, $ZrO_2 + CaO$) has been demonstrated provided the cubic structure is maintained (BERMAN et al., 1960). Thus, although experiments over a wide range of temperature and burn-up are essential before firm conclusions can be drawn, it appears at this stage that radiation-induced crystal damage will be of only secondary importance to fuel element behaviour. An allied topic, the destruction of the cubic lattice at high burn-up by the accumulation of large quantities of fission products, will be dealt with later.

An important influence on fuel performance is exerted by the effects of temperature gradients in the bulk fuel. Although, in the strictest sense, these effects lie outside the realm of radiation chemistry since only the thermal energy generated during the arrest of fission fragments is of consequence, the topic may be designated a radiation effect in so far as most of the existing knowledge has derived from post-irradiation examination of test fuel pellets. An outstanding contribution has been made by workers at Chalk River, and details of their irradiation tests have been published by ROBERTSON et al. (1958, 1959). Work carried out at the Bettis Plant, U.S.A., has been described by EICHENBERG et al. (1957) and by BLEIBERG et al. (1960). A useful study which illustrates the value of metallographic techniques in pre- and post-irradiation examination of $UO_2$ pellets has been published by BRADBURY and HARRISON (1961).

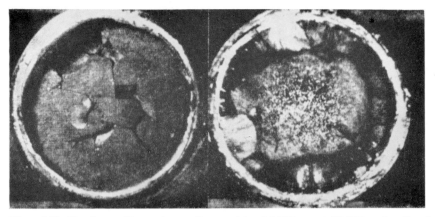

*Figure 4.22.* Uranium oxide specimens of composition (a) $UO_{2\cdot0}$ and (b) $UO_{2\cdot15}$ irradiated under similar conditions (sheath outer diameter 1·05 cm) (Bain and Robertson, 1960) (by courtesy of Atomic Energy of Canada Ltd. and North Holland Publishing Co. (Journal of Nuclear Materials (1959) **1**, 109)).

*Figure 4.25.* Cross-section of fuel element plate showing swelling of fuel after burn-up of 9 at. % ($21\cdot5 \times 10^{20}$ fissions $cm^{-3}$) (Bleiberg *et al.*, 1960) (by courtesy of U.S.A.E.C.)

*To face page* 149

*The effect of non-stoichiometric oxygen*

It has been established without doubt that the presence of non-stoichiometric oxygen is undesirable; grain growth takes place much more readily than with stoichiometric material irradiated under comparable conditions, and the release of fission products is considerably higher.

Following strong qualitative evidence of such behaviour during loop tests, a carefully controlled experiment was carried out by BAIN and ROBERTSON (1959). These workers compared the irradiation behaviour of stoichiometric pellets with that of pellets having a composition $UO_{2.15}$: both sets of pellets had a density of $10.4–10.5$ g cm$^{-3}$, and each was subjected to essentially identical conditions of irradiation (burn-up 4,400 MWd/tonne U, surface temperature 325°C, $\int kd\theta$ 25–27 watt cm$^{-2}$, see page 151). The contrasting appearance of the specimens at the end of this test is shown in *Figure 4.22*. Whereas the stoichiometric material shows only cracking, the non-stoichiometric pellet has suffered extensive grain growth over a central region covering nearly half of its total cross-sectional area. This change in structure resulted in a release of volatile fission products corresponding to nearly 20 per cent of the total, which contrasted sharply with the level of about 0.1 per cent released from the stoichiometric material.

The deleterious effect of excess oxygen most probably arises from a combination of the poorer thermal conductivity of non-stoichiometric material (Section 4.1.2) and the greater ease of grain growth at higher temperatures, which results from a higher rate of self-diffusion of oxygen. From observations of melting and grain growth following short-term irradiations RIDAL et al. (1961) deduce that the mean thermal conductivity of $UO_{2.12}$ is about 20 per cent lower than that of $UO_{2.0}$ under similar conditions.

Evidence has been obtained at Harwell that at higher centre temperatures, non-stoichiometric pellets can develop central cavities which differ in structure from those developed in stoichiometric material during centre melting (q.v.). MURRAY and WILLIAMS (1958) postulate that volatilization of $UO_3$—a process which has been observed during sintering of non-stoichiometric oxide in an inert atmosphere (Section 4.1.3)—takes part in this process. They point out that mass transfer might be expected to continue indefinitely, since $UO_3$ would distil from the central parts of a fuel element and on depositing in cooler portions would decompose, evolving oxygen which would re-diffuse into hotter sections. This cyclic process would promote a continuous change in grain structure, and would ensure a high release of volatile fission products.

Regardless of the precise mechanism it is clear that the structural changes which can take place in non-stoichiometric $UO_2$ under irradiation make it unacceptable as a fuel material. The tolerable limit of deviation from an O/U ratio of 2.00 cannot be rigidly defined (ROBERTSON (1960) has estimated an upper limit of 2.01 for CANDU fuel on the basis of fission gas release), but it is certain that all sintering schedules must end with treatment of the oxide fuel in a reducing atmosphere. The implications of this requirement on the utilization of non-stoichiometric oxygen as an aid to sintering have already been discussed (Section 4.1.3).

It is not yet clear what method of estimating the O/U ratio of fuel pellets is best suited to production control. The gravimetric technique involving conversion to $U_3O_8$ requires large quantities of material if the deviation from stoichiometry is small. Laboratory methods which are capable of precision of the order $\pm 0.001$ include the carbon monoxide reduction technique of ROBERTS and HARPER (1952) and the controlled potential coulometric method of STROMATT and CONALLY (1961) (involving estimation of U(VI) after dissolution in $H_3PO_4$). A solid state electrochemical method first proposed by KIUKKOLA and WAGNER (1957) holds promise as a non-destructive technique for measuring O/U ratios. This involves measuring the potential of a couple consisting of an anion defect lattice (e.g. $ZrO_2 \cdot CaO$) and $UO_{2+n}$ against a metal/metal oxide couple of known potential (e.g. Fe/FeO, Ni/NiO). The temperature variation of the e.m.f. can be calibrated against the value of $n$. Progress in the development of this technique has been reported by ARONSON and BELLE (1958) and by MARKIN and ROBERTS (1962).

ROBERTSON (1960) has proposed a mineralogical 'streak' test as a control method for determining U/O ratios. Apparently a streak of $UO_{2+n}$ on white porcelain varies in colour from 'milk chocolate' through 'plain chocolate' to 'black' as $n$ changes from 0.005 through 0.010 to 0.15. A simple method such as this is appealing, but a careful assessment of its reliability is required.

### Irradiation behaviour of stoichiometric material

Although the absence of non-stoichiometric oxygen ensures the best performance of uranium dioxide under a given set of irradiation conditions, these conditions are still limited by the need to avoid grain growth,* and—in the extreme case—melting at the central region of the fuel, which may result in the formation of an annular void. Cracking of pellets during thermal cycling is a common occurrence, and appears to be an unavoidable consequence of mechanical strain introduced during fabrication. Apart from underlining the need for structural strength to be supplied by the fuel element cladding, the consequences of cracking alone do not appear to be very serious since cracks are usually radial and do not therefore seriously affect the thermal path to the surface. If the centre temperature is high enough for grain growth to take place, however, healing and fresh cracking may occur during every thermal cycle, with a consequent increase in the release of volatile fission products. Moreover, above a temperature of 1,800°C, it is possible that precipitation of uranium metal will take place (ROTHWELL, 1961).

Ideally, to make a precise prediction of physical changes which may occur in the fuel during operation, a knowledge of the temperature distribution within the fuel element is required. This may be obtained either from direct measurement of the temperature at different points, or by computation from a knowledge of the power output, the surface temperature and the variation of thermal conductivity with temperature. Unfortunately, direct measurement of the temperature distribution is exceedingly difficult to carry out, and the method of computation is unreliable because of ignorance of the dependence of thermal conductivity upon temperature and irradiation conditions.

ROBERTSON (1959) has shown that the temperature drop through a cylindrical fuel element can be usefully expressed in terms of a parameter

* A valuable out-of-pile study of grain growth in sintered $UO_2$ compacts over the temperature range 1,550–2,440°C has been reported by MACEWAN (1961).

which is a function only of power output, surface temperature and rod diameter. This parameter is defined by

$$\int_{\theta\text{surface}}^{\theta r} k(\theta)\, d\theta = \frac{q}{4\pi} f(ha, r)$$

where $k(\theta)$ is the thermal conductivity at temperature $\theta$, $q$ is the rate of heat production per unit length of fuel, $r$ is a radial distance from the axis of the cylinder, $a$ is the radius and $h$ is a quantity which allows for the depression of thermal neutron flux inside the rod. The most important practical case arises when $r = 0$ and $\int k\, d\theta$ relates to the temperature drop from the surface to the centre of the fuel. Values of $f(ha)$ under these conditions for oxide cylinders

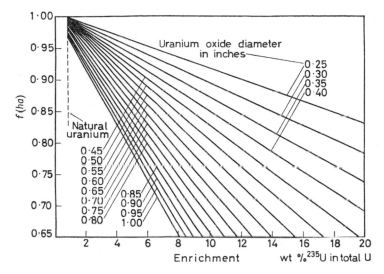

*Figure 4.23.* The dependence of $f(ha)$ on $UO_2$ diameter and enrichment for oxide cylinders of 95 per cent theoretical density (Runnalls, 1959) (by courtesy of Atomic Energy of Canada Ltd.).

of 95 per cent theoretical density have been calculated at Chalk River, and are reproduced in *Figure 4.23*. Using this diagram $f(ha)$ may be obtained directly for a fuel element of known diameter and isotopic enrichment, and $\int k\, d\theta$ may then be calculated for any value of $q$. Derivations for other geometries have been presented by Robertson (1959).

Having calculated

$$\int_{\theta\text{(surface)}}^{\theta\text{(centre)}} k(\theta)\, d\theta$$

for a given fuel element, it is possible to estimate $\theta$(centre) by using a suitable calibration curve relating values of the integral to the temperature difference itself. RUNNALLS (1959) examined the value of the integral in experiments where a reasonably reliable estimate of $\theta$(centre) could be obtained: for example, appreciable grain growth was assumed to take place at 1,500–1,600°C,

151

and centre melting (which was observed in irradiations of short duration by BAIN and ROBERTSON (1959) ) at 2,800°C. The experimental points were found to be in agreement with a curve calculated from the data of HEDGE and FIELD-HOUSE (1956) (*Figure 4.3*) corrected to 95 per cent theoretical density and extrapolated up to the melting point. This calibration curve is therefore

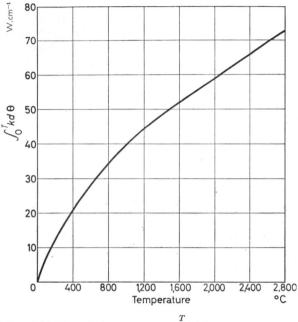

*Figure 4.24.* The relationship between $\int_0^T kd(\theta)$ and $T$ for $UO_2$ of 95 per cent theoretical density (Robertson, 1959) (by courtesy of Atomic Energy of Canada Ltd.).

recommended by Robertson for application to experimental data, and is reproduced in *Figure 4.24.* From the curve, values of $\theta$(centre) at known values of

$$\int_{\theta(\text{surface})}^{\theta(\text{centre})} k(\theta) \, d\theta$$

can be obtained by using the relationship

$$\int_{\theta(\text{surface})}^{\theta(\text{centre})} k(\theta) \, d\theta = \int_0^{\theta(\text{centre})} k(\theta) \, d\theta - \int_0^{\theta(\text{surface})} k(\theta) \, d\theta$$

By way of illustration the maximum permissible values of

$$\int_{\theta(\text{surface})}^{\theta(\text{centre})} k(\theta) \, d\theta$$

for assumed values of $\theta$(surface) derived from *Figure 4.24* are presented in *Table 4.5*: it has been assumed that extensive grain growth will occur above $\theta$(centre) of 1,500°C, and melting at 2,800°C. From the maximum value of

152

the integrated thermal conductivity, a maximum value of the power per unit length $q$ can be obtained for a fuel element of given dimensions.

It must be emphasized at this stage that the figures in *Table 4.5* should be used only as a rough guide, since they may well be revised as better data become available. For example, some evidence is available that the values of integrated conductivity for centre melting derived from *Figure 4.24* may be too low: a value for

$$\int_{250}^{\theta(\text{melting})} k(\theta)\,d\theta$$

as high as 75 watt cm$^{-1}$ has been observed in hydraulic rabbit irradiations of $UO_2$ having a density 95 per cent of theoretical (BAIN and ROBERTSON, 1959). Limiting values for grain growth are rendered uncertain by the arbitrary definition of the process (usually an increase in grain size to 15–20 microns, but often without reference to the time at temperature), although the figures for a surface temperature of 400°C quoted from Chalk River of $30 \pm 3$ watt cm$^{-1}$ (ROBERTSON et al., 1959) and from Harwell of 28 watt cm$^{-1}$ (SAYERS et al., 1960) are in good agreement with the value in *Table 4.5*.

TABLE 4.5

MAXIMUM PERMISSIBLE VALUES OF $\displaystyle\int_{\theta(\text{surface})}^{\theta(\text{centre})} k(\theta)\,d\theta$

TO AVOID (*a*) GRAIN GROWTH, AND (*b*) CENTRE MELTING
(Fuel density 95 per cent of theoretical)

| $\theta$ (surface) °C | $\displaystyle\int_{\theta(\text{surface})}^{\theta(\text{centre})}$ (watt cm$^{-1}$) | |
|---|---|---|
| | (*a*) To avoid grain growth | (*b*) To avoid centre melting |
| 250 | 34 | 58 |
| 300 | 32 | 56 |
| 350 | 30 | 54 |
| 400 | 28 | 52 |
| 500 | 24 | 48 |
| 600 | 21 | 45 |
| 700 | 17·5 | 41·5 |
| 800 | 14·5 | 38·5 |

Many irradiations have been carried out with a gas-filled gap between the zircaloy-2 or stainless steel sheath and the fuel. Under such conditions allowance must be made for the gradient across the gas gap in estimating the temperature of the fuel surface from that of the sheath. This gap could change during irradiation owing to fragmentation of the fuel: however, evidence from Chalk River indicates that such changes are of only minor importance in estimating the integrated conductivity. Moreover, evidence from numerous short-term irradiations carried out by BAIN *et al.* (1961) indicates that the surface temperature of fuel pellets is not significantly affected by gas gaps smaller than one per cent of the pellet diameter.

It is important that future work should lay emphasis on defining maximum permissible values of $\int k(\theta)\,d\theta$ in relation to the release of volatile fission products, particularly as visual observation of grain growth in post-irradiation examination seems rather uncertain. Studies are also needed of the effect of changes in fuel density on the curve in *Figure 4.24*: preliminary data obtained by Bain and Robertson (1959) indicate, as expected, that values of

$$\int_0^\theta k(\theta)\,d\theta$$

for cold-swaged powders are considerably lower than for dense pellets.

In the early work, centre melting and grain growth appeared to be the salient phenomena which required to be related to integrated conductivity and fission gas release. A third phenomenon has now been identified; that of 'columnar grain growth'. This takes place at a temperature (*ca.* 2,400°C), considerably below the melting point of $UO_2$, and the formation of long radial grains may be accompanied by central void formation. The phenomenon has been reproduced out of pile in experiments reported by MACEWAN and LAWSON (1960, 1962): these workers applied electrical heating to the inner surface of annular $UO_2$ pellets while cooling the outer surface with water, thus producing a steep temperature gradient (*ca.* 2,800°C cm⁻¹) at an inner surface temperature of up to 1,400°C. After 12 hours of this treatment the development of long columnar grains was evident, accompanied by small flat voids perpendicular to the radial direction. MacEwan and Lawson obtained strong evidence that this phenomenon is related to the evaporation of $UO_2$ from hotter to colder regions. Such a process would be expected to enhance fission product release as much as centre melting: if so, column (*b*) in *Table 4.5* might be usefully replaced by values of

$$\int_{\theta\text{surface}}^{2,400} k(\theta)\,d\theta$$

being upper limits of the integral to avoid columnar grain growth. Further studies of this important effect are obviously needed.

*Effects of high burn-up*

In discussion so far, the effects of high burn-up on the properties of $UO_2$ have been ignored. However, even if heavy particle damage to the fuel is of no great importance, and the temperature distribution is such that no grain growth takes place, accumulation of fission product atoms in the lattice must eventually lead to distortion. The first evidence of this was obtained by BARNEY (1958, 1959), who carried out irradiations of fully enriched $UO_2$ (either in a stainless steel cermet or as a loose powder) to high burn-ups (up to 50 per cent total uranium). He found that internal porosity developed in the solid due to the accumulation of fission product gases, and that swelling tended to take place, though this could be restrained by the matrix. It is difficult to make quantitative deductions from this work, however, largely because the degree of retention of volatile fission products was not measured.

Later observations of BLEIBERG *et al.* (1960) allow firmer conclusions to be drawn. From data obtained during irradiation in pressurized water of $UO_2$ platelets of varying $^{235}U$ content (14–52 per cent) clad with zircaloy-2, these workers concluded that a definite burn-up of bulk $UO_2$ exists beyond which serious dimensional changes take place.* A cross-sectional photograph of a fuel plate, showing the swelling of the $UO_2$ after 9 at. % burn-up is reproduced in *Figure 4.25*: microscopic examination of sections of the fuel plate

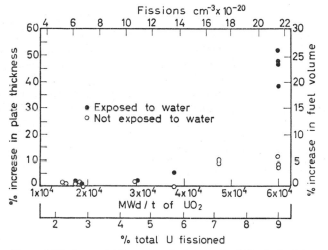

*Figure 4.26.* Average dimensional changes in $UO_2$ fuel plates irradiated to various burn-ups (Bleiberg *et al.*, 1960)(by courtesy of U.S.A.E.C.).

revealed the existence of uniformly dispersed fine pores in the structure. The percentage fission gas release was about two powers of ten higher than that from corresponding samples irradiated to burn-ups of about 3·5 at.%.

Seven fuel elements were tested to different burn-ups, and a plot of average dimensional changes in the fuel plates against burn-up is shown in *Figure 4.26*. It is evident that dimensional changes become appreciable above a burn-up of about 5 at. %. Filled points in *Figure 4.26* refer to specimens which were exposed to water because of defection of the fuel cladding. At the highest burn-up, dimensional changes under these conditions were particularly serious: this may have been due to entry of water into open pores in the fuel during reactor shut-down, leading to the development of high internal pressure when the operating temperature of about 300°C was reattained.

It must be emphasized that the limiting burn-up of about 5 at. % to avoid swelling in undefected fuel, which may be deduced from *Figure 4.26*, is not of

* The claim that damage resulted in the total destruction of the fluorite lattice has been retracted in the light of further evidence (PWR PROJECT, 1961).

general application. All the tests of Bleiberg *et al.* were carried out in high temperature water under external pressures not less than 80 atmospheres. In reactors cooled by a gas, an organic liquid or a liquid metal, the external pressure will probably be at least a power of ten lower than this figure; data on the dependence of swelling upon restraining pressure (including that exerted by the cladding) are therefore needed before general conclusions can be drawn.

### 4.2 THORIUM DIOXIDE AND THORIA-URANIA SYSTEMS

#### 4.2.1 Chemical and Physical Properties

##### Thoria

Thorium dioxide (thoria) is the only known oxide of thorium. It is an extremely stable compound with a high heat of formation ($\Delta H_{298} = 293$ kcal mole$^{-1}$), and is the most refractory of all the metallic oxides, with a melting point as high as 3,300°C (LAMBERTSON *et al.*, 1953). It has a fluorite structure ($a_0 = 5.5859$Å), and a theoretical density of 10.00 g cm$^{-3}$. The mean coefficient of linear thermal expansion varies from $7.1 \times 10^{-6}$ c.g.s. units at 300°C to $10.4 \times 10^{-6}$ c.g.s. units at 1,500°C (WHITTEMORE and AULT, 1956), being slightly lower than that of uranium dioxide over a comparable range of temperature (*Table 4.2*, p. 118).

Values of the thermal conductivity of thoria at various temperatures are summarized in *Table 4.6*.

TABLE 4.6

THERMAL CONDUCTIVITY OF THORIA AT VARIOUS
TEMPERATURES (Kingery, 1955)

| Temp. (°C) | $\kappa$ (cal cm$^{-1}$ sec$^{-1}$ deg$^{-1}$ C) |
|---|---|
| 130 | 0.022 |
| 400 | 0.016 |
| 600 | 0.010 |
| 1000 | 0.006 |

The values are the same as those for $UO_2$ (*Figure 4.3*) within the limits of uncertainty of the latter.

The mean value of the specific heat over the temperature range 3–100°C is 0.044 cal g$^{-1}$ deg$^{-1}$ K (SKINNER *et al.*, 1950); over the range 320–1170°K it is expressed by the equation

$$C_p = 0.0647 + 7.53 \times 10^{-6} \, T - 1,050 T^2 \, \text{cal g}^{-1} \text{deg}^{-1} \text{K}$$

(VICTOR and DOUGLAS, 1961).

Important mechanical properties of thoria and thoria + 0.5 wt.% calcium oxide have been reported by LANG and KNUDSEN (1956).

## Thoria–urania

Both thoria and urania have a fluorite cubic structure and form a complete series of solid solutions (SLOWINSKI and ELLIOT, 1952), with miscibility extending to the liquid phase over the whole range of composition (LAMBERTSON et al., 1953; *Figure 4.27*). Although, like pure $UO_2$, the solid solutions will oxidize when heated in air, the presence of $Th^{4+}$ imparts a remarkable degree of stability to the structure. ANDERSON et al. (1954) observed that the fluorite cubic structure of a solid solution containing 78 mole per cent $UO_2$ was stable in air up to 1,400°C (composition

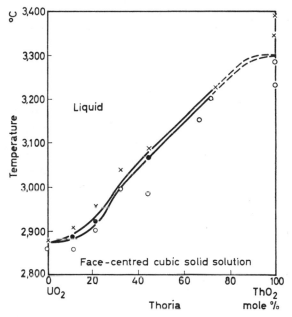

*Figure 4.27.* $UO_2 \cdot ThO_2$ phase equilibrium diagram. × liquid, ○ solid, ● solid and liquid (Lambertson et al., 1953) (by courtesy of the American Ceramic Society).

$U_{0.78}Th_{0.22}O_{2.53}$). HUND and NIESSEN (1952), on the other hand, found that the fluorite structure was stable in air only to a composition of 56·5 mole per cent $UO_2$. Anderson et al. attribute this discrepancy to differences in the method of preparation, which might have facilitated the nucleation of the $U_3O_8$ phase in Hund's material. However, the structural stability of a solid solution containing up to 50 mole per cent $UO_2$ seems assured. This has been confirmed during thermal cycling studies in air of thoria–urania compacts (LYNCH et al., 1960).

SMITH (1960a) reports the complete oxidation of a $ThO_2 \cdot 10\% UO_2$ sintered pellet in oxygen (1 atm) without physical deterioration. The oxidation proceeded at a linear rate described by the equation

$$R(\text{mole } O_2\,\text{cm}^{-2}\,\text{min}^{-1}) = 3\cdot7 \times 10^{-3}\exp\left(\frac{-22,500}{RT}\right)$$

Little information is available on the physical properties of thoria–urania bodies. The coefficients of thermal expansion of $ThO_2.6\%$ $UO_2$ and $ThO_2.10\%$ $UO_2$ from 25 to 800°C are little different from those of thoria over the same range.

### 4.2.2 Densification Studies
#### Thoria

Numerous studies have been made of the densification of thoria in relation to its use as a refractory container material: particular attention has been paid to the formation of green bodies by slip casting prior to firing (MURRAY et al., 1956; MURRAY and LIVEY, 1956; STODDARD and HARPER, 1957; CURTIS, 1959), and some effort has also been devoted to hot pressing at temperatures up to 2,000°C (MURRAY and LIVEY, 1956; CURTIS, 1959). In this section we shall confine ourselves to data obtained in studies of cold-pressing and firing, since this technique is most likely to be applied in the production of dense material for breeder and fuel application.

The sintering of thoria in relation to its mode of preparation has been investigated by KANTAN, RAGHAVAN and TENDOLKAR (1958). Thoria was prepared from nitrate solution by direct decomposition, and by precipitation and calcination of the hydroxide, the carbonate and the oxalate; all powders were sieved, and only the $-200$ mesh fraction was used for sintering tests which were carried out by dry pressing at 30 ton in.$^{-2}$ and sintering at temperatures of up to 1,500°C for 1 hour.

It was found that the sintered densities obtained varied appreciably with the mode of preparation of the thoria, and that material from oxalate showed oustanding behaviour in giving a high sintered density despite a low green density: this is exemplified by the data in *Table 4.7*.

TABLE 4.7

SINTERING BEHAVIOUR OF THORIA PREPARED BY DIFFER-
ENT METHODS (CALCINING TEMP. 900°C; COMPACTING
PRESSURE 30 TON IN.$^{-2}$; SINTERING FOR 1 HOUR AT
1,500°C IN AIR) (Kantan et al., 1958)

| Starting Material | Density | |
|---|---|---|
| | Green | Fired |
| Hydroxide | 7·50 | 7·86 |
| Carbonate | 7·70 | 8·09 |
| Nitrate | 7·23 | 8·20 |
| Oxalate | 6·50 | 9·35 |

Following these findings, a more detailed investigation was made of oxalate-prepared material to elucidate the effects of compacting pressure, sintering temperature, and mode of precipitation and calcination of the oxalate.

It was found that changing the sintering atmosphere between air, oxygen, hydrogen and vacuum had no significant effect on the sintered density, and for ease of operation most tests were performed in air. The general conclusions may be summarized as follows:

(a) Sintered density tended to increase with compacting pressure over the range 5 to 30 ton in.$^{-2}$, but the increase above 20 ton in.$^{-2}$ was slight.

(b) Density increased with sintering temperatures up to 1,500°C, but a further increase of the temperature to 1,700°C produced no significant improvement.

(c) Density decreased significantly if the parent oxalate was precipitated at a temperature above 30°C. This is probably related to an increase in the mean particle size of the final oxide, established by ALLRED et al. (1957). (See *Figure 4.19, Volume 2.*)

(d) The optimum density was achieved with material from oxalate calcined at 900°C. Calcination at lower temperatures may have produced incomplete decomposition of the oxalate (the calcination times are not stated) which could have led to slight 'bloating' during sintering. Calcination at temperatures above 1,000°C, on the other hand, could have produced material of low specific surface.

Unfortunately no physical characterization of their powders was carried out by Kantan et al., and it is therefore impossible to draw firm conclusions. It seems likely, however, that the same general relations between physical properties and sinterability hold for thoria as for urania (with the exception, of course, of the effect of non-stoichiometric oxygen), i.e. the powder should have a surface area greater than 1–2 m$^2$ g$^{-1}$, and should contain the minimum of large agglomerates. If a reasonable analogy can be drawn between thoria and plutonia prepared by different methods, it seems likely that ThO$_2$ obtained by calcining the hydroxide or the nitrate at or above 800°C will have a much lower surface area than the corresponding material from the oxalate (Volume 2, Chapter 4), and this might contribute to its poorer sintering behaviour. Moreover Kantan et al. state explicitly that material obtained from hydroxide, nitrate or carbonate is much coarser than that from the oxalate.

Some experiments have been reported on the effect of additives as a means of enhancing the sinterability of thoria at moderate temperatures (JOHNSON and CURTIS, 1954; WARDE and JOHNSON, 1955; LANG and KNUDSEN, 1956). Most success was obtained with the alkaline earth oxides, particularly with calcium oxide: an addition of 0·5 per cent CaO raised the density obtained after sintering for 1 hour at 1,700°C from 86 to 98 per cent of theoretical, though the improvement was lost when sintering was carried out in a hydrogen atmosphere. There is evidence that the rate of sintering in this system is controlled by the surface migration of anion vacancies, and a more detailed study of the sintering kinetics would be worthwhile. There seems little doubt that the effectiveness of calcium is related to the closeness of the ionic size of Ca$^{2+}$ (0·99 Å) to that of Th$^{4+}$ (1·02 Å). The Sr$^{2+}$ ion (1·13 Å) is somewhat less effective than calcium, while ions of a very different size such as Be$^{2+}$ (0·31 Å), Mg$^{2+}$ (0·65 Å), Zr$^{4+}$ (0·74 Å), Al$^{3+}$ (0·50 Å) were without effect up to a concentration of 30 weight per cent (CURTIS, 1959). It has been established that additions of calcium fluoride can act in the same way as the oxide (ARENBERG et al., 1957), but it is unlikely that the deliberate addition of fluorides would ever become an accepted practice.

The preparation by hot pressing techniques of thoria compacts containing molybdenum or niobium fibres has been described by BASKIN *et al.* (1959). Later work by the same authors (1960) has shown that although the thermal conductivity of these bodies is little better than that of thoria at room temperature, it is markedly better at elevated temperatures. The physical strength of the compacts, however, is poor.

### *Thoria–urania*

The formation of thoria–urania bodies by sintering compacted mixtures of $ThO_2$ and $U_3O_8$ in air has been studied by HANDWERK (1957). The employment of $U_3O_8$ is essential if firing is to be carried out in air, for if $ThO_2 + UO_2$ is used, the volume expansion during oxidation to $U_3O_8$ at 600°C shatters the green compact. Over the temperature range 1,150–1,400°C the $U_3O_8$

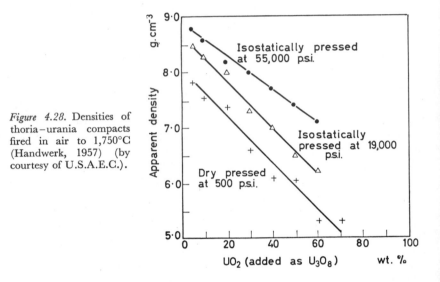

*Figure 4.28.* Densities of thoria–urania compacts fired in air to 1,750°C (Handwerk, 1957) (by courtesy of U.S.A.E.C.).

decomposes to $UO_2$ and a solid solution with $ThO_2$ is formed: although the decomposition involves a volume contraction and gas evolution, this does not appear to cause disruption of the pellet. If the resulting compact is cooled in air, oxidation takes place, but the fluorite structure is maintained at least up to a composition of 50 per cent uranium (Section 4.2.1).

No systematic studies have been made of the variation of sinterability with powder properties, but judging from the data of Handwerk the method tends to give compacts of low density, which decreases with uranium content: this is exemplified by *Figure 4.28*. The low densities are not surprising in view of the fact that bloating of the compacts must take place as oxygen is expelled during decomposition of $U_3O_8$.

A more promising method of fabrication involves the cold pressing and sintering of $(U, Th)O_{2+n}$ powders prepared by calcination of thorium–uranyl oxalates obtained from coprecipitation (SHAPIRO and POWERS, 1959a). By this method it is possible to prepare powders containing up to 20 per cent uranium, which achieve densities of up to 96 per cent of theoretical after sintering for several hours in air at temperatures within the range 1,300–1,500°C. No measurements of the final value of the oxygen–metal ratio were recorded; it is important that this should be known for irradiation test pieces. It would also be of interest to know the effect of excess oxygen on the rate of sintering, and to compare the sintering behaviour in hydrogen with that in air. Shapiro and Powers observed that the incorporation of 1 per cent $Y_2O_3$ (at the oxalate coprecipitation stage) brought about no improvement in the sintered density under a given set of conditions. They found also that coprecipitation with ammonia produced a powder with poor sintering properties.

### 4.2.3 Irradiation Studies

A series of irradiation tests of fuel elements of $ThO_2.^{235}UO_2$ has been carried out under the auspices of the Argonne National Laboratory, and the details are described in a number of publications (HANDWERK, 1957; KITTEL and HANDWERK, 1958; NEIMARK and KITTEL, 1959; HANDWERK and NOLAND, 1959; NEIMARK, 1961). The fuel was fabricated as cylindrical elements 0·25 in. diameter and 0·5 in. length by dry pressing $ThO_2$–$U_3O_8$ powders and firing in air to 1,800°C. The specific gravity of the specimens measured by water immersion lay between 9·0 and 10·0 g cm$^{-3}$. As the cooling cycle is not specified and no analyses are reported the oxygen content of the specimens is uncertain. Two sets of test samples were irradiated; one containing 2·5 and the other 10 per cent by weight of highly enriched $UO_2$. Some specimens were irradiated bare, while others were sheathed in cans of zircaloy-2, stainless steel or aluminium-1 wt.% nickel alloy. The annular fuel-can gap in the sheathed specimens was filled either with gas (air, helium–argon) or with metal (NaK, lead).

In general, the irradiation behaviour of the test pieces was very good. Particularly notable was the stability of bare $ThO_2.2·5\%\ UO_2$, which showed no mechanical damage after irradiation to a burn-up of 0·75 per cent total atoms at a centre temperature of ca. 480°C and a surface temperature of ca. 200°C. A number of other pellets showed cracking, however, which appeared to be unrelated to the burn-up and the temperature distribution. Sheathed fuel which was irradiated at a centre temperature of less than 2,000°C showed negligible distortion, but at higher centre temperatures failures took place which were particularly serious as centre melting was approached. It is not clear how these changes could have been influenced by extensive grain growth, though one test piece with a centre temperature estimated at not more than 2,740°C had developed a central cavity. Further tests will be necessary to determine whether a process of columnar grain growth takes place, analogous to that observed in $UO_2$ fuel.

A charge of $ThO_2.6·35$ wt. %$^{235}UO_2$ fuel elements and $ThO_2$ breeder elements has been made for the boiling water reactor BORAX-IV (HANDWERK and NOLAND, 1959). Presumably post-irradiation examination of this fuel will yield a fund of evidence on the behaviour of thoria-based ceramic fuels. It is desirable, however, that some attempt should be made to relate the performance of thoria fuels to the concept of integrated thermal conductivity (Section 4.1.6). In future tests, it is also desirable to control the oxygen content carefully, and so evaluate its importance. WILSON (1959) has observed that $UO_3$

is expelled from $(Th, U)O_{2+n}$ at high temperature; this indicates that the presence of excess oxygen may be deleterious to irradiation performance.

### 4.3 PLUTONIUM DIOXIDE AND PLUTONIA–URANIA SYSTEMS

These systems have recently assumed growing importance in reactor fuel technology as interest in plutonium as a fissile material has increased. Fuels containing both $UO_2$ and $PuO_2$ may be of particular value: at plutonium levels of the order of one per cent, plutonia–urania could be employed in a thermal reactor (in which $^{235}U$ is replaced by $^{239}Pu$), while at plutonium levels greater than about 10 per cent the mixed oxide has potential as a fast reactor fuel. It is doubtful if pure $PuO_2$ would constitute an economic fast reactor fuel, for at the high rate of burn-up in a fast reactor it is important to achieve a fair degree of breeding in the core. However $PuO_2$ fuel elements have been employed in the Russian experimental fast reactor, BR-5 (LEIPUNSKY *et al.*, 1958).

#### 4.3.1 Chemical and Physical Properties

#### Plutonium oxides

Plutonium forms three stable oxides, listed in *Table 4.8*.

TABLE 4.8

THE OXIDES OF PLUTONIUM

| Composition | Crystal structure | Theoretical density (g cm$^{-3}$) |
|---|---|---|
| $PuO_2$ | Face-centred cubic | 11·46 |
| $\alpha$-$Pu_2O_3$ | Body-centred cubic | 10·2 |
| (Composition probably $PuO_{1\cdot62}$) | | |
| $\beta$-$Pu_2O_3$ | Hexagonal | 11·47 |

The compound $\beta$-$Pu_2O_3$ is well defined, being isomorphous with the rare earth sesquioxides, and can be prepared easily by reducing the dioxide with plutonium metal at about 1,500°C (HOLLEY *et al.*, 1958). The nature of $\alpha$-$Pu_2O_3$ was for some years obscure, and the phase was stated to vary in composition between $Pu_2O_3$ and $Pu_4O_7$ (MOONEY and ZACHARIASEN, 1949); it can be prepared by heating $PuO_2$ at temperatures above 1,500°C *in vacuo* or in an inert atmosphere, or by reducing it with carbon or hydrogen (ROBERTS *et al.*, 1958; RUSSELL, 1961). The experiments of HOLLEY *et al.* (1958), and the more recent work of RILEY (1961) have led to greater understanding of the nature of the oxygen-deficient cubic phase, and a tentative phase diagram of the plutonium–oxygen system can be constructed. The diagram proposed by Holley *et al.* is reproduced in *Figure 4.29*; according to Riley it is probable that the O/Pu ratio for 'cubic $Pu_2O_3$' is too low, and should be revised to a value of approximately 1·62. Riley carried out experiments on the effect of heating plutonium dioxide in an atmosphere of pure argon, and found that the O/Pu ratio of the resultant cubic phase depended both on the temperature and on the time of heating. Of particular note was the unusual metastability of the composition approximating to $PuO_{1.75}$ (observed by Mooney and Zachariasen) consisting of roughly 50 per cent of face-centred cubic $PuO_2$ and 50 per cent of a body-centred cubic phase: on prolonged heating above 2,000°C, however, further oxygen was lost, and when the proportions of the b.c.c. phase had reached about 90 per cent (O/Pu ratio about 1·62 depending upon the temperature), $\beta$-$Pu_2O_3$ was formed.

From the viewpoint of ceramic fuels, interest has centred on plutonium dioxide, which is thermodynamically stable in air up to temperatures of at

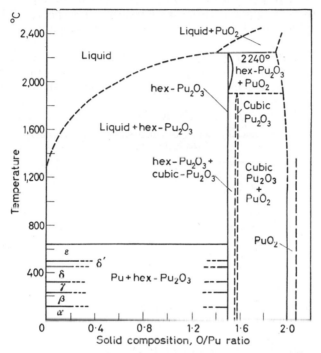

*Figure 4.29.* A tentative Pu–O phase diagram (Holley *et al.*, 1958)
(by courtesy of United Nations).

least 2,000°C (Riley has determined the pressure of oxygen in equilibrium with $PuO_2$ at this temperature to be 0·07–0·08 atmosphere). Plutonium dioxide may be prepared by thermal decomposition of a number of plutonium salts, and details of calcination temperatures and their influence on the micro-structure of the product oxide are presented in Volume 2, Chapter 4. In *Figure 4.29* the dioxide is shown to be capable of exhibiting an O/Pu ratio of up to 2·09 at lower temperatures. This fact was first established by DRUMMOND and WELCH (1957) who showed that the ratio varied with the method of preparation, though the value for all samples was reduced to $2·002 \pm 0·008$ after ignition in air at 1,200°C. ROBERTS *et al.* (1958) showed that the oxygen content of a number of samples increased on heating in oxygen at 900°C, though no change in the size of the unit cell could be detected. Later experiments (RAND and JACKSON, 1962) indicate strongly that excess oxygen

163

is retained by a process of chemisorption, and that reduction of the O/Pu ratio to 2·00 following calcination at high temperature may be attributed to reduction in surface area and possibly deactivation.

Measurements of the physical properties of plutonium dioxide have so far been rather limited, but some work has been reported on the melting point and the coefficient of thermal expansion. Melting point data are somewhat confused because of loss of oxygen on heating *in vacuo*: under these ill-defined conditions, melting points of between 2,170 and 2,355°C have been reported (HOLLEY et al., 1958; CHIKALLA, 1960). However more recent work by RILEY (1961) indicates that the oxygen pressure in equilibrium with the dioxide at its melting point is approximately one atmosphere, and measurement under these conditions yields a value for the melting point close to 2,400°C.

Values of the thermal expansion coefficient of $PuO_2$ are listed in *Table 4.9*. Experiments of BRETT and RUSSELL (1960) yield a mean value of $9·7 \times 10^{-6}$ c.g.s. units over the temperature range 25–1,000°C: these authors have

TABLE 4.9

THE COEFFICIENT OF LINEAR THERMAL EXPANSION OF $PuO_2$
(Chikalla, 1960)

| Temp. (°C) | Mean coefficient of linear expansion (c.g.s. units $\times 10^6$) |
|:---:|:---:|
| 75–100 | 9·04 |
| 25–500 | 10·02 |
| 75–775 | 11·16 |
| 775–950 | 14·38 |

shown, furthermore, that the coefficient rises for 'oxygen depleted' samples up to a mean value of $13 \times 10^{-6}$ c.g.s. units (25–1,000°C) at the approximate composition $Pu_4O_7$.

The microstructural properties of $PuO_2$ powders prepared by various methods have been described by FRANCIS and SOWDEN (1959). (See Volume 2, Section 4.6.1.)

*Plutonia–urania*

It was shown by MULFORD and ELLINGER (1958) that $UO_2$ and $PuO_2$ form a continuous series of solid solutions, with essentially linear variation in the lattice parameter over the whole range of composition. Moreover, $PuO_2$ exerts a stabilizing effect on the fluorite structure of $UO_2$ analogous to that produced by $ThO_2$ (Section 4.2.1), so that above a $PuO_2$ content of about 40 per cent, the cubic structure is retained on heating in air (Fox and BRETT, 1962). Although the exact limit of this stabilization has not been accurately defined, it is doubtful if $UO_2 . PuO_2$ powders up to the maximum composition likely to be of interest to fast reactors (*ca.* 30 per cent $PuO_2$) could be sintered in air without nucleation of the $U_3O_8$-like phase.

The $UO_2 . PuO_2$ system is complicated by the fact that one oxide has a tendency to oxidize and the other a tendency to reduce. The tendency of $PuO_2$ to lose oxygen with the formation of the $\alpha$-$Pu_2O_3$ phase is unfortunately retained even when the oxide is in solid solution with $UO_2$, at least when the concentration of $PuO_2$ is greater than 20 per cent, and this introduces complications into the sintering technology which are absent from $UO_2 \cdot ThO_2$. The phase information so far available has emerged from studies primarily devoted to sintering, and it is best discussed under this heading (q.v.).

Only limited information is available on the physical properties of $UO_2 \cdot PuO_2$ solid solutions. Preliminary studies of the melting point over a limited range of composition have been made by PIJANOWSKI and DELUCA (1960) whose results are reproduced in *Figure 4.30*. The melting points

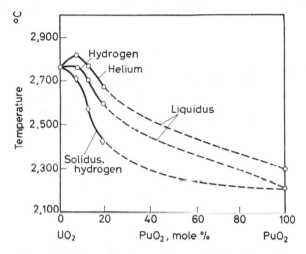

*Figure 4.30.* Approximate melting points in the system $UO_2 \cdot PuO_2$ (Pijanowski and DeLuca, 1960) (by courtesy of U.S.A.E.C.).

obtained in a hydrogen atmosphere are lower than those in a helium atmosphere, apparently due to formation of $\alpha$-$Pu_2O_3$ under reducing conditions; no quantitative estimates of the degree of reduction were made, however. A liquidus line in helium has also been reported by CHIKALLA (1959), and this is in fair agreement with that of Pijanowski and DeLuca. For the present, however, the data in *Figure 4.30* should be regarded only as approximate, particularly as no account has been taken of possible dissociation in a helium atmosphere.

The only data on thermal expansion has been reported by BRETT and RUSSELL (1960), who found that the presence of one per cent of $PuO_2$ has no significant effect on the coefficient of thermal expansion of $UO_2$.

### 4.3.2 Densification Studies

*Plutonium dioxide*

Work on the production of dense pellets of plutonium dioxide was carried out at Harwell by RUSSELL (1961), who was able to prepare compacts having a density up to 94 per cent of theoretical by dry-pressing powder (derived from oxalate) and sintering at 1,500°C in hydrogen saturated with water vapour at room temperature.

The mode of preparation of the powder exerted a significant influence on the sintering behaviour. It was found that the highest densities were obtained using oxide prepared by calcination of the oxalate at 700–800°C. Presumably powder calcined at lower temperatures retained traces of oxalate which decomposed during sintering and caused 'bloating' of the pellet (cf. the behaviour of thoria prepared from oxalate, Section 4.2.2), while calcination above 800°C promoted crystallite growth within the pseudomorphs and decreased the surface area of the oxide (cf. Volume 2, *Figure 4.35*).

Russell made interesting observations of the effect of oxygen in the sintering atmosphere. The densities in *Table 4.10* were obtained after sintering for four hours in hydrogen–oxygen mixtures.

TABLE 4.10

SINTERING OF PLUTONIUM DIOXIDE IN HYDROGEN (1 atm) CONTAINING
VARIOUS PARTIAL PRESSURES OF OXYGEN (Russell, 1961)

| Temperature (°C) | Partial pressure of oxygen (atm) | Sintered density (g cm$^{-3}$) |
|:---:|:---:|:---:|
| 1,300 | $10^{-15}$ | 8·5 |
|  | $10^{-10}$ | 9·4 |
| 1,400 | $10^{-15}$ | 9·3 |
|  | $10^{-10}$ | 10·0 |
|  | $10^{-5}$ | 9.5 |
| 1,500 | $10^{-15}$ | 10·0 |
|  | $10^{-10}$ | 10·4 |
|  | $10^{-5}$ | 9·7 |
| 1,600 | $10^{-15}$ | 10·2 |
|  | $10^{-10}$* | 10·5 |
|  | $10^{-5}$ | 10·0 |

\* Hydrogen saturated with water vapour at room temperature.

The highest density at each temperature was achieved with a partial pressure of oxygen about $10^{-10}$ atm; at this pressure the oxide has an equilibrium O/Pu ratio between 1·98 and 2·00 at all the temperatures studied. It would be of interest to ascertain if this slightly substoichiometric composition exerts a parallel effect on the self-diffusion of plutonium in the oxide.

*Plutonia–urania*

Studies of the sintering behaviour of $UO_2 . PuO_2$ solid solutions and of $UO_2 + PuO_2$ mixed mechanically have been carried out in several laboratories and, although the mechanism of the process is not yet fully understood, it is possible to deduce general relationships between the densities obtained and important parameters such as mode of preparation of the oxide, sintering temperature and sintering atmosphere.

When separately prepared $UO_2$ and $PuO_2$ powders are mechanically mixed, cold pressed and heated at temperatures around 1,500°C, two processes take place simultaneously: a solid solution is formed by inter-diffusion of the cations, and densification occurs, presumably by a bulk diffusion process. Studies of the densification of mixed powders in atmospheres of argon and of hydrogen were made by RUSSELL *et al.* (1960) using $UO_2$ from ADU (surface area 6 $m^2$ $g^{-1}$) and $PuO_2$ from oxalate (surface area 28 $m^2$ $g^{-1}$). It was found that mixtures which were sintered within the temperature range 1,400–1,700°C in argon resulted in pellets consisting only of a fluorite phase. Mixtures sintered in hydrogen, on the other hand exhibited (above a $PuO_2$ concentration of 20 per cent) a second phase of $\alpha$-$Pu_2O_3$, probably formed by reduction of $PuO_2$ before solid solution was complete. The sintered densities attained in each atmosphere after firing for 2 hours at 1,650°C are shown

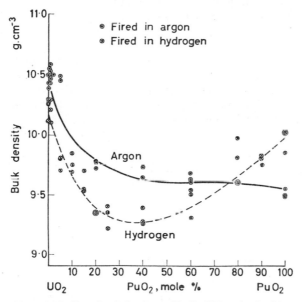

*Figure 4.31.* Sintering behaviour of $PuO_2$–$UO_2$ mixed oxides at 1,650°C in argon and hydrogen (Russell *et al.*, 1960) (by courtesy of U.K.A.E.A.).

in *Figure 4.31.* Curves similar to that in hydrogen have been observed by CHIKALLA (1959, 1960) over a range of sintering temperatures between 1,200 and 1,600°C (though a report of the absence of $\alpha$-$Pu_2O_3$ formation made by this author has been modified in the light of later experience).

Further work at Harwell by HARRISON *et al.* (1961) has established that hydrogen-sintered compacts (prepared from mixed powders) containing 5 to 15 per cent plutonium had an oxygen/metal ratio of 1·98–1·99, and moreover that about 30 per cent of the plutonium was insoluble in nitric acid. Solid solution formation could be promoted by sintering in an oxidizing atmosphere. Carbon dioxide was particularly effective and, following prolonged ball-milling of the powders, 99·7 per cent of the plutonium was found to pass into solid solution after a sintering period of 4 hours at 1,400°C, giving a compact density about 95 per cent of theoretical. The resulting pellet, however, had an oxygen/metal ratio of about 2·1, and, if an analogy can be drawn with pure $UO_2$, would be expected to exhibit poor behaviour under irradiation. Harrison *et al.* have shown that near-stoichiometric material can be produced by using a less oxidizing atmosphere of $CO_2/CO$ (though this tends to decrease the rate of formation of solid solution), or alternatively by sintering in $CO_2$ and cooling in the mixed atmosphere. Other possible gaseous mixtures for controlling the O/M ratio are wet hydrogen or nitrogen/oxygen mixtures. The precise composition of the mixed atmosphere has yet to be determined in relation to the U/Pu ratio desired, but the work of Harrison has pointed the way, starting from mechanically mixed powders, to obtain high density, solid solution and a good control of oxygen/metal ratios. The tolerable deviation from an O/M ratio of 2·00 (particularly on the substoichiometric side) can only be ascertained by irradiation tests.

A method alternative to mixing separately prepared $PuO_2$ and $UO_2$—and one more attractive from the viewpoint of recycling—is to coprecipitate plutonium and uranium from nitrate solution as a compound which can be reduced to a solid solution of the oxide. This method of fuel production is favoured by workers on the Fast Oxide Breeder Programme of the U.S.A.E.C. (DAVIDSON *et al.*, 1957, 1959), who have employed co-precipitation from nitrate solution with ammonia, followed by reduction in hydrogen to a $UO_2.PuO_2$ powder, which is cold-pressed and sintered.

TABLE 4.11

DATA OBTAINED DURING PREPARATION OF $UO_2.PuO_2$ SINTERED PELLETS
(Harrison *et al.*, 1961)

| Plutonium content % | Mixed (M) or co-precipitated (C) | Atmosphere | Sintering temp. °C (4 h) | Density g cm⁻³ | Per cent theoretical |
|---|---|---|---|---|---|
| 1 | M | $H_2$ | 1,400 | 8·4 | 76 |
| 1 | M | $H_2$ | 1,500 | 10·1 | 92 |
| 1 | C | $H_2$ | 1,500 | 10·6 | 96·5 |
| 1 | M | $CO_2$ | 1,400 | 10·6 | 96·5 |
| 1 | C | $CO_2$ | 1,550 | 9·9 | 90 |
| 10 | M | $CO_2$ | 1,550 | 10·6 | 96·5 |
| 10 | M | $H_2$ | 1,650 | 9·7 | 88 |
| 10 | C | $CO_2$ | 1,550 | 10·0 | 91 |
| 10 | C | $H_2$ | 1,550 | 10·5 | 96 |

At first sight, it would appear that the employment of a powder with the oxides in solid solution would eliminate the possibility of reduction on sintering in hydrogen. Preliminary results obtained at Harwell by BRETT (1962), however, indicate that at levels of plutonium higher than about 40 per cent, some reduction does take place with the formation of a second cubic phase, $(U, Pu)O_{2-n}$: at lower plutonium levels the position is still obscure, and any slight reduction taking place would seem to be tolerable if it does not result in inferior irradiation behaviour. At all events, powders prepared by coprecipitation certainly sinter to higher densities in hydrogen than do those prepared by mixing, as shown by the data in *Table 4.11*, obtained with mixed and coprecipitated powders at plutonium levels of 1 and 10 per cent.

Conversely, mixed powders at the one per cent level show better sintering behaviour in $CO_2$ than do the coprecipitated powders, though a systematic study of the effect of coprecipitation is needed before this can be regarded as a general effect.

A detailed study of the preparation of $UO_2.1\%$ $PuO_2$ powders by co-precipitation has been made by workers at Harwell (SOWDEN, AINSLEY and STOCKDALE, 1962), who used precipitation with ammonia from mixed nitrate solution as an initial step, and reduced the precipitate either directly in hydrogen at 900°C or else by way of $U_3O_8.PuO_2$ at 700°C. Batchwise precipitation tended to yield powders with irreproducible sintering characteristics, and the best results were obtained using continuous precipitation at a constant pH. A wide range of precipitation conditions (pH 7–10, temperature 25–98°C, aqueous or gaseous ammonia) yielded powders which sintered readily to a density of $10.5 \pm 0.15$ g cm$^{-3}$ on firing for 2 hours in hydrogen at 1,500–1,550°C. Considerably lower densities ($\sim 9$ g cm$^{-3}$) were obtained if a sintering atmosphere of carbon dioxide was employed instead of hydrogen. In the absence of plutonium, $UO_2$ prepared under identical conditions sintered at 1,550°C in hydrogen to low densities mostly in the range 8.6–9.6 g cm$^{-3}$; this indicates that the presence of one per cent $PuO_2$ is beneficial to the sintering of $UO_2$ in hydrogen. At such low concentrations, it is impossible to decide from x-ray data whether or not the powder contains $PuO_2$ completely in solid solution prior to sintering, but the fact that all powders dissolved readily in nitric acid without the addition of fluoride is strong evidence for the absence of crystallites containing a high proportion of plutonium.

Interesting observations were made of the effect of plutonium valency on the efficiency of co-precipitation. It was established that true coprecipitation took place only between U(VI) and Pu(IV) (as 'ADU/Pu(OH)$_4$'), and that Pu(VI) formed a stable colloid at high pH, which tended to become adsorbed on the surface of the ADU. To rely on such an uncontrolled adsorption process would be undesirable in a full-scale production process, and it is better that the plutonium should be conditioned to the quadrivalent state with hydrogen peroxide prior to precipitation.

Alternative methods to coprecipitation and powder mixing may be applicable in the production of $UO_2.PuO_2$ fuel, particularly when the plutonium is at the low level required in thermal reactors. It is possible (i) to adsorb the plutonium as Pu(IV) colloid on to the surface of finely divided $UO_2$ or (ii) to introduce plutonium dissolved in a suitable solvent (e.g. Pu(VI) in hexone) which also contains the organic binder. Preliminary experiments by Sowden et al. have shown that both of these techniques appears to be capable of successful development.

Ammonium diuranate precipitated continuously tends to settle and filter slowly (Section 4.1.4), and the properties of plutonium-bearing ADU are no better. SOWDEN, AINSLEY and STOCKDALE (1962) have investigated other methods of coprecipitating plutonium and uranium at a plutonium level varying between 15 and 50 per cent, the range of interest for fast reactor fuel. A precipitate of outstanding filtration and settling qualities was produced by coprecipitation from a solution of U(IV), Pu(III) nitrate with oxalic acid.

In *Table 4.13* are compared the filtration and settling properties of continuously precipitated ADU and oxalate having plutonium contents between

0 and 50 per cent. The specific filtration resistance is the parameter of CARMAN (1938) and the settling constant is derived by approximating the Kozeny equations quoted by ALLISON and MURRAY (1953): the volume of filtrate passing in time $t$ is proportional to $r_1^{-1/2}$ and the hindered settling rate at a given concentration of solids to $(\rho/S)^2$. The properties of the oxalate precipitates are vastly superior over the whole range of composition. Sintering tests on oxides derived from both materials (15 per cent Pu) demonstrated that densities of between 10·0 and 10·5 g cm$^{-3}$ could be attained on sintering for 4 hours at 1,550°C in an atmosphere of either $H_2$ or $CO_2$.

TABLE 4.12

COMPARISON OF THE PROPERTIES OF TWO TYPES OF PRECIPITATE AT VARIOUS CONCENTRATIONS
OF PLUTONIUM: U(VI) Pu(IV)—AMMONIA, AND U(IV) Pu(III)—OXALIC ACID
(Sowden, Ainsley and Stockdale, 1962)

| | Plutonium content (relative to total metal %) | Conditions of precipitation | Specific filtration resistance, $r_1$ (c.g.s. units $\times 10^{-10}$) | Settling constant $\rho/S$ (c.g.s. units $\times 10^5$) | Density of settled bed at onset of compaction (g l.$^{-1}$) |
|---|---|---|---|---|---|
| U(VI) Pu(IV) —ammonia | 0 | pH 9·0 ± 0·2 | 38 | 0·67 | 25 |
| | 15 | ,, | 22 | 0·84 | 35 |
| | 30 | ,, | 24 | 1·10 | 40 |
| | 50 | ,, | 30 | 1·32 | 45 |
| U(IV) Pu(III) —oxalic acid | 0 | 10% excess oxalic acid | 0·060 | 8·1 | 420 |
| | 15 | ,, | 0·032 | 10·6 | 490 |
| | 30 | ,, | 0·071 | 14·0 | 570 |
| | 50 | ,, | 0·10 | 10·2 | 300 |

The aim of most of the work on urania–plutonia systems so far reported has been to produce a dense body having plutonium distributed throughout it as homogeneously as possible. At Chalk River, however, MICHAUD and BOUCHER (1961) have pursued a novel approach, and have endeavoured to keep the plutonia as discrete refractory solid particles embedded in a matrix of $UO_2$. This type of fuel might permit the plutonium bred from the uranium during residence in the reactor to be separated from the original plutonium, and so reduce contamination with higher plutonium isotopes. Michaud established (by using a coarse, high fired sample of $PuO_2$ and minimizing the time of sintering) that the extent of solid solution of a $UO_2 . 2\% PuO_2$ mixture could be reduced to a few per cent (as measured by the proportion of plutonium soluble after prolonged leaching with nitric acid). No irradiation tests have been reported so far however, and it is likely that considerable solid solution formation would take place during the residence of the fuel in a reactor. In any case, it seems that the economic advantages of such a dispersion type fuel would be marginal.

In summary, although the groundwork for the production of $UO_2 . PuO_2$ fuels has now been covered, detailed studies are required to define the optimum production conditions. Particular attention must be given to investigating the irradiation properties of fuel pieces having sub-stoichiometric composition, $(U, Pu)O_{2-n}$: only when evidence on this point is available can the importance or otherwise of fabricating fuel of stoichiometric composition be assessed.

### 4.3.3 Irradiation Studies

It is somewhat anomalous that most of the irradiation experiments on $UO_2 . PuO_2$ fuels so far reported have been carried out with powders. Although the expense of high-temperature sintering is avoided in a powder fuel element, the fission gas release is inevitably high: this penalty is a large one, and although it might be tolerated if the external pressure on the fuel can were large (as, for example, in a pressurized water reactor), it is unlikely to be accepted for a gas-cooled thermal reactor. In a fast reactor, a strong can might make the powder concept worthy of serious consideration, though the implications of an extremely low thermal conductivity in a very highly rated system must be carefully assessed.

The first results on the irradiation of $UO_2 . PuO_2$ powders were obtained with oxide containing 20 per cent plutonium prepared by co-precipitation, and dry-pressed to small compacts ($0 \cdot 19$ in. diameter $\times 1$ in. length) having a density 65 per cent of theoretical (CASHIN, 1957; HANDWERK, 1957). Samples were irradiated in stainless steel cans, one to a burn-up of 5 per cent of the Pu atoms (surface temperature ca. 700°C). No distortion of the stainless steel cans was noted, but the powder had sintered, and it had melted in the centre and formed a void. No gas release measurements were made, and no quantitative deductions can be drawn from these tests.

Irradiation experiments in support of the Hanford Plutonium Recycle Programme have been reported by BATES and ROAKE (1959). A powder of nominal composition $UO_2 . 1\% PuO_2$ was prepared by mixing $UO_2 . 20\%$ $PuO_2$ with natural $UO_2$, and this was vibrationally compacted into zircaloy tubes (9·37 in. long, 0·56 in. o.d.) to a density of 4·7 g cm$^{-3}$. The fuel element was irradiated in water at 40°C in a flux of $1 \cdot 2 \times 10^{14}$ n cm$^{-2}$ sec$^{-1}$ to a total fissile atom burn-up of about 0·15 per cent. As in the experiments of Cashin, considerable sintering took place, and a central void was formed. A second phase (possibly $(U, Pu)O_{2-x}$) was found in the region of high density columnar grains which were formed adjacent to the central void.

The only experience on the irradiation of sintered pellets has been reported by SAYERS and WORTH (1961) who have compared the behaviour of $UO_2 . 1\%$ $PuO_2$ pellets with that of enriched $UO_2$ pellets irradiated under essentially identical conditions (ratings 25–35 W g$^{-1}$, centre temperatures 1,700–2,500°C, burn-up 2,000–3,000 MWd/T). From post irradiation examination, they conclude that fission gas release and grain growth behaviour are the same for both fuels.

There is clearly a need for further irradiation data on high density pellets of known history and composition, and experiments now in progress at Harwell and Hanford should give valuable information. The concept of integrated thermal conductivity should be applied to the results at the outset, and careful attention must be given to the release of volatile fission products and its dependence upon the plutonium and the oxygen contents of the fuel.

### 4.4 URANIUM CARBIDES

Compared with the enormous effort which has been devoted to the development of oxides as ceramic fuels, the work on other compounds has so far been very limited. However, it is obvious that the need in highly rated systems for a fuel having improved thermal conductivity, coupled with a possible demand for a higher fissile atom density than the maximum afforded by oxides, will give impetus to the development of other fuel systems, particularly carbides and nitrides.

At the time of writing, interest in carbides is quickening. It has been established that uranium monocarbide retains a fairly good thermal conductivity at higher temperatures (cf. $UO_2$, Section 4.1.2), and moreover that its irradiation stability (at least when fabricated by melting and casting) appears to be very good. These observations have encouraged more intensive studies of carbide systems, and a number of laboratories have embarked on extensive programmes involving the carbides of uranium and plutonium: although much of this work is of a preliminary nature, the following sections will review the progress reported up to the time of writing, and will indicate what difficulties must be overcome for the development of carbide fuels to be successful.

#### 4.4.1 Phase Relationships and General Properties

Three carbides of uranium have been identified; their general properties are summarized in *Table 4.13*.

TABLE 4.13

THE CARBIDES OF URANIUM

| Composition | Crystal Structure | Theoretical density (g cm⁻³) | Melting point (°C) |
|---|---|---|---|
| UC | Face-centred cubic | 13·63 | 2,400 ± 100 |
| $U_2C_3$ | Body-centred cubic | 12·88 | Decomposes to $UC + UC_2$ at *ca.* 1,700°C |
| $UC_2$ | Tetragonal [cubic fluorite (or pyrites) structure exists above 1,800°C.] Tetragonal $UC_2$ is unstable with respect to $U_2C_3 + C$ below ∼ 1,300°C | 11·68 | 2,475 ± 25 |

The structure of the monocarbide and dicarbide was determined by LITZ *et al.* (1948), and RUNDLE *et al.* (1948); the existence of the sesquicarbide was established by MALLET, GERDS and VAUGHAN (1950), who showed that the compound could be formed by heating a mixture of the monocarbide and dicarbide between 1,250 and 1,800°C: a slight amount of physical stressing was necessary to initiate the reaction.

A phase diagram for the uranium–carbon system was first published by

MALLET *et al.* (1952). Since that time work at the Batelle Memorial Institute has continued, and a number of refinements have been introduced. A diagram published by CHUBB and ROUGH (1960) is reproduced in *Figure 4.32*; the details of this may be subject to later modification. Thus, workers at Harwell (WILLIAMS *et al.*, 1960) have found a retrogressive solubility of uranium in UC which reaches a maximum of about 1 at. % at 1,800°C, and details at the carbon-rich end of the diagram at high temperature are still in considerable doubt. The difficulties of determining the phase diagram are accentuated by the ready inclusion of oxygen and nitrogen impurities.

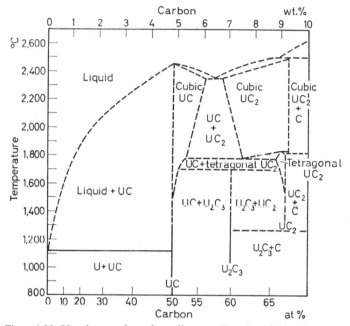

*Figure 4.32.* Uranium–carbon phase diagram (Rough and Chubb, 1960)
(by the courtesy of U.S.A.E.C.).

A high temperature x-ray investigation of the uranium–carbon system has been reported by WILSON (1960), and neutron diffraction studies at room temperature by AUSTIN (1959). Confirmation of the tetragonal-cubic transformation of $UC_2$ at 1,850°C has been obtained by the high temperature x-ray studies of BREDIG (1960).

Most fuel development work so far has concentrated on the monocarbide, which has the highest theoretical density. It is probable that the dicarbide will also assume importance, particularly as a fuel contained in a graphite matrix (BENZIGER and ROHWER, 1961).

*Physical properties*

Although the melting point data of various authors (e.g. MALLET *et al.* (1952), NEWKIRK and BATES (1959)), range from 2,250 to about 2,500°C there is little doubt that UC melts at a temperature some three hundred degrees lower than $UO_2$. This disadvantage is offset, however, by a greatly improved thermal conductivity which appears to show little dependence upon temperature up to 1,100°C (*Figure 4.33*). Comparing these data with those in *Figure 4.3*, it is apparent that the thermal conductivity of UC is about six times as high as that of $UO_2$ at 1,000°C; moreover, it appears that variation in carbon content over the range 4·8 to 5·3 w/o does not have a pronounced effect upon thermal conductivity.

No examination of the dependence of the thermal conductivity of $UC_2$ upon temperature has yet been reported; the value at 50°C is high (0·082 cal $sec^{-1}$ $cm^{-1}$ $deg^{-1}$ C at a density of 10·0 g $cm^{-3}$) (BAKER, 1946).

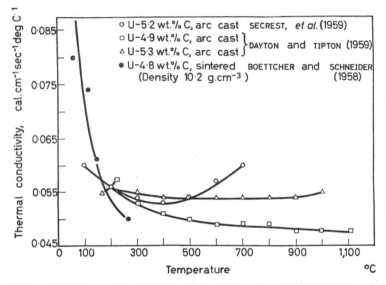

*Figure 4.33*. Thermal conductivity of uranium monocarbide (Rough and Chubb, 1960) (by courtesy of U.S.A.E.C.).

Values of the specific heat of the monocarbide and dicarbide up to 2,000°C are reported as follows:

UC : $\quad C_p = 7\cdot6 + (2\cdot85.10^{-3})\,T$ $\quad$ (TRIPLER *et al.*, 1959)
$UC_2$: $\quad C_p = 8\cdot92 + (3\cdot95.10^{-3})\,T$ $\quad$ (BOETTCHER and SCHNEIDER, 1958)

Recorded values of the mean coefficients of thermal expansion over the range of temperature 200–950°C are

UC : $\quad 11\cdot4.10^{-6}\,deg^{-1}\,C$ $\quad$ (SECREST *et al.*, 1959)
$UC_2$: $\quad 14\cdot2.10^{-6}\,deg^{-1}\,C$ $\quad$ (TRIPLER *et al.*, 1959)

In view of the now established instability of $UC_2$ below about 1,300°C, it is uncertain whether these physical properties refer to a metastable dicarbide or to a mixture of $UC_2$, $U_2C_3$ and C.

A summary of the mechanical properties of UC and $UC_2$ has been presented by STRASSER (1960). The mechanical properties of uranium monocarbide are in general superior to those of $UO_2$; for example, the bend strength at room temperature is greater by a factor of three.

*Chemical properties*

All the carbides of uranium react readily with oxygen and water, particularly when they are in a finely divided state, though quantitative data on the reactivities are lacking. Qualitative claims have been made, for example, that UC ignites spontaneously in air if the particle diameter is less than 40 microns, and that $UC_2$ is more readily hydrolysed than UC, but these claims deserve further scrutiny. It is generally accepted that carbides in powder form must be handled in an inert atmosphere, though the tolerable limits of oxygen and water vapour with respect to carbon content and physical condition of the carbides have yet to be specified.

The compatibility of bulk uranium monocarbide with cladding materials and coolants will be discussed in Section 4.4.3.

### 4.4.2 Production and Densification

*Production*

The carbides of uranium may be prepared by one of three main routes:

(i) **The** direct combination of metal with carbon
(ii) **The** reaction of finely divided metal with a gaseous hydrocarbon
(iii) **The** reduction of an oxide with carbon.

The first method may involve the melting of uranium metal with graphite, and has been employed as a prelude to casting the bulk carbide (e.g. SECREST *et al.*, 1959). Another technique consists of cold compacting metal powder with graphite, and forming the carbide *in situ* by heating to about 1,100°C *in vacuo*: this has been used to produce dense bodies of the carbide, and will be discussed in more detail below.

*The methane–metal reaction.* The production of uranium monocarbide by the reaction

$$U + CH_4 \xrightarrow{\text{600–900°C}} UC + 2H_2$$

was first employed by LITZ *et al.* (1948). Finely divided metal is required for the reaction, and this can be produced by first reacting bulk metal with hydrogen at 275°C; the $UH_3$ subsequently decomposes on raising the temperature. Several hydriding and carburization stages may be necessary to ensure complete reaction, and it is advisable to remove surface oxide from the bulk uranium (e.g. by treating with nitric acid) prior to hydriding the metal. The reaction sequence can result in a finely divided carbide powder, but the work of several laboratories indicates that controlling the carbon content of the final product presents considerable difficulty (BARNES *et al.*, 1956; KALISH and LYTTON, 1959, 1960, 1961; KORCHYNSKY, 1960, 1961; FINLEY *et al.*, 1960; MOREAU, 1960; ROUGH and CHUBB, 1960). According to STANDRING and TWIGG (1960) the reaction tends to be incomplete below 700°C and the product is a mixture of UC and uranium metal, while at temperatures above 800°C a mixture of the dicarbide and monocarbide is formed. The optimum reaction temperature appears to be in the neighbourhood of 750°C, under which conditions Kalish and Lytton have obtained 100 g batches of UC after reaction with methane (flow rate 5 l. min⁻¹) for 2 hours. It is most important to use highly pure methane, as nitrogen and oxygen will react readily with the finely divided metal. Carefully controlled

175

preparations described by FINLEY et al. (1960) resulted in oxygen levels of between 0·13 and 1·1 wt. % Kalish and Lytton have carried out carburization with propane at 700°C, but extensive deposition of free carbon was observed: a similar difficulty was encountered earlier by LITZ (1948) and by LOCH et al. (1956), using acetylene. The preparation of 'pure' uranium monocarbide by reaction between pre-hydrided metal and propane at 700°C in a static system has been claimed by SANO et al. (1959) but no analytical details are given.

It appears at present that although gas carburization seems to be an attractive method for producing carbide from metal on a laboratory scale, considerable development work will be necessary to adapt the method to a large-scale production process, particularly with regard to control of carbon content and purity of the product.

*The oxide–carbon reaction.* Direct reduction of an oxide with carbon has a particular appeal as a method of large-scale production in that it eliminates the need for production of the metal as an intermediate process.

It was originally considered (e.g. LOCH et al., 1956; BARNES et al., 1956) that a temperature of 1,800–1,900°C was necessary for the reaction

$$UO_2 + 3C \rightarrow UC + 2CO$$

to proceed in the direction of carbide at a reasonable rate, and a temperature of 1,800°C was advocated by LITZ et al. (1948) for the carbon reduction of $U_3O_8$. However, recent work at Harwell by AINSLEY and SOWDEN (1961) has established that, provided carbon monoxide is removed rapidly enough to maintain a low pressure of the gas over the reacting mixture, a reasonably high rate of reaction can be achieved at temperatures in the region of 1,400°C. The Harwell workers have established that the equilibrium pressure of carbon monoxide over the reaction mixture can be expressed approximately by the equation

$$\log p \, (\text{atm}) = 8\cdot57 - \frac{18,500}{T \, (°K)}$$

over the range 1,150–1,400°C. Thus at 1,400°C, the pressure of CO at which reaction ceases entirely is only $3\cdot2 \times 10^{-3}$ atm.

Kinetic experiments have been performed under high vacuum conditions, using the rate of evolution of gas as a measure of the reaction. It was shown that first order kinetics (with respect to oxide) were obeyed approximately: first order rate constants (1,200–1,450°C) obtained with powders of fused $UO_2$ (particle size 2–20 microns) mixed with carbon (30 m² g⁻¹) and pelleted at 10 ton in.⁻² fell within a range expressed by

$$k \, (\text{sec}^{-1}) = (7\cdot5 \pm 1\cdot5) \times 10^8 \exp \left( \frac{-92,000}{RT} \right)$$
$$\text{(zero pressure CO)}$$

The rate showed no significant variation with particle size over the range examined. After heating the mixture for 2 hours at 1,450°C, the level of oxygen was reduced to $\leqslant 0\cdot3$ wt. %. In American laboratories LIED (1960) has prepared kilogramme batches of UC containing 0·1 wt. % oxygen by heating oxide–carbon pellets at 1,600°C for 8 hours, while TAYLOR (1960) has reduced the

176

oxygen level to 0·2 wt. % after reacting at 1,750°C for 4 hours. Further research is required to ascertain the final level of oxygen attainable and its dependence upon time and temperature: it is worth noting, however, that the oxygen contents usually quoted for material obtained from the methane–metal reaction are higher than the figures given above.

Little is so far known of the mechanism of the $UO_2$–C reaction, though there is some evidence that the dicarbide (which has been found in incompletely reacted mixtures) is an intermediate product. The equilibrium pressures observed probably refer to the reaction

$$UO_2 + 4C \rightleftharpoons UC_2 + 2CO$$

but there is some discrepancy between this assumption and existing thermodynamic data for $UC_2$ (RAND and KUBASCHEWSKI, 1960).

It is clear that the reduction of oxides with carbon offers wide scope for fundamental study. From the technical viewpoint, the reaction appears to offer a promising method of manufacturing uranium carbides, both as stock for melting and casting and as powder for pressing and sintering; in the latter case, the oxygen content of the product may exert an important effect on the sintering behaviour, and therefore deserves careful attention. A possible improvement on the vacuum production process would be to remove the carbon monoxide in a stream of flowing inert gas: at temperatures below 1,500°C, however, the reaction rate might be slowed down considerably if a laminar layer of carbon monoxide were formed adjacent to the surface of the solid reactants.

Other methods of producing uranium carbides have shown little promise. Preliminary work on the reduction of $UF_6$ with hydrogen and acetylene at 1,800°C has been carried out at Battelle Memorial Institute (CHUBB and ROUGH, 1960); although uranium monocarbide is formed the product is invariably heavily contaminated with fluoride, and the method is therefore unsuited to large-scale development.

*Densification*

*Melting and casting.* Because the melting point of UC is several hundred degrees lower than that of $UO_2$, the fabrication of dense bodies by melting and casting becomes a more practical proposition, and considerable effort has been devoted to the development of suitable techniques (e.g. GRAY et al., 1958; SECREST et al., 1958, 1959; KALISH et al., 1959; ROUGH and CHUBB, 1960; PHILLIPS, CHUBB and FOSTER, 1960; BROWN and STOBO, 1961). In most of the work reported so far, a mixture of uranium and graphite has been used as starting material, and great care is necessary to obtain a homogeneous mixture; however the same processes could be applied to ready formed UC powder (prepared, for example, by the oxide–carbon reaction).

For the preparation of small casts (up to ca. 100 g), melting on a water-cooled copper hearth has been employed, followed by drop-casting in a graphite mould: by this method, sound cylindrical castings of diameter up to $\frac{3}{8}$ in. have been fabricated having a density between 98 and 99·5 per cent of theoretical. Melting is effected by striking an arc between a non-consumable graphite electrode and the charge, and although conditions must be carefully controlled to minimize carbon pickup, it is possible to reproduce the carbon content in a sample to within $\pm 0\cdot1$ wt. %. For the preparation of larger pieces, it is expedient to employ a skull melting technique (again using a graphite electrode) in which a molten bath of carbide is built up in a solid 'skull' of the same composition; the melt is then tilt-poured into a preheated graphite mould, which is slowly cooled. Control of composition appears to be more difficult by this technique and $\pm 0\cdot3$ wt. % carbon in the final product is usually quoted: the use of tungsten electrodes has resulted in a high degree of contamination of the product (up to 3 per cent tungsten). It is possible that better control of composition will be afforded by the development of electron beam melting (ACCARY and CAILLAT, 1961), in which granulated carbide is melted continuously in an intense electron beam from which it runs into a mould; it appears that a better control of grain size and homogeneity is also attainable by this method.

Although melting and casting seems potentially a good technique for producing carbide shapes having a density very close to theoretical, considerable development work on quality control is required, and it seems certain that the method will be rather expensive. It is therefore desirable to seek alternative means of preparing dense compacts by the pressing and sintering of powders at temperatures below the melting point.

*Pressing and sintering of uranium monocarbide.* In Section 4.1.3 it was shown how, by using suitable cold-pressing and sintering techniques, uranium dioxide powder can be fabricated into dense bodies at temperatures of little more than half the melting point. Although similar work with uranium monocarbide is much less advanced, there is ample evidence that powders of this material sinter much less readily than $UO_2$, and that either higher sintering temperatures or a judicious choice of sintering atmosphere or of additives will be necessary to obtain bodies approaching theoretical density.

The sintering of powders produced by grinding arc-melted uranium monocarbide has been studied by TRIPLER *et al.* (1959). Powder of two size-fractions was employed, having average particle size of $14\cdot7$ and $6\cdot2$ microns respectively; cold pressing was carried out hydrostatically and the green compacts were sintered *in vacuo*. The data obtained are summarized in *Table 4.14*. In the latter half of the Table are later results reported by ROUGH and CHUBB (1960), who carried out extensive analyses on the material before and after sintering: these workers used end-pressing with binder-lubricants selected from cetyl alcohol in petroleum ether, camphor in methyl alcohol and Carbowax-6000 in methyl alcohol.

A striking general feature of *Table 4.14* is the low densities obtained after sintering at quite high temperatures. In only one example—using the finest powder and sintering at 1,900°C for 2 hours—was a density greater than 90 per cent of theoretical achieved: in other cases there was no distinct effect of particle size or forming pressure, though the final density tended to increase with sintering temperature and time. The changes in carbon content during sintering (measured for the last three samples) are intriguing.* There was insufficient oxygen initially present in the samples to account for loss by oxidation, and it must be concluded that a slight leak of oxygen into the furnace was sufficient to remove the carbon. This hypothesis is partly borne out by metallographic examination, for many of the sintered specimens were

* The carbon content of stoichiometric UC is 4.80 wt. %.

TABLE 4.14

SINTERING DATA OBTAINED WITH POWDERS OF GROUND, ARC-MELTED CARBIDE (Tripler et al, 1959; Rough and Chubb, 1960)

| Total carbon wt.% | | Oxygen wt.% | | Nitrogen wt.% | | Average particle diameter of powder (microns) | Forming pressure (p.s.i. × 10⁻³) | Sintering conditions | | Density of compact g cm⁻³ | | Sintered density % theoretical (relative to UC = 13·63) |
|---|---|---|---|---|---|---|---|---|---|---|---|---|
| Powder | Sintered compact | Powder | Sintered compact | Powder | Sintered compact | | | Time (h) | Temp. (°C) | Green | Sintered | |
| 4·96 | — | — | — | — | — | 6·2 | 50 | 1 | 1,600 | — | 10·3 | 75·6 |
| 5·06 | — | — | — | — | — | 14·7 | 50 | 1 | 1,600 | — | 10·0 | 73·3 |
| 4·96 | — | — | — | — | — | 6·2 | 100 | 1 | 1,600 | — | 10·0 | 73·3 |
| 5·06 | — | — | — | — | — | 14·7 | 100 | 1 | 1,600 | — | 10·3 | 75·6 |
| 4·96 | — | — | — | — | — | 6·2 | 100 | 3 | 1,600 | — | 11·2 | 82 |
| 4·96 | — | — | — | — | — | 6·2 | 100 | 1 | 1,800 | — | 11·3 | 83 |
| 4·96 | — | — | — | — | — | 6·2 | 100 | 3 | 1,800 | — | 11·8 | 87 |
| 4·94 | — | 0·27 | — | 0·015 | — | 20 | 30 | 0·5 | 1,700 | 9·2 | 10·5 | 77 |
| 4·94 | — | 0·27 | — | 0·015 | — | 20 | 30 | 2 | 1,700 | 9·2 | 10·8 | 79 |
| 4·94 | 4·55 | 0·27 | 0·19 | 0·015 | 0·011 | 20 | 30 | 2 | 1,900 | 9·2 | 11·3 | 83 |
| 4·83 | 4·37 | 0·079 | 0·14 | 0·011 | — | 25 | 30 | 1 | 1,950 | 8·8 | 11·2 | 82 |
| 4·94 | 4·32 | 0·79 | 0·36 | 0·015 | 0·012 | 4 | 30 | 2 | 1,900 | 9·1 | 12·8 | 94 |

179

found to possess two concentric regions of different grain size, the large grains in the outer region containing a uranium-rich grain boundary phase. Because of this finding the data must be treated with some reserve, though it is doubtful if the general conclusions are affected, for the presence of free uranium would be expected to improve the sintering qualities.

Cold-pressing and sintering of powders produced from hydrocarbon–metal or from oxide–carbon reactions has led to results very similar to those obtained with the arc-melted material; this is indicated by a brief summary of the available data in *Table 4.15*. The carbon content after sintering is reported only for the oxide-prepared material tested by Taylor *et al*. In most other cases the presence of metallic uranium in the sintered compact cannot be ruled out. The single experiment of Taylor in which the final carbon content was substantially below that of UC showed a final sintered density of 13·0: the values attained by Barnes *et al*. may well have been partly due to the presence of metallic uranium, for the carbon content of the starting product was significantly lower than 4·8 wt. %. Effects have been obtained with powder prepared by the metal–methane reaction which can be ascribed to the presence of free uranium. STANDRING and TWIGG (1960), for example, found that powder obtained after carburization of the metal for 8 hours at 750°C sintered in 30 min at 1,850°C to a density of 13·0 g cm$^{-3}$ or greater, while powder carburized for 13 hours gave a density of only 10·0 g cm$^{-3}$ after sintering under the same conditions. Similar observations were made by KALISH *et al*. (1959). When free uranium is present in the structure it is, of course, an artifice to consider the densities in relation to the theoretical density of uranium monocarbide. Thus the sintered density of the best sample in *Table 4.15* corresponds strictly to 89 per cent of theoretical; it is not possible to make this correction in the majority of the examples cited, since analysis of the sintered compact is not reported.

In summary, it must be concluded that many of the data on the sintering behaviour of uranium monocarbide are complicated by the presence of metallic uranium; although this might be expected to aid sintering, temperatures of the order of 2,000°C are needed to achieve densities of about 90 per cent of theoretical except with fine material (particle size $\sim 1\mu$) where a sintering temperature of 1,700–1,800°C might be sufficient. It is not possible from existing information to draw even qualitative conclusions about the effects of particle shape, and no attempt to measure surface areas has been recorded. Further careful experimental work is needed, with particular emphasis on maintaining purity both of materials and of sintering atmosphere; it is most important that the carbon content both before and after sintering should be measured.

If it is established that the sintering quality of uranium monocarbide powders cannot be substantially improved by changes in the mode of preparation or physical treatment, it becomes desirable to explore the possibility of reducing the sintering temperature by the use of additives. BARNES *et al*. (1956) obtained evidence that the addition of up to 10 wt. % of iron could lower the sintering temperature of UC prepared from oxide, a density of 11·9 g cm$^{-3}$ being attained on firing at a temperature as low as 1,500°C (time unspecified). More recent work at the University of Sheffield (WHITE *et al*., 1961) has provided information on the phase behaviour of metal–UC systems, and

TABLE 4.15

THE SINTERING PROPERTIES OF UC PRODUCED BY THE METHANE–METAL AND OXIDE–CARBON REACTIONS

| Powder preparation method | Total carbon wt. % | Oxygen wt. % | Nitrogen wt. % | Average particle size (microns) | Compacting pressure (p.s.i × 10³) | Sintering conditions (vacuum except where specified) | | Sintered density | | Reference |
|---|---|---|---|---|---|---|---|---|---|---|
| | | | | | | Time (h) | Temp. (°C) | g cm⁻³ | % theoretical (with respect to UC) | |
| Propane–metal | 4·68† | 0·56 | 0·16 | 8 | 30 | 1 | 1,900 | 11·4 | 84 | (a) |
| | 5·98† | 0·69 | 0·095 | 12 | 30 | 1 | 1,900 | 11·4 | 84 | (b) |
| Methane–metal | 4·84† | 0·70 | 0·70 | 10 | 40–200 | 1·5 | 2,050 | 10·7–12·5 | 79–92 § | |
| | 4·47–4·62† | — | — | 50–100 | 11 | 0·5 | 1,700 | 11·5 | 84 | (c) |
| | ,, | — | — | 50–100 | 11 | 0·5 | 1,900 | 12·1 | 89 | |
| | ,, | — | — | 20–40 | 22 | 1 | 2,000* | Up to 12·9 | Up to 95 | |
| | ,, | — | — | 20–40 | 22 | 0·5 | 2,100* | Up to 12·0 | 88 | |
| Oxide–carbon | 3·96† | 0·09 | 1·8 | 5 | 40 | 0·5 | 1,800* | 13·0 | 95 | (d) |
| | 4·72† | — | 0·1 | 5 | 40 | 1 | 1,800* | 8·6 | 63 | |
| | 4·80† | 0·04 | 0·02 | 5 | 40 | 1 | 1,800* | 10·0 | 73 | |
| | 4·87† | 0·63 | 0·04 | 5 | 40 | 0·5 | 1,800 | 9·4 | 69 | |
| | 4·75† | — | — | 5 | 40 | 1 | 1,900 | 10·0 | 73 | |
| | 4·75† | — | — | 2·5 | 40 | 1 | 1,950 | 10·65 | 78 | |
| | 4·75† | — | — | 0·5 | 40 | 1 | 1,850 | 12·50 | 92 | |

* Flowing argon.
† Before sintering.
‡ After sintering.
§ Following ballmilling of the powders, densities of up to 12·6 g cm⁻³ were obtained after 4 hours at 1,700°C

(a) Rough and Chubb (1960).
(b) Finley et al. (1959).
(c) Barnes et al. (1956).
(d) Taylor et al (1959, 1960).

181

indicates conditions under which sintering in the presence of a liquid phase might be attainable at a relatively low temperature. The tie lines of UC–UFe$_2$, UC–Fe and UC–Cr (in which no sign of solid solubility has been detected) are reproduced in *Figure 4.34*. In these three systems it is possible to obtain a liquid phase at 1,040, 1,160 and 1,420°C respectively. No work has so far been reported on the sintering of prepared UC in the presence of these additions; the sintering of U–C–X mixtures will be discussed below. Preliminary investigation of the tie lines of UC with nickel and cobalt has established that reaction with UC takes place above 1,300°C, and free carbon is deposited (WHITE *et al.*, 1961; BOETTCHER and SCHNEIDER, 1958). Nevertheless, it has

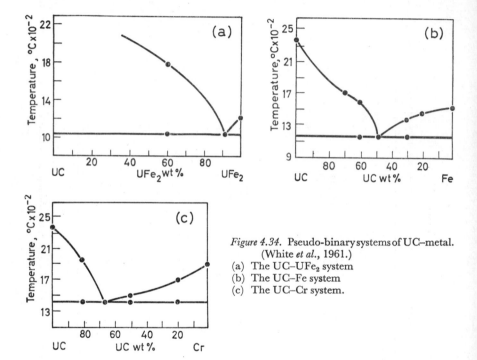

*Figure 4.34.* Pseudo-binary systems of UC–metal. (White *et al.*, 1961.)
(a) The UC–UFe$_2$ system
(b) The UC–Fe system
(c) The UC–Cr system.

been demonstrated that small quantities of nickel can greatly enhance the sintering of UC (KORCHYNSKY *et al.*, 1961; STRASSER and TAYLOR, 1961): the mechanism of this process is worthy of careful investigation. Reaction has been found to take place between UC and aluminium (THURBER ann BEAVER, 1959) molybdenum, tantalum (BOWMAN, 1959) and silicon (BOETTCHER and SCHNEIDER, 1958). Tentative ternary phase diagrams for a selection of U–C–metal systems have been presented by ROUGH and CHUBB (1960), but little sintering information is available.

No systematic study of the effect of sintering atmosphere has yet been made. It is possible that the presence of nitrogen, which would react at sintering temperature with monocarbide or free metal to form nitride, would assist in the elimination of voids: the mononitride and monocarbide form a continuous series of solid solutions (WILLIAMS and SAMBELL, 1959). There is, however, no firm evidence at the time of writing that the presence of nitrogen is beneficial.

Preliminary studies have been reported on hot pressing as a means of reducing the sintering temperature of UC. BARNES *et al.* (1956) attempted to hot press powders in a graphite die, but abandoned the method on account of the extensive formation of the dicarbide which took place at temperatures above about 1,200°C. Similar experience has been reported more recently by MEERSON *et al.* (1960). Workers at Batelle (ROUGH and CHUBB, 1960) have combined densification by hot pressing with metallurgical bonding to a can. For example, UC powders in a niobium can sintered to a density better than 95 per cent of theoretical after isostatic pressing in helium (5 ton in$^{-2}$) for 30 min at 1,430°C, and a metallurgical bond was formed between the specimen and the can. Even higher densities (up to 99 per cent of theoretical) could be obtained by adding 9 wt. % of molybdenum to the carbide powder. The method is worthy of further development, particularly as can-fuel bonding is very desirable in fuel elements for service in highly rated reactors.

*Pressing and sintering of the elements—'reaction sintering'.* The first work on the pressing and sintering of the powdered elements to form dense monocarbide *in situ* was carried out at Harwell by BARNES *et al.* (1956), and subsequent experience in several laboratories has been described by ROUGH and CHUBB (1960); ACCARY (1960); ACCARY and CAILLAT (1961); HEDGER and REGAN (1960); SINIZER (1960); REGAN and WILLIAMS (1961); BROWN and STOBO (1961); REGAN and HEDGER (1961).

It has been established that compacted uranium and graphite powders begin to react at approximately 800°C to give the monocarbide, and that after about 2 hours at 1,100°C the reaction is essentially complete. The density of the monocarbide is governed largely by the density of the compacted mixture before reaction: accordingly by choosing conditions under which a high degree of cold compaction is achieved, 'reaction sintered' monocarbide bodies having a density up to 92 per cent of theoretical can be prepared at a temperature of only 1,100°C. Important secondary effects on sintered density are attributable to the physical and chemical nature of the reactant powders. The highest sintered densities appear to have been obtained using a uranium powder of mean particle size 30 $\mu$ and a fine graphite of mean particle size 1–2 $\mu$ pressed at 40 ton in.$^{-2}$. The use of coarser graphites had little effect on the green density, but led to lower sintered densities: similar deleterious effects were observed on using uranium powder with an oxidized surface, and pickling in nitric acid to remove the oxide film is recommended.

An essential requirement of the method is rapid heating of the uranium–carbon compact. Hedger found that heating at 100–500°C h$^{-1}$ led to a volume expansion of up to 20 per cent, whereas heating at 300°C min$^{-1}$ by plunging specimens into a hot furnace reduced expansion to the 1–2 vol. % expected for the formation of monocarbide from the elements. The precise reasons why 'plunge sintering' is necessary are at present obscure; they are probably related to differences in diffusion processes which occur when uranium is present as a liquid rather than as a solid, for thermal analysis has shown than the heat of reaction raises the temperature above the melting point of uranium for some minutes at the early stages of the reaction. The effect of the furnace temperature over the range 1,075–1,200°C is relatively slight, as is exemplified by data for U–4·85 wt. % C compacts plunge sintered *in vacuo* for a period of 2 hours (*Figure 4.35*).

Regan and Williams have studied plunge sintering of mixed elemental powders ( – 300 B.S.S. mesh uranium powder and Acheson 'Dag 621' graphite) in the presence of iron and uranium–iron alloys (as – 240 B.S.S. mesh powders). $UFe_2$ was found to be the most effective in increasing the sintered density, the optimum conditions being an addition of 10 wt. % followed by sintering for 2 hours at 1,100°C. The effects of $UFe_2$ content on sintered density and porosity are shown in *Figure 4.36*; the open porosity of the sintered compact is relatively small in all cases. Metallographic examination showed that the structure consisted of rounded grains of UC embedded in a matrix of $UFe_2$.

A final assessment of the possibility of using additives to promote sintering can only be made when irradiation tests have been completed. If $UFe_2$ is employed, considerable fission fragment damage to the metallic matrix is

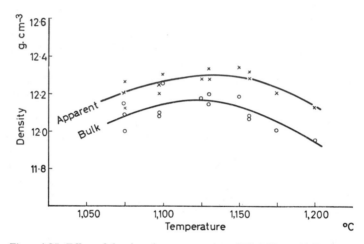

*Figure 4.35.* Effect of the sintering temperature of U–4·85 wt. % C mixtures on sintered density (Regan and Williams, 1961) (by courtesy of U.K.A.E.A.).

inevitable, and the possibility of swelling exists. This might be minimized if a process using small additions of iron could be developed, for cooling conditions could in principle be selected under which separation of the UC–Fe eutectic would take place. The resulting fuel compact would then be a cermet type consisting of spheres of UC embedded in a matrix of iron, but unless the fuel spheres were unusually large ( ~ 100 $\mu$), considerable radiation damage to the matrix would still be encountered.

The preparation of pure UC by hot-pressing the elemental powders has been described by DUBUISSON *et al.* (1958), SINIZER (1960) and TAYLOR and MCMURTRY (1961). By hot-pressing uranium–carbon mixtures at 2,800 p.s.i. in a double-acting graphite die at 900°C for 3 hours, Dubuisson was able to prepare monocarbide bodies having a density greater than 98 per cent of theoretical: it is surprising in view of the experience of BARNES *et al.* (1956) that no appreciable pickup of carbon from the die was encountered.

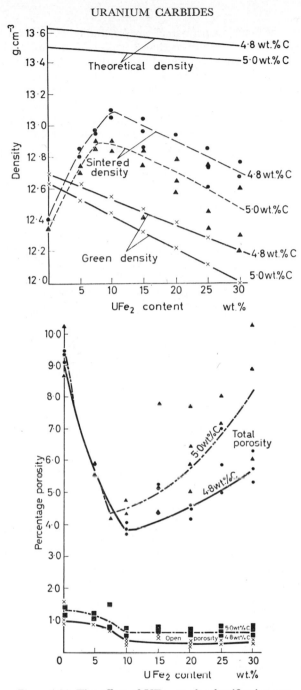

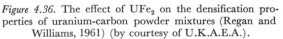

*Figure 4.36.* The effect of $UFe_2$ on the densification properties of uranium-carbon powder mixtures (Regan and Williams, 1961) (by courtesy of U.K.A.E.A.).

(a) On sintered density
(b) On porosity

In summary, the block diagram in *Figure 4.37* indicates the likely techniques which are available for preparing dense bodies of uranium monocarbide, taking the dioxide (obtained by any of the methods indicated in *Figure 4.17*) as starting material. Until more experience is gained on a large scale, selection of the most economic route can be little more than speculative.

Melting and casting is undoubtedly attractive in that highly dense ( > 98 per cent of theoretical) bodies are assured, and the stock material for melting can be prepared by the direct reduction of the oxide with carbon. The main problems seem to lie in control of the product composition, particularly in

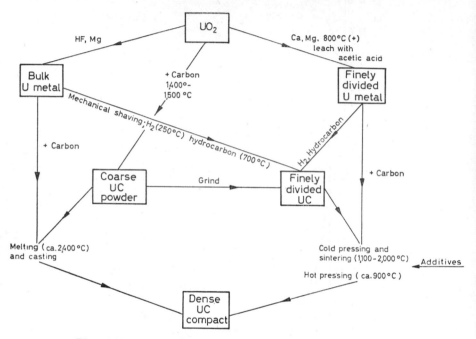

*Figure 4.37.* Possible steps in the production of uranium monocarbide.

scaling up the method to a fuel production level. Cold-pressing and sintering of UC powder has at present little to recommend it, for densities greater than 90 per cent of theoretical can only be obtained by sintering at temperatures approaching 2,000°C. However further work—particularly the development of suitable additives to lower the sintering temperature—may modify this conclusion. The most promising powder metallurgical technique at present available is the cold-pressing and sintering of metal powder–carbon mixtures, which requires a sintering temperature no greater than 1,100°C. This method, however, has less attraction in the mixed U–Pu system (Section 4.6.2).

### 4.4.3 *The Chemical Reactivity of Uranium Carbides*

*Reactivity with fluids*

Because of great differences in stability between the oxides and carbides of uranium (e.g. $-\Delta H_{298}(UO_2) = 260$ kcal mole$^{-1}$; $-\Delta H_{298}(UC) \sim 30$ kcal mole$^{-1}$), the carbides have a marked tendency to oxidize. Thus the high degree of reactivity with water precludes carbide fuels entirely from the enormous field of water-cooled reactors: their application must be confined to reactors cooled by liquid metals, molten organic compounds or gases. The limited information available on the reactivity with fluid coolants will now be considered; oxygen will be included because of its importance in handling atmospheres, as well as an impurity in coolants.

*Oxygen, Nitrogen and Water.* Both UC and $UC_2$ powders are attacked by oxygen: the rate of reaction at a given temperature undoubtedly depends upon the physical state of the compounds, but only limited data are available. Thus BARNES *et al.* (1956) claim that UC powders having a mean particle size less than 40 microns take fire spontaneously in air at room temperature. It is important that more quantitative data be gathered, particularly in regard to the safe storage of powder specimens in oxygen-contaminated atmospheres.

Only semi-quantitative data are available on the stability of bulk uranium monocarbide in air, but there is sufficient evidence to indicate stability in dry air at room temperature. STANDRING and TWIGG (1960) found that arc-melted specimens weighing 0·5 g (surface area 0·5 $cm^2$) increased in weight by only 2 mg $h^{-1}$ when held in air at 600°C. Quantitative measurements on the reaction of the bulk dicarbide (89 per cent theoretical density) with oxygen (1 atm) over the temperature range 150–300°C have been reported by ALBRECHT and KOEHL (1958), who established a parabolic rate equation

$$\text{weight gain } (\mu\text{g cm}^{-2}) = kt^{0·5}$$

where
$$k = 5·6 \times 10^{11} \exp\left(\frac{-21,200 \pm 1,100}{RT}\right)$$

The equation predicts indefinite stability of bulk $UC_2$ in dry air at room temperature. The time taken for a $UC_2$ cylinder, 1 cm in diameter and 1 cm in length (density 13·6 g $cm^{-3}$) to suffer 1 per cent oxidation at various temperatures calculated from Albrecht and Koehl's equation are as follows:

| Temperature (°C) | Time to suffer 1% oxidation |
|---|---|
| 27 | $10^6$ years |
| 50 | $10^4$ years |
| 100 | 1 year |
| 150 | 11 hours |
| 200 | 3 min |

Application of the data to powders predicts that a powder composed of 1 micron particles will undergo 1 per cent oxidation after 1 year at room temperature. This erroneous conclusion (in view of the known pyrophoricity of such fine powders) may be attributed partly to a very large effect of surface energy upon reactivity: and it must be concluded that caution is necessary in applying Albrecht and Koehl's equation to compacts of high porosity.

Preliminary studies on the oxidation of (aged) arc-melted uranium in a static oxygen atmosphere (as a head-end treatment in chemical processing) have been reported by MURBACH (1961). It was found that oxidation took place rapidly at temperatures above 275°C in oxygen and 350°C in air. The rate of oxidation increased with the partial pressure of oxygen, occurring in most cases as a two stage process proceeding first to $UO_{2+n}$ (activation energy 7·1 kcal in 7 mm of oxygen) and then to $U_3O_8$ at higher temperatures.

Albrecht and Koehl also studied the reaction of $UC_2$ with nitrogen (1 atm, 400–700°C) to give $UN_x$ ($x = 1·5$–2). As with oxygen, a parabolic rate law was obeyed, where

$$k = 4·4 \times 10^8 \exp\left(-\frac{22,600 \pm 1,200}{RT}\right)$$

and the stability of bulk compacts at room temperature is therefore assured. Studies of the reaction between uranium monocarbide and nitrogen have been carried out by AUSTIN and GERDS (1958) who reported that at 1,000°C and above, UC underwent complete reaction with nitrogen at 1 atmosphere, giving $U_2N_3$ and free carbon. The same products were found on reacting the dicarbide up to 1,550°C, but above 1,800°C the product was U(N, C) plus free carbon.

It is important that the reactivity of finely divided monocarbide and dicarbide with nitrogen should be carefully investigated, particularly to test the suitability of nitrogen as an inert atmosphere alternative to argon.

There is ample evidence that bulk uranium carbides react readily with water. Work at Batelle Memorial Institute has shown that compacts will disintegrate completely in boiling water in less than 1 hour (TRIPLER et al., 1959). The rate at which cast specimens containing between 4·5 and 9·2 wt. % carbon gained weight while suspended in water at 60°C varied widely and erratically but all showed serious attack after 1 hour (ROUGH and CHUBB, 1960). BRADLEY and FERRIS (1961) found that when uranium monocarbide was hydrolysed with water at 80°C, the principal products were 'a finely divided U(IV) compound',* methane (86 vol. %) and hydrogen (11 vol. %) along with ethane and propane. Hydrolysis of UC–$UC_2$ mixtures revealed a decrease in the volume of gas produced as the proportion of $UC_2$ increased (from 86 ml g$^{-1}$ with pure UC to 32 ml g$^{-1}$ with a specimen containing 63 per cent $UC_2$).

Albrecht and Koehl showed that, in contrast to observations with nitrogen and oxygen, $UC_2$ reacted with water vapour (0·038 atm, 150–300°C) according to a linear law, where $k$ ($\mu$g cm$^{-2}$ sec$^{-1}$) could be expressed by

$$k = 1·88 \times 10^4 \exp\left(-\frac{8,350 \pm 710}{RT}\right)$$

This equation predicts that a theoretically dense cylinder (1 cm diameter × 1cm in height) in contact with water vapour at 25°C will oxidize at the rate of 1 per cent in 24 hours. ROUGH and CHUBB (1960) advanced qualitative evidence that cast specimens of UC were attacked slowly in moist air, but in time flaking and spalling took place in a manner indicative of selective attack along cleavage planes.

Although more data are needed, particularly on fine powders, there is no doubt that particular steps are necessary to exclude water vapour from an

---

* This was identified by x-ray analysis as $UO_2$ in independent work by NEWKIRK (1959).

atmosphere in which the uranium carbides are handled. It has been reported that the dicarbide corrodes more rapidly in moist air than the monocarbide (CHIOTTI, 1951), but no quantitative data are available.

*Inorganic acids.* The dissolution of carbides is important to recycling of feed material and aqueous reprocessing of irradiated fuel. Work in the Windscale and Dounreay laboratories of the U.K.A.E.A., however (PHILLIPS, 1959; SIMPSON and HEATH, 1959), indicates that hydrolysis of UC by nitric acid (resulting in the evolution of $CO_2$, hydrocarbons and oxides of nitrogen), gives a solution containing organic acids, including substantial amounts of oxalic acid. This would be likely to interfere with any subsequent solvent extraction process, and it therefore seems likely that controlled oxidation to $U_3O_8$ before dissolution is desirable: MURBACH (1960) has demonstrated that arc-melted UC can be oxidized smoothly to $U_3O_8$ in about 1 hour at a nominal temperature of 350–400°C. Alternatively, HARTLEY and McLENNEN (1961) propose hydrolysis with boiling water prior to dissolution in nitric acid.

BRADLEY and FERRIS (1961) showed that UC reacted with 5·6M HCl at 80°C to give essentially the same gaseous products as from the reaction with water, though hydrolysis took place more slowly. The resultant solution was green, and more than 99% of the uranium was in the tetravalent state.

*Carbon dioxide.* Measurements of the rate of change of weight of sintered uranium monocarbide specimens in dry carbon dioxide over the temperature range 500–830°C were made by ANTILL *et al.* (1957). The rate of attack was surprisingly constant (wt. increase 120–170 mg h⁻¹). Thus at 500°C UC was oxidized about 100 times as fast as uranium metal, while at 700°C the order of reactivity was reversed, the metal being oxidized three times as fast as UC. In essentially confirming these observations, BROWN and STOBO (1961) have established that the rate of the reaction increases with carbon content. No in-pile experiments have been reported, but from the aspect of reactivity under conditions of defected cladding UC is expected to be markedly inferior to $UO_2$ up to surface temperatures of at least 700°C.

*Hydrogen.* STANDRING and TWIGG (1960) exposed pellets of UC (6 g, density 11·2 g cm⁻³) to hydrogen (0·25–0·9 atm) at temperatures from 200–350°C over periods up to 65 hours without any changes taking place in pressure or in the weight of the specimens; the tests were made on material prepared both from the methane–metal reaction and by direct sintering of the elements. Stability was greatly impaired, however, by the presence of $UC_2$ or free uranium metal.

*Organic coolants.* BOETTCHER and SCHNEIDER (1958) found that no corrosion of uranium monocarbide was detectable in tests of short duration (5 hours) with diphenyl, crude terphenyl and *p*-terphenyl at temperatures up to 350°C. ROUGH and DICKERSON (1960) report a rate of attack of 6 mg cm⁻² h⁻¹ of cast UC specimens (5·0 wt. % C) in terphenyl at 350°C. For specimens containing a substantial proportion of $UC_2$ (6–8 wt. % C) the rate of attack was reduced to 0·3 mg cm⁻² h⁻¹. These figures are upper limits only, for no special precautions were taken to exclude moisture (ROUGH and CHUBB, 1960).

*Liquid metals.* MURRAY and WILLIAMS (1958) report that uranium monocarbide shows good stability in liquid sodium, at least up to 500°C. STANDRING and TWIGG (1960) and BROWN and STOBO (1961) obtained negligible weight changes over a period of 1 month when sintered UC compacts were exposed to NaK alloy at temperatures of 600 and 800°C, and similar experience has been reported by workers at Batelle Memorial Institute (PRICE et al., 1958; PRICE and GOLDTHWAITE, 1958; HARE and ROUGH, 1960). During irradiation tests (Section 4.4.4) attack on UC in contact with NaK was observed, but this was attributable to the presence of oxygen impurity. There is no reason to doubt that UC is compatible with pure NaK and sodium at all temperatures of reactor interest. The transfer of carbon from $UC_2$ to stainless steel by liquid sodium is considered in Volume 3, Chapter 1.

Only fragmentary information on compatibility with other liquid metals is available. It was found that UC did not react with liquid bismuth after 3 hours at 600°C (STRASSER, 1960). Sintered material is wetted by molten zinc, but not by molten lead or tin (BOETTCHER and SCHNEIDER, 1958).

*Reactivity with metals*

As with uranium oxide it is difficult to employ thermodynamic data to predict the possibility of reaction of carbides with metals. When the metals themselves do not form carbides or dissolve carbon appreciably it is reasonably certain that no reaction will take place: thus the inertness of UC towards Na and NaK is not surprising. In the case of the transition metals, however, many of which form stable carbides, theoretical prediction is impossible. The free energies are of comparable magnitude, and even if the data were sufficiently accurate to differentiate, the formation of intermetallic compounds and solid solutions might invalidate conclusions based on the assumption of simple carbon displacement.

Empirical tests therefore constitute the only method of establishing compatibility. The information in many cases is sparse and requires supplementing, but on the basis of some of the data available ROUGH and CHUBB (1960) have attempted to construct crude ternary U–C–M phase diagrams. As is so often the case, few data have been obtained under irradiation conditions.

*Aluminium.* THURBER and BEAVER (1959) found that UC had reacted with aluminium after 27 hours at 620°C; the intermetallic compounds $UAl_3$ and $UAl_4$ were identified by x-ray analysis, but no $Al_4C_3$ was detected. In contrast, no reaction between $UC_2$ and aluminium was found, and a pseudo-binary system was suggested.

*Beryllium.* MURRAY and WILLIAMS (1958) reported that no reaction occurred between UC and beryllium up to 600°C. However, after 12 hours at 650°C and a contact pressure of 1,500 kg cm⁻², BOETTCHER and SCHNEIDER (1958) found that firm bonding took place, while BOLTA and STRASSER (1960) obtained evidence of considerable reaction after 167 days at 825°C. Recent quantitative studies at ORNL (HARMS and MURDOCK, 1961) have shown that interdiffusion involves the formation of $UBe_{13}$: the diffusion coefficient has an activation energy of $\sim 25$ kcal mole⁻¹ and at 1,000°C the value of $D$ is $2 \cdot 5 \times 10^{-10}$ cm² sec⁻¹.

*Chromium.* No interaction between UC and chromium has been found up to 2,000°C (IVANOV and BADAJEVA, 1958; WHITE et al., 1961): the system constitutes a pseudo-binary (see *Figure 4.34*).

*Cobalt.* Cobalt reacts with UC at 1,300–1,500°C with the formation of (unidentified) intermetallic compounds (WHITE et al., 1961). This finding contradicts the suggestion (BOWMAN, 1959) that the system is pseudo-binary.

*Copper.* There is agreement (BOWMAN, 1959; WHITE *et al.*, 1961) that no reaction occurs with copper up to the melting point of UC. A pseudo-binary system is suggested, with a eutectic point very close to 100 per cent copper.

*Iron.* The pseudo-binary nature of UC–Fe has been discussed earlier (Section 4.4.2 and *Figure 4.34*). Interaction of UC with stainless steel at 800–1,200°C and with mild steel at 1,000–1,200°C (SECREST *et al.*, 1958; NICHOLS, 1958; ROUGH and CHUBB, 1960) may be ascribed to reaction with chromium and/or nickel. Reported penetrations of stainless steel are, at 1,200°C (type 304) 0·010 in. in 24 hours (Rough and Chubb), and at 1,100°C (type unspecified) 0·004 in. in 6 days (Nichols). BOLTA and STRASSER (1960) observed a penetration of less than 0·001 in. after 167 days at 820°C (type 304).

*Magnesium.* No reaction has been detected after 24 hours at 600°C (ROUGH and DICKERSON, 1960).

*Molybdenum.* It is claimed that molybdenum reacts with UC (temperature unspecified) to give $Mo_2C$ (ROUGH and CHUBB, 1960). CREAGH (1960) reports a rapid reaction at 2,000°C with the production of a liquid phase.

*Nickel.* There is evidence that nickel reacts with UC at 1,000–1,600°C. BOETTCHER and SCHNEIDER (1958) claim that $U_6Ni$ is formed at 1,000°C, but after reaction at 1,300–1,600°C, WHITE *et al.* (1961) identified the intermetallic species as $UNi_5$. The work of both laboratories contradicts the contention of BOWMAN (1959) that the system is pseudo-binary. It is desirable that more work be carried out in this system, particularly on account of the apparent success of nickel as a sintering additive to UC (e.g. KORCHYNSKY *et al.*, 1961).

*Niobium.* BOLTA and STRASSER (1960) detected no reaction between niobium and UC after 167 days at 825°C while KORCHYNSKY *et al.* (1961) demonstrated similar compatibility during 100 hours at 1,000°C. A 'strong reaction' was observed at 2,300°C (CREAGH, 1960).

*Rhenium.* It has been found that this metal forms a simple eutectic at 1,850°C and a pseudo-binary system is implied (ROUGH and CHUBB, 1960).

*Silicon.* There is evidence for the formation of $USi_3$ at 1,000°C (BOETTCHER and SCHNEIDER, 1958).

*Tantalum.* It has been reported (PHILLIPS and FOSTER, 1959; ROUGH and DICKERSON, 1960) that no reaction with UC took place over a period of 24 hours at 1,000°C and a period of 2 hours at 1,800°C. However BOWMAN (1959) found that reaction occurred at temperatures above 1,800°C to give free uranium and tantalum carbides.

*Titanium.* NICHOLS (1958) observed reaction with UC: at 1,100°C, 0·005 in. penetration took place in 6 days, while at 1,200°C there was 'very marked' attack.

*Tungsten.* CREAGH (1960) found no reaction between UC and tungsten below a temperature of 2,350°C, when a slight roughening of the surface took place. It therefore appears that tungsten is an excellent container material for UC at high temperatures.

*Zirconium.* BOETTCHER and SCHNEIDER (1958) observed reaction between UC and Zr (compressed together at 1,500 kg $cm^{-2}$) after 12 hours at 650°C, while ROUGH and DICKERSON (1960) report a marked reaction in 24 hours at 1,000°C (conditions of contact unspecified). These observations are confirmed in compatibility tests on zircaloy-2 reported by STRASSER (1960).

*Reactivity with carbides*

The solubilities of UC in other carbides, particularly those of the transition metals, have been reviewed by ROUGH and CHUBB (1960): most of the data is derived from the work of BROWNLEE (1958), NOWOTNY *et al.* (1957, 1958), and BURDICK *et al.* (1955). Uranium monocarbide forms a complete series of solid solutions with ThC and with the non-fissile carbides ZrC, TaC, and NbC. An account of the preparation of ZrC–UC solid solution by hot pressing of ZrC, $UO_2$ and carbon at 2,000°C has been given by STEPHAS and HOYT (1961); such solid solutions of high melting point have potential application as fuel in thermionic converters (LING YANG and CARPENTER, 1961).

The reaction of UC with other carbides at high temperature has been qualitatively examined by CREAGH (1960). It was found that on contact for 30 min at 2,300°C, SiC, VC and $Mo_2C$ all reacted to produce a liquid phase (unidentified), whereas no reaction was apparent with ZrC, NbC, HfC, WC, $W_2C$, TiC and 4 TaC–ZrC (solid solution).

*Reactivity with oxides*

Few data are available on the compatibility of UC with oxides. CREAGH and DRELL (1960) report that no reaction took place with zirconia and thoria respectively after 30 min at 2,450°C in an atmosphere of argon. ROUGH and CHUBB (1960) observed the formation of uranium metal on heating a mixture of $UO_2$ and UC *in vacuo* at 1,800°C.

UC–UN *solid solutions*

It has been established by WILLIAMS and SAMBELL (1959) that uranium mononitride exhibits complete solid solubility with the monocarbide, at least above 1,200°C. It is probable that U(C,N) would constitute an acceptable fuel material, and its properties compared with the pure compounds are worth investigating.

*4.4.4 Irradiation Studies*

The most important irradiation data available at the time of writing have emerged from a programme carried out jointly by teams at the Batelle Memorial Institute and Atomics International (SMITH and ROUGH, 1959; ROUGH *et al.*, 1960; HARE *et al.*, 1961; HARE and ROUGH, 1960, 1961). The tests were carried out exclusively on arc-cast enriched UC cylinders $\frac{3}{8}$ in. diameter and 2 in. long. Specimens were irradiated unclad, immersed in sodium/potassium alloy and contained in stainless steel baskets; surface and centre temperatures were measured by thermocouples mounted respectively in the liquid metal and in holes drilled in the specimens.

A summary of the data reported, which covers a considerable range of carbon content, burn-up and temperature conditions, is given in *Table 4.16*. In general the behaviour under irradiation is most encouraging; changes in specific gravity (measured by weighing in air and in carbon tetrachloride) are small up to quite high burn-ups, and release of [85]Kr up to the highest burn-up level at which this was measured (*ca.* 8,000 MWd/T) corresponds very satisfactorily with that predicted assuming escape only by fission fragment recoil

192

from the available free surface. This is in contrast with the earlier work of BARWOOD *et al.* (1957) who found that irradiation of UC pins of 80–85 per cent theoretical density to 3,000 MWd/T at 630°C resulted in the release of 10 per cent of the fission product gases. Extensive cracking of many of the cast specimens could be ascribed to the strain produced by thermal gradients, while surface damage was attributable to reaction with oxygen (present at a level of about 50 p.p.m.) in the NaK.

Although changes in carbon content over the range 4·6–5·3 wt. % do not appear to have any gross effect on the irradiation performance, there is firm evidence, at least in the case of the carbon-rich specimens, that microstructural changes take place. Cast specimens containing more than 4·8 wt. % carbon originally contained platelets of $UC_2$ embedded in a matrix of UC, but after irradiation it was found that a substantial fraction of the $UC_2$ phase had disappeared, particularly from the centre of the specimen. The reason for this change is not yet established with certainty, though Batelle workers have obtained some evidence that it may be related to decomposition of $UC_2$ accompanied by diffusion of carbon down the thermal gradient. Evidence on the behaviour of specimens containing less than 4·8 wt. % carbon is incomplete, though there is some indication that swelling takes place at higher burn-ups if free uranium is present.

Fundamental studies of damage to single crystals of uranium monocarbide by irradiation at low temperatures (nominally 65°C) have been described by FOX and WAIT (1961). These authors have found quite different behaviour from that observed with $UO_2$ (Section 4.1.6). A lattice dilation of 0·14 per cent was found after a burn-up of 0·46 MWd/T ($5 \times 10^{-7}$ fissions/atom of uranium),* increasing relatively slowly at higher burn-ups to a value of 0·22 per cent after a burn-up of 1,750 MWd/T ($1·9 \times 10^{-3}$ fissions/atoms of uranium). The development of considerable inhomogeneous strain which increased in magnitude with dose was also noted, and above a burn-up of 280 MWd/T crystal fragmentation was observed. Most of the strain could be relieved from the lower-irradiated crystals by annealing at 480°C for 18 hours, but samples which had suffered a burn-up greater than about 100 MWd/T disintegrated on heating.

It appears from the existing evidence that radiation-induced fragmentation will be unlikely to occur at fuel element temperatures greater than 500°C because of continuous annealing of the damage. However further irradiation experiments with single crystals at intermediate temperatures are desirable to establish the temperature limit below which a serious problem may exist.

Preliminary data on fission gas release from lightly irradiated specimens of UC (prepared by reaction sintering and by direct reduction of oxide) are discussed in Chapter 5.

### 4.5 THORIUM CARBIDES

#### 4.5.1 *Phase Relationships and Chemical Properties*

A preliminary investigation of the thorium–carbon phase diagram has been reported by WILHELM and CHIOTTI (1950) and CHIOTTI (1950) (*Figure 4.38*).

---

* A similar effect has been reported by ADAM and RODGERS (1961) at burn-ups of up to 3·5 MWd/T.

TABLE 4.16

SUMMARY OF IRRADIATION DATA ON CAST SPECIMENS OF URANIUM MONOCARBIDE (for references, see text)

| Carbon content before irradiation (wt. %) | Burn-up (MWd/T uranium from dosimetry measurements) | Average temperature (°C) | | Change in specific gravity (%) | Fission gas release (cm³ of ⁸⁵Kr) | |
|---|---|---|---|---|---|---|
| | | Surface | Centre | | Measured | Estimated from recoil |
| 5·0-5·6 (3 specimens) | 400 | 600 | 660 | 0·29-0·44 | — | — |
| 5·2 | 1,420 | 770 | 1,300 | 0·7-0·9 | $2·4 \times 10^{-5}$ | $2·5 \times 10^{-5}$ |
| 5·2 | 1,780 | 540 | 880 | 2·5 | — | — |
| 5·3 | 5,600 | 920 | 1,370 | 0·6-2·0 | $9·7 \times 10^{-5}$ | $8·8 \times 10^{-5}$ |
| 5·1 | 7,800 | 700 | 1,060 | 2·5 | — | — |
| 4·6 | 6,500 | 880 | 1,330 | 2·4 | $8·2 \times 10^{-5}$ | $8·7 \times 10^{-5}$ |
| 4·7 | 6,400 | 770 | 1,250 | 1·6 | — | — |
| 4·6 | ~5,000 | 500-700 | 800-1,100 | 1·6 | $8·4 \times 10^{-5}$ | $9·4 \times 10^{-5}$ |
| 4·8 | ~5,000 | 850-780 | 1,300-1,600 | 1·2 | — | — |
| 5·0 | 12,200 | 760 | 1,180 | 1·8 | — | — |
| 5·0 | 12,800 | 620 | 1,090 | 1·8 | — | — |
| 5·2 | 18,000 | 580-760 | 990-1,250 | 3·4 | — | — |
| 5·3 | 22,000 | 460-590 | 800-1,040 | 4·4 | — | — |

194

Thorium forms only two carbides, ThC (melting point 2,625 ± 25°C) which has a face-centred cubic lattice, and ThC₂ (melting point 2,655 ± 25°C) which has a highly anisotropic monoclinic structure (HUNT and RUNDLE, 1951). All compositions between the metal and ThC are said to show complete miscibility above about 1,980°C, but below this temperature a miscibility gap exists having a temperature peak at 2 wt.% carbon and a range 0·25 to 3·8 wt.% carbon at room temperature. Similarly ThC and ThC₂ form a complete series of solid solutions above about 2,300°C, but show little or no mutual solid

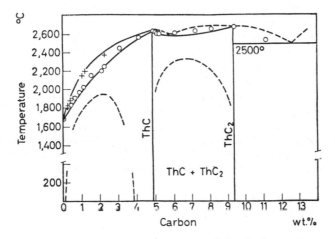

*Figure 4.38.* Tentative phase diagram of the thorium–carbon system (Chiotti, 1950) (by courtesy of U.S.A.E.C.).

solubility at room temperature. It is claimed that the dicarbide forms a eutectic with graphite containing approximately 12·6 wt.% carbon and having a melting point of 2,500 ± 35°C. Work on this system would be of interest, particularly directed to defining more accurately the regions of miscibility: it is important to ascertain if Th₂C₃ can be formed under conditions analogous to those required for U₂C₃ (Section 4.4.1).

Little information is available on the chemical properties of the carbides of thorium. SCAIFE and WYLIE (1958) report that the dicarbide is readily hydrolysed in moist air, and that fine powders are pyrophoric. Quantitative studies of the oxidation of bulk ThC₂ (prepared by sintering or arc-melting of the elements) in moist air have been carried out by ENGLE (1961): the weight gain-time curves were complex, but it was established that complete conversion to thoria and gaseous products (hydrogen, methane, ethane and higher hydrocarbons) proceeded to completion after about 1 hour at 50°C, about ten times the rate of corresponding samples of UC₂. Limited evidence on the hydrolysis of ThC₂ with liquid water (HUNT and RUNDLE, 1951) indicates that methane is the predominant gaseous product. ENGLE found a negligible rate of reaction between the dicarbide and nitrogen at 50°C; SCAIFE and WYLIE found a rapid reaction to give 'nitride or carbon-nitride' at 2,170°C.

## 4.5.2 Preparative Studies

The carbides of thorium have been prepared by reaction of the elements either by sintering or arc-melting (BRETT, LAW and LIVEY, 1960; WILHELM and CHIOTTI, 1950) or by reaction of thoria with carbon (SCAIFE and WYLIE, 1958; SAMSONOV et al., 1960). No studies of preparations using a hydrocarbon–metal reaction have been reported. Scaife and Wylie found that thoria–carbon mixtures heated in a current of dry argon could be converted to $ThC_2$ (99 per cent) after 30 min at 2,100°C. Samsonov et al., working in vacuo, were able to achieve essentially complete conversion of thoria to either ThC or $ThC_2$ after 2 hours at 1,800°C.

As well as preparing $ThC_2$ from the elements by sintering at 1,800°C in argon, BRETT et al. (1960) were able to obtain $(U, Th)C_2$ by sintering uranium and thorium metal powders with carbon at 1,700°C. X-ray examination showed that the product was single phase over a range of metal ratios from 9:1 to 1:9, indicating solid solubility over this range of composition; however poor crystallinity was in evidence in the middle of the range. More limited evidence on preparations consisting principally of the monocarbides indicated that this system is also one of complete solid solubility.

Stability tests carried out in dry oxygen showed that resistance to oxidation over the temperature range 200–400°C increased with the uranium content of $(U, Th)C_2$. A similar tendency was noted by ENGLE (1961) for oxidation in moist air.

No studies devoted specifically to the preparation of dense bodies of $ThC_2$ or of $(U, Th)C_2$ have been reported.

## 4.6 PLUTONIUM CARBIDES

### 4.6.1 Phase Relationships and Chemical Properties

A detailed study of the plutonium–carbon system has been carried out at Los Alamos by MULFORD et al. (1960): the phase diagram advocated by these workers is reproduced in Figure 4.39. There are two well-established phases, the monocarbide and the sesquicarbide.

TABLE 4.17

THE CARBIDES OF PLUTONIUM

| Composition | Crystal structure | Theoretical density (g cm⁻³) | Melting point (°C) |
|---|---|---|---|
| $PuC_{1-x}$ | Face-centred cubic | 13·99 | 1,650°C, with peritectic decomposition |
| $Pu_2C_3$ | Body-centred cubic | 12·70 | 2,050°C, with peritectic decomposition |

The lattice parameter of $PuC_{1-x}$ (4·958–4·974 Å) depends upon the composition and the oxygen content of the sample: for $Pu_2C_3$ the observed range is narrower (8·126–8·131 Å) and there seems to be little, if any, range of composition.

In addition to these two compounds there is evidence for the existence below 575°C of a carbon-deficient 'zeta phase' and above about 1,750°C of a higher carbide, tentatively designated $PuC_2$. The zeta phase has a cubic

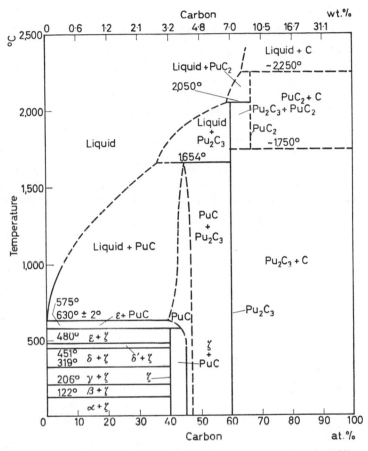

*Figure 4.39.* The plutonium–carbon phase diagram (Mulford *et al.*, 1960) (by courtesy of Cleaver-Hulme Press Ltd.).

structure similar to that of the monocarbide and contains 40 at. % carbon; the higher carbide shows a complicated x-ray pattern which has not been indexed.

A striking feature of the monocarbide phase is the relatively low melting point (1,650°C) at which it decomposes peritectically into plutonium-rich liquid and $Pu_2C_3$. The kinetics of this transformation are of considerable importance to reactor fuel technology and are worthy of further attention. Some features of the Los Alamos phase diagram have been essentially confirmed at Fontenay-aux-Roses by PASCARD (1961) who finds, however, that the region of the diagram where the zeta-phase exists is more complicated than that proposed by Mulford *et al.*; Pascard also considers that $PuC_{1-n}$ has

197

a narrower range of composition than in *Figure 4.39* (46–47 per cent as against 45–47 per cent).

Some physical properties investigated by Pascard include coefficients of thermal expansion, values of which are reported as follows:

$$PuC_{1-n} \qquad 28 \times 10^{-6}\,deg^{-1}\,C$$
$$Zeta\ phase \qquad 40 \times 10^{-6}\,deg^{-1}\,C$$
$$PuC_{1-n}+Pu_2C_3\ (total\ 48\ at.\ \%\ C) \quad 17 \times 10^{-6}\,deg^{-1}\,C$$

No quantitative work has been published on the chemical reactivity of plutonium carbides, though there seems little doubt that they will be highly susceptible to oxidation and hydrolysis, particularly in a finely-divided state. DRUMMOND *et al.* (1957) claim that the sesquicarbide is more stable than the monocarbide to oxidation on heating and to hydrolysis by boiling water and acids.

Preliminary data have been obtained on the system $(U, Pu)C$ (*Figure 4.40*). Above about 35 per cent UC, the system appears to be single phase, consisting probably of a stoichiometric solid solution $(U, Pu)C$. At higher levels of plutonium, separation into two phases corresponding to $(U, Pu)C_{1-x}$ and $(U, Pu)_2C_3$ takes place. Although further work is obviously desirable, it is

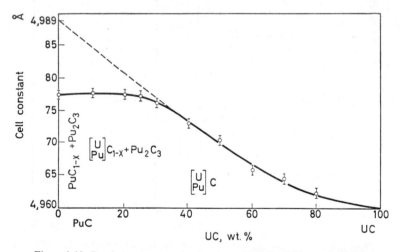

*Figure 4.40.* Lattice parameters in the system UC–PuC (Pascard, 1961).

encouraging to note that the single phase region extends beyond the plutonium levels likely to be of interest to fast reactor fuels though the range of carbon composition (q.v.) is in doubt. No melting point data on the mixed system have appeared up to the time of writing, and the possibility of peritectic decomposition of $(U, Pu)C$ has yet to be investigated.

### 4.6.2 Preparative Studies

Plutonium carbides have been prepared by reaction of the elements or by reduction of the oxide with carbon (DRUMMOND *et al.*, 1957; MULFORD *et al.*, 1960; PASCARD, 1961; OGARD *et al.*, 1961).

Pascard prepared finely divided plutonium powder by hydriding bulk metal at 100–200°C and decomposing *in vacuo* at 500–550°C: the powder was then mixed with carbon and reaction to carbide carried out at about 550°C. Alternatively decomposition of the hydride and reaction with carbon could be carried out as a one-stage process. Mulford and Ellinger, on the other hand, employed arc melting of bulk metal and graphite, numerous inversions and re-meltings being necessary to ensure homogeneity of the product.

Several laboratories have experienced difficulty in preparing single-phase plutonium monocarbide by reduction of the oxide with carbon *in vacuo* at 1,400–1,500°C (DRUMMOND *et al.*, 1957; OGARD *et al.*, 1961; PASCARD, 1961; SOWDEN *et al.*, 1961), the product being almost invariably contaminated with sesquicarbide even when a $PuO_2:C$ mole ratio as low as $1:2·6$ is employed. The persistence of sesquicarbide may be attributed to (a) the retention of oxygen as $Pu(C,O)$, which would leave excess carbon to form $Pu_2C_3$, or (b) the volatilization of a plutonium-rich species during reaction, which would similarly upset the carbon balance. There is insufficient evidence to conclude whether either or both of these factors is contributing to the phenomenon. A similar difficulty has been encountered in the preparation of $(U,Pu)C$ containing about 20 per cent plutonium: using mixed oxide prepared either mechanically from the separately prepared powders or by coprecipitation from mixed nitrate solution, the product of reacting a $1:3$ mole ratio of $(U,Pu)O_2–C$ often contains appreciable quantities (up to 30 per cent) of $(U,Pu)_2C_3$. Ogard has found that a single monocarbide phase, $(U_{0·8}Pu_{0·2})C_{0·95}$ can be obtained if the mole ratio of reactants is reduced to $1:2·95$, while Sowden *et al.* have obtained evidence that if steps are taken to ensure that the oxides are in solid solution, the sesquicarbide phase can be greatly reduced even at a reactant mole ratio of $1:3$. Further work on this reaction as a production process is required, particularly in relation to the effect of carbon and oxygen contents on the subsequent behaviour of the product.

Densification studies of plutonium-bearing carbides are as yet in the early stages. OGARD *et al.* (1961) carried out sintering studies on $PuC.Pu_2C_3$ mixtures which had been prepared by carbon reduction of the oxide *in vacuo* at 1,450°C; the product of the reaction was ground, pressed at 60 ton in.$^{-2}$ and sintered for 4 hours at 1,600–1,650°C. For material containing between 20 and 50 per cent of $Pu_2C_3$, and carbon contents between 41·5 and 47 at. % pellets were obtained having densities between 90 and 93 per cent of theoretical. Arc-melting of similar material produced compacts of almost theoretical density; this process also led to a considerable reduction in the levels of both oxygen and of sesquicarbide, giving some support to the contention that the contamination of PuC with sesquicarbide is in some way related to the retention of oxygen.

Essentially pure plutonium sesquicarbide was obtained by reacting carbon and oxide in a mole ratio of $3·5:1$. Upon grinding, pressing and sintering at 1,650–1,750°C, densities of up to 99 per cent of theoretical were attained.

Results obtained by Ogard on the densification of $(U,Pu)C_{0·95}$ powders obtained by reduction of the oxide indicate that the presence of plutonium is beneficial to sintering, though careful tests are necessary on UC powders having the same history and physical properties before this can be established with certainty. For powders of composition $U_{0.9}Pu_{0.1}C_{0.95}$ and $U_{0.8}Pu_{0.2}C_{0.95}$ densities of up to 94 per cent of theoretical were achieved after sintering for 4–6 hours at 1,650°C; no impurities were detected by x-ray analysis or metallographic examination, and subsequent arc melting of sintered pellets led to buttons of single-phase material approaching theoretical density.

PASCARD (1961) has carried out tests on the sintering of (U, Pu)C powders prepared from the oxide in the presence of 0·5 per cent nickel as an additive. The densities obtained under these conditions were considerably lower than those achieved with similarly prepared UC powders (Section 4.4.2) but the meaning of this is obscure because of the presence of oxide and sesquicarbide impurities in the (U, Pu)C tested. Better results were obtained with powders prepared by reacting a mixture of $UH_3 + PuH_3$ with carbon at 900–1,100°C for 15 hours. On pressing at 20 ton in.$^{-2}$ with 0·5 per cent Ni and 1·5 per cent naphthalene binder, the powders sintered to densities of 96–97·5 per cent of theoretical after 4 hours at 1,450°C; corresponding tests in the absence of nickel led to densities of only about 82 per cent of theoretical.

It is obviously too early at present to choose between any of the methods so far explored for the preparation of dense (U, Pu)C powders. Direct reduction of the oxides with carbon, which minimizes the number of stages and avoids the handling of finely divided metal, has particular appeal in the case of plutonium-bearing fuels; present indications support a route commencing with $(U, Pu)O_2$ rather than with the separate oxides. Ogard's sintering experience is encouraging, and the data of Pascard on the benefits of nickel addition indicate that detailed attention should be devoted to this aspect (cf. Section 4.4.2).

The final test of any fuel must be its behaviour under irradiation, and such experience is totally lacking at the time of writing.

Experience gained to date on fissile carbides in general indicates that many problems remain to be solved, especially in production and densification. In particular it is not yet known what degree of control of the metal/carbon ratio is required to ensure satisfactory irradiation performance. An assessment of this is a matter of great importance which may exert an overriding influence on the choice of a production route for the fuel.

### 4.7 URANIUM NITRIDES

Nitrides are as yet in a very early stage of development, but have considerable potential as nuclear fuels. The fissile atom density of UN, for example, is about 4 per cent greater than that of UC, and recent data indicate that the thermal conductivity at higher temperatures is at least as good. Furthermore the final cation/anion ratio of the material can be in principle controlled (as with oxides) by equilibration with a gas atmosphere. The importance of this advantage over carbides may become more apparent as experience with the latter accumulates.

#### 4.7.1 Phase Relationships and Chemical Properties

No phase diagram of the U–N system has yet been reported but RUNDLE et al. (1948) have identified the three compounds shown in *Table 4.18*.

TABLE 4.18

THE NITRIDES OF URANIUM

| Composition | Crystal structure | Theoretical density | Melting point |
|---|---|---|---|
| UN | Face-centred cubic | 14·32 | $\begin{cases} 2{,}650\pm100 \text{ (a)} \\ 2{,}480\pm50 \text{ (b)} \end{cases}$ |
| $U_2N_3$ | Body-centred cubic | 11·24 | — |
| $UN_2$ | Fluorite | 11·73 | — |

(a) Chiotti (1952), ammonia atmosphere.
(b) Newkirk and Bates (1959), atmosphere of flowing helium.

The higher nitrides decompose to the mononitride *in vacuo* at about 1,300°C. According to Rundle *et al.*, $U_2N_3$ shows a sharp phase boundary on the low nitrogen side, but absorbs excess nitrogen up to about $UN_{1.75}$ with expansion of the lattice.

PAPROCKI *et al.* (1959) found that coarse UN powders ($-200+325$ mesh) were not pyrophoric, but picked up oxygen slowly on standing in air at room temperature. On the other hand, fine powders ($<2\ \mu$) are pyrophoric (TAYLOR and McMURTRY, 1961) though KELLER *et al.* (1961) claim that UN powders are less reactive than UC powders. Bulk mononitride was considerably more stable to water than the monocarbide; there were no signs of attack after 16 days in contact at 100°C, but after 14 days at 200°C it was found that disintegration of pellets took place.

### 4.7.2 Preparative Studies

The only route which has been successfully employed to prepare pure uranium nitride is the reaction of uranium metal or $UH_3$ with nitrogen or ammonia (RUNDLE *et al.*, 1948; KATZ and RABINOWITCH, 1951; CHIOTTI, 1952; MALLET and GERDS, 1955; SHEINHARTZ and ZAMBROW, 1958; TRIPLER *et al.*, 1959; TAYLOR and McMURTRY, 1961; KELLER *et al.*, 1961).

Two main sequences of reactions have been employed

$$U + N_2 \xrightarrow{850°C} U_2N_3 \xrightarrow[\text{in vacuo}]{1{,}300°C} UN$$

$$U + H_2 \xrightarrow{250°C} UH_3 \xrightarrow[800°C]{N_2} U_2N_3 \xrightarrow[\text{in vacuo}]{1{,}300°C} UN$$

$$U + NH_3 \xrightarrow{300-400°C} UH_3 + U_2N_3 \xrightarrow[700°C]{N_2} U_2N_3 \xrightarrow[\text{in vacuo}]{1{,}300°C} UN$$

The second and third routes lead to a fine powder of mean particle size of several microns, and the first route to a much coarser powder.

Taylor and McMurtry have investigated the preparation of UN directly from the oxide

$$2UO_2 + 4C + N_2 \rightarrow 2UN + 4CO$$

by heating an oxide–carbon mixture in flowing nitrogen at 1,400–1,850°C. It appears difficult to obtain a product largely free of oxygen and carbon, but the method has potential advantages as a production route and is worthy of further study. Methods which involve gross contamination of the product with another solid, e.g. reaction of $UCl_4$ with ammonia or of the metal with $Mg_3N$ (KATZ and RABINOWITCH, 1951), are less appealing for large-scale development.

The dinitride has been prepared only by reacting uranium metal with nitrogen at high pressures (126 atm); the pure compound can be obtained only with difficulty (RUNDLE et al., 1948).

Densification studies have so far been few in number. CHIOTTI (1952) prepared small crucibles by pressing coarse powders (average particle size about 50 microns) to 25 ton in.$^{-2}$ and sintering at 2,000–2,100°C in vacuo to densities around 84 per cent of theoretical, while KELLER (1961) obtained densities 75 per cent of theoretical on sintering similar powders at 1,800°C for 2 hours. Similarly poor sintering performance has been observed by workers at the Battelle Memorial Institute (PAPROCKI et al., 1961). Using finer powders (6–8 microns) TAYLOR and McMURTRY (1961) were able to obtain densities as high as 95 per cent of theoretical on sintering in vacuo at 1,850°C for 1 hour. The results of the nitrogen analyses carried out by these workers on the final pellets appear to be in some doubt, however, and there is a possibility that the compacts contained free uranium metal: KELLER et al. (1961) state specifically that nitrogen was lost from UN on heating above 1,800°C.

It is clear that data on the equilibrium between nitrogen and UN at elevated temperatures are essential to further densification studies. ENDEBROCK et al. (1961) have encountered difficulties in controlling the nitrogen content of the product during formation of the mononitride by melting and casting of uranium in a nitrogen atmosphere; they recommended a nitrogen pressure of ten atmospheres to obviate decomposition of UN at the melting point. Densification at lower temperatures by hot pressing was investigated by PAPROCKI et al. (1961), who obtained densities up to 95 per cent of theoretical on isostatically pressing (4 ton in.$^{-2}$, 3 hours) in cans of niobium or molybdenum at 1,400–1,500°C, while KELLER et al. (1961) obtained 90 per cent dense material on pressing (5 ton in.$^{-2}$) at 1,290°C for 3 hours. There is little doubt, however, that isostatic hot pressing is too expensive to be considered as a large scale production process.

Impetus to the development of nitride fuels has recently been provided by the measurements of Taylor and McMurtry on the thermal conductivity of the mononitride: within the large scatter of their data, the parameter lies between 0·10 and 0·15 cal cm$^{-1}$ sec$^{-1}$ deg$^{-1}$ C over the temperature range 280–1,000°C. Thus to the advantage over carbides of a higher fuel density may be added an improved thermal conductivity at elevated temperatures. Further work is required to verify this, however.

The only irradiation data available at the time of writing is that of ADAM and RODGERS (1961) who observed a small lattice dilation at low burn-ups (up to 3·5 MWd/T) analogous to that found with UC (Section 4.4.4).

### 4.8 THORIUM AND PLUTONIUM NITRIDES

Work on these compounds has so far been of a fundamental nature only, and no fuel development studies have been reported.

There is firm evidence in the literature only for a sesquinitride and a mono-nitride of thorium: the compound 'Th$_3$N$_4$' reported in early work was most probably Th$_2$N$_3$. On passing ammonia over thorium shavings at 900°C, Th$_2$N$_3$ is formed which is subsequently decomposed to ThN at 1,750°C (CHIOTTI, 1951). RUNDLE (1948) reports that the mononitride has a face-centred cubic (sodium chloride) structure; according to Chiotti the melting point is 2,630°C.

Work on the preparation and properties of plutonium mononitride has been carried out by BROWN, OCKENDEN and WELCH (1955), who prepared the compound by the reactions

$$\text{Pu} \xrightarrow[200°\text{C}]{\text{H}_2} \text{PuH}_{2\cdot7} \xrightarrow[230°\text{C}]{\text{N}_2} \text{PuN}$$

The hydriding step was essential, for bulk plutonium metal reacted slowly and incompletely with nitrogen at temperatures well above the melting point (up to 1,000°C).

Plutonium mononitride is isomorphous with UN and ThN. Presumably if other nitrides of plutonium exist they decompose below 230°C. PuN was found to be unstable in air, particularly in the presence of moisture, and was hydrolysed rapidly by hot water and by cold, dilute mineral acids giving ammonia salts and a mixture of colloidal and soluble plutonium.

### 4.9 URANIUM SILICIDES

#### 4.9.1. Phase Relationships and Chemical Properties

The complex phase diagram of the uranium and silicon system was first examined by Kaufmann and co-workers in the days of the Manhattan Project, and the findings were eventually published (KATZ and RABINOWITZ, 1951). Crystallographic studies were reported by ZACHARIASEN (1949), and the phase diagram was subsequently revised by KAUFMANN et al. (1957); this version, the details of which may well be subject to further revision, is reproduced in Figure 4.41. Table 4.19 contains a summary of the compounds which have been

TABLE 4.19

THE SILICIDES OF URANIUM

| Compound | Structure | Theoretical density (g cm$^{-3}$) | Melting point (°C) |
|---|---|---|---|
| ε phase ($\sim$U$_3$Si) | Body-centred tetragonal | 15·58 | 930 |
| U$_3$Si$_2$ | Tetragonal | 12·20 | 1,665 |
| USi | Orthorhombic | 10·40 | 1,575 |
| U$_2$Si$_3$ (designated β USi$_2$ by Zachariasen) | Hexagonal | 9·25 | 1,640 |
| USi$_2$ | Body-centred tetragonal | 8·98 | $\sim$1,700 |
| USi$_3$ | Cubic | 8·15 | 1,315 |

identified. Of these, $U_3Si_2$ and USi, by virtue of their high density and relatively high melting point, have the greatest potential as candidates for reactor fuels.

The mean coefficients of linear expansion ($\alpha$) of the silicides over the temperature range 20–900°C have been reported by SNYDER and DUCKWORTH

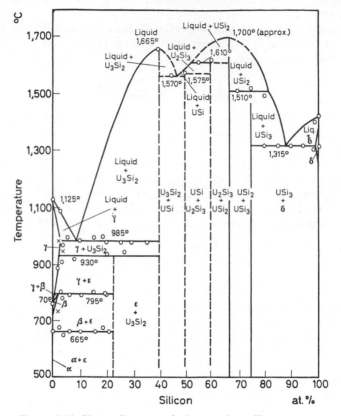

*Figure 4.41.* Phase diagram of the uranium–silicon system (Kaufmann *et al.*, 1957) (by courtesy of the Metallurgical Society of A.I.M.E. and Journal of Metals).

(1957) as follows:

| Compound | $U_3Si$ | $U_3Si_2$ | USi | $USi_2$ | $USi_3$ |
|---|---|---|---|---|---|
| $\alpha \times 10^6$ (deg$^{-1}$ C) | 17·5 | 14·6 | 16·5 | 16·8 | 12·0 |

and the mean specific heat of three of the compounds (0–300°C):

| Compound | $USi_2$ | $USi_3$ | $U_3Si$ |
|---|---|---|---|
| $C_p$ (cal g$^{-1}$ deg$^{-1}$ C) | 0·065 | 0·078 | 0·038 |

Data on the thermal conductivity of $U_3Si_2$ have been obtained by TAYLOR and McMURTRY (1961), who found a decrease with temperature from 0·09 cal cm$^{-1}$ sec$^{-1}$ at 230°C to 0·05 cal cm$^{-1}$ sec$^{-1}$ at 1,000°C: the same authors reported a number of other physical properties of this material.

Like the carbides and nitrides, the silicides of uranium are pyrophoric when finely divided (NICHOLS, 1958). KOENIG (1960) found that arc-cast specimens of $U_3Si_2$, while stable for long periods in air at 100°C, oxidized according to a parabolic rate law at 200°C and disintegrated completely after 16 hours at 315°C. SNYDER and DUCKWORTH (1957) have studied the initial stages of the oxidation in air of dense castings of $U_3Si_2$, $USi_2$ and $USi_3$, and found a parabolic rate law up to 400°C in all cases. The same authors have shown that these silicides reacted with nitrogen (300–700°C) faster than uranium metal under comparable conditions. Citing the results of isolated qualitative compatability tests, NICHOLS (1958) claims that $U_3Si$ is more resistant than uranium metal to corrosion by steam and water (see also Volume 2, Chapter 6), while $U_3Si_2$ oxidizes in carbon dioxide (700°C) at about the same rate as the metal. $U_3Si$ showed no signs of attack after a static test of 1 week in NaK at 800°C. LOCH et al. (1956) found that bulk specimens of $U_3Si$ and $USi_2$ showed only slight gains in weight (0·1–0·6 per cent) after 1 hour in hydrogen at 500°C.

### 4.9.2 Preparation and Densification

The only successful syntheses of pure uranium silicides have been carried out by direct combination of the elements (ISSEROW, 1956; LOCH et al., 1956; KAUFMANN et al., 1957). TAYLOR and McMURTRY (1961) prepared essentially single phase $U_3Si_2$ either by heating the elements in a crucible of magnesia to 1,500–1,550°C and cooling slowly, or heating to 1,750°C and quenching rapidly: slow cooling from 1,750°C resulted in the crystallization of a considerable proportion of $USi_2$. The same authors attempted to prepare $U_3Si_2$ by the reaction

$$3UO_2 + 2SiC + 4C \rightarrow U_3Si_2 + 6CO$$

but the results were not encouraging due to incomplete reaction and the formation of other silicides.

Densification of $U_3Si_2$ has been carried out by cold pressing and sintering. NICHOLS (1958) reports that after pressing at 25 ton in.$^{-2}$, powders of unspecified physical properties could be sintered to a density 95 per cent of theoretical after 2 hours at 1,400°C. Even higher densities (96·8–98·4 per cent of theoretical) were obtained by Taylor and McMurtry after sintering for 1 hour at 1,400°C in argon. The powders in this case were reduced to an average particle size of less than two microns and were pressed at about 2·5 ton in.$^{-2}$ (Carbowax-6000 binder); higher forming pressures (6–8 ton in.$^{-2}$) tended to result in cracked pellets.

The same authors performed hot pressing of uranium–silicon powders. Densities 90 per cent of theoretical were attained after 1 hour at 925°C and a pressure of 1,500 p.s.i. using a graphite die. For higher temperatures and shorter holding times other die materials (e.g. boron nitride, aluminium nitride) appear to be necessary.

No details of the sintering of other silicides of uranium are available, though mention of tests in general terms is made by LOCH et al. (1956).

### 4.9.3 Irradiation Behaviour

Irradiation tests on samples of $U_3Si$ clad with zircaloy-2 were carried out by BLEIBERG and JONES (1958), who observed a significant decrease in density accompanied by increases in hardness and electrical resistivity. The decrease in density (3·8 per cent) was independent of the maximum centre temperature over the range 160–250°C and of burn-up over the range 0·01–0·10 at.% uranium. X-ray examination showed that irradiation caused complete disappearance of the diffraction pattern (presumably due to crystallite fracture), and a great increase in brittleness of the specimens was indicative of considerable strain. The authors propose that these changes are due to radiation-induced disordering of the $U_3Si$ phase with a subsequent transformation of the lattice from face-centred tetragonal to face-centred cubic (which would account for the observed density decrease).

Some doubt has since been thrown on the conclusions of Bleiberg and Jones by the work of KITTEL and SMITH (1960), who observed no appreciable dimensional changes in cast $U_3Si$ test pieces irradiated under similar conditions to comparable burn-ups: changes in dimensions were observed only in extruded pieces, which showed moderate anisotropic growth. Furthermore, irradiations at higher centre temperatures (up to 660°C) have been reported by HOWE (1960), who found only a small decrease in density up to a burn-up of 0·06 at.%. At higher burn-ups, the rate of density decrease rose sharply, and a 7 per cent increase in volume was attained after 1·2 at.% burn-up; Howe considered this swelling to be due to the accumulation of fission product gases.

No irradiation work on other silicides of uranium has been reported: an examination of the behaviour of $U_3Si_2$ would be of particular value.

### 4.10 THORIUM AND PLUTONIUM SILICIDES

Until quite recently only one silicide of thorium ($ThSi_2$) was known, but detailed examinations of the thorium–silicon system by JACOBSON et al. (1956) and later by BROWN and NORREYS (1961) have established the existence of the compounds in *Table 4.20*.

TABLE 4.20

THE SILICIDES OF THORIUM

| Compound | Structure | Theoretical density (g cm$^{-3}$) | Melting point (°C) |
|---|---|---|---|
| $Th_3Si_2$ | Tetragonal | 9·75 | 1,850 |
| $ThSi$ | Orthorhombic | 8·92 | > 1,900 |
| $Th_3Si_5$ | Hexagonal | 7·91 | 1,750 |
| $\alpha–Th_6Si_{11}$ | Tetragonal | 7·89 | Indeterminate |
| $\beta–Th_6Si_{11}$ | Hexagonal | 7·88 | Transforms at ~ 1,300°C to $\alpha$-form |
| $\alpha–ThSi_2$ | Tetragonal | 7·79 | Indeterminate |
| $\beta–ThSi_2$ | Hexagonal | 7·78 | Transforms at ~ 1,300°C to $\alpha$-form |

A tentative phase diagram advanced by Brown and Norreys is reproduced in *Figure 4.42*.

In the system plutonium–silicon, only $PuSi_2$ has so far been identified (ZACHARIASEN, 1949).

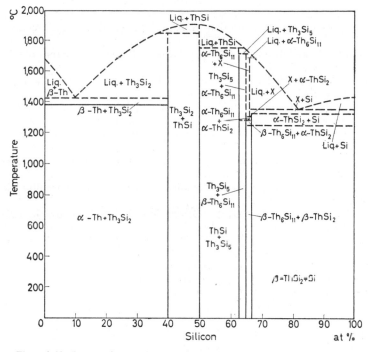

*Figure 4.42.* Proposed phase diagram for the thorium–silicon system (Brown and Norreys, 1961) (by courtesy of the Institute of Metals).

**REFERENCES**

*Oxides*

ACKERMAN, R. J., GILLIES, P. W. and THORN, R. J. (1956). 'High temperature thermodynamic properties of uranium dioxide.' *J. Chem. Phys.*, **25**, 1089

AINSCOUGH, J. B. (1961). 'The characteristics and sintering behaviour of uranium dioxide prepared by a homogeneous precipitation route.' *J. Appl. Chem.*, **11**, 365

AINSLEY, R. and SOWDEN, R. G. (1961). Unpublished work at A.E.R.E., Harwell

ALLEN, P. L. and SAUM, C. W. (1961). Unpublished work at U.K.A.E.A. Laboratories, Capenhurst

ALLISON, A. G. and DUCKWORTH, W. H. (1955). 'Ceramic investigations of $UO_2$.' U.S.A.E.C. Report, BMI-1009

ALLISON, E. B. and MURRAY, P. (1953). 'Sedimentation from concentrated suspensions in relation to particle size.' *Trans. Brit. Ceram. Soc.*, **52**, 204

ALLRED, V. D., BUXTON, S. R. and McBRIDE, J. P. (1957). 'Characteristic properties of thorium oxide particles.' *J. Phys. Chem.*, **61**, 117

ANDERSON, J. S., HARPER, E. A., MOORBATH, S. and ROBERTS, L. E. J. (1952). 'The properties and microstructure of uranium dioxide; their dependence upon the mode of preparation.' U.K.A.E.A. Report, AERE C/R 886

ANDERSON, J. S., EDGINGTON, D. N., ROBERTS, L. E. J. and WAIT, E. (1954). 'The oxides of uranium. Part IV. The system $UO_2$–$ThO_2$–O.' *J. Chem. Soc.*, 3324

ANDERSON, J. S. and JOHNSON, K. D. B. (1953). 'The oxides of uranium. III. The system $UO_2$–MgO–O.' *J. Chem. Soc.*, 1731

ANDERSON, J. S., ROBERTS, L. E. J. and HARPER, E. A. (1955). 'The oxides of uranium, Part VII. The oxidation of uranium dioxide.' *J. Chem. Soc.*, 3946

ANDERSON, J. S., SAWYER, J. O., WORNER, H. W., WILLIS, G. M. and BANNISTER, M. J. (1960). 'Decomposition of uranium dioxide at its melting point.' *Nature, Lond.*, **185**, 915

ARENBERG, C. A. and JAHN, P. (1958). 'Steam sintering of uranium dioxide.' *J. Amer. Ceram. Soc.*, **41**, 179

ARENBERG, C. A., RICE, H. H., SCHOFIELD, H. Z. and HANDWERK, J. H. (1957). 'Thoria ceramics.' *Bull. Amer. Ceram. Soc.*, **36**, 302

ARONSON, S. (1958). 'Oxidation of $UO_2$ in water containing oxygen.' Bettis Technical Review (Reactor Metallurgy). U.S.A.E.C. Report, WAPD-BT-10

ARONSON, S. and BELLE, J. (1958). 'Non-stoichiometry in uranium dioxide.' *J. Chem. Phys.*, **29**, 151

ARONSON, S., ROOF, R. B., JR. and BELLE, J. (1957). 'Kinetic study of the oxidation of uranium dioxide.' *J. Chem. Phys.*, **27**, 137

AUSKERN, A. B. and BELLE, J. (1961). 'Uranium ion self diffusion in uranium dioxide.' *J. Nucl. Materials*, **3**, 311

AUSKERN, A. B. and BELLE, J. (1961a). 'Oxygen ion self-diffusion in uranium dioxide.' *J. Nucl. Materials*, **3**, 267

BAIN, A. S. and Robertson, J. A. L. (1959). '$UO_2$ irradiations of short duration.' Atomic Energy of Canada Ltd. Report, CRFD-825

BAIN, A. S. and ROBERTSON, J. A. L. (1959). 'Effects of O:U ratio on the irradiation behaviour of uranium oxide.' *J. Nucl. Materials*, **1**, 109

BAIN, A. S., ROBERTSON, J. A. L. and RIDAL, A. (1961). '$UO_2$ irradiation of short duration. Part III.' Atomic Energy of Canada Ltd. Report, CRFD-955 (AECL-1192)

BAIRD, J. B. and WEST, K. B. C. (1959). Unpublished work at A.E.I./John Thompson Nuclear Energy Co. Ltd., under contract to U.K.A.E.A.

BANCROFT, A. R. and WATSON, L. C. (1958). 'Preparation of uranium dioxide for use in ceramic fuels. Part III. Ammonium diuranate reduction studies'. Atomic Energy of Canada Ltd. Report, CRCE-716, Part III

BARNEY, W. K. (1958). 'Irradiation effects in $UO_2$.' *Proc. Second Geneva Conf.*, **6**, 677

BARNEY, W. K. (1959). 'The swelling of $UO_2$ at high burn-up.' *Nuclear Metallurgy*, Vol. VI. A Symposium on the Effects of Irradiation on Fuel and Fuel Elements. IMD Special Report Series No. 9

BASKIN, Y., ARENBERG, C. A. and HANDWERK, J. H. (1959). 'Thoria reinforced by metal fibres.' *Ceram. Bull.*, **38**, 345

BASKIN, Y., HARADA, Y. and HANDWERK, J. H. (1960). 'Some physical properties of thoria reinforced by metal fibres.' *J. Amer. Ceram. Soc.*, **43**, 489

BATES, J. L. (1961). 'Thermal conductivity of $UO_2$ improves at high temperatures.' *Nucleonics*, **19**, No. 6, 83 (June)

BATES, J. L. and ROAKE, W. E. (1959). 'Irradiation testing of plutonium–uranium oxide nuclear fuel.' *Nuclear Metallurgy*, Vol. VI. A Symposium on the Effects of Irradiation on Fuel and Fuel Elements. IMD Special Report Series No. 9

BEL, A. and CARTERET, Y. (1958). 'Contribution to the study of sintering of uranium dioxide.' *Proc. Second Geneva Conf.*, **6**, 612

BEL, A., FRANCOIS, B., DELMAS, D. and CAILLAT, R. (1959). 'Frittage d'oxyde d'uranium de surface specifique elevée.' *C. R. Acad. Sci.*, **249**, 1045

BEL, A., DELMAS, R. and FRANCOIS, B. (1959a). 'Frittage de l'oxyde d'uranium dans l'hydrogène à 1,350°C.' *J. Nucl. Materials*, **3**, 259

# REFERENCES

BELBEOCH, B., PIEKARSKI, C. and PERIO, M. P. (1961). 'Influence des dimensions cristallines sur la cinétique d'oxydation de $UO_2$.' *J. Nucl. Materials*, **3**, 60

BELLE, J. (1958). 'Properties of uranium dioxide.' *Proc. Second Geneva Conf.*, **6**, 569

BELLE, J. and AUSKERN, A. B. (1958). 'Self-diffusion of oxygen in uranium dioxide.' *J. Chem. Phys.*, **28**, 171

BELLE, J. and LUSTMAN, B. (1957). 'Properties of uranium dioxide.' Proceedings of the Paris Fuel Elements Conference, 1957. U.S.A.E.C. Report TID-7546, Book 2

BERMAN, R. M., BLEIBERG, M. L. and YENISCAVICH, W. (1960). 'Fission fragment damage to crystal structures.' *J. Nucl. Materials*, **2**, 129

BLACKBURN, P. E. (1957). 'Oxygen dissociation pressures over uranium oxides.' Westinghouse Research Laboratories Report, 100 FF 942-P1

BLACKBURN, P. E., WEISSBART, J. and GULBRANSEN, E. A. (1958). 'Oxidation of uranium dioxide.' *J. Phys. Chem.*, **62**, 902

BLEIBERG, M. L., MASKARINEC, G., CLARK, D. and YENISCAVICH, W. (1960). 'Burn-up limitations of bulk $UO_2$ prototype fuel elements.' Bettis Technical Review (Reactor Technology). U.S.A.E.C. Report, WAPD-BT-18

BOURNS, W. T. and WATSON, L. C. (1958). 'Preparation of uranium dioxide for use in ceramic fuels. Part I. Batch precipitation of ammonium diuranate.' Atomic Energy of Canada Ltd. Report, CRCE-716, Part I

BOYKO, E. R., EICHENBERG, J. D., ROOF, R. B. JR. and HALTEMAN, E. K. (1960). 'X-ray examination of irradiated uranium dioxide.' Bettis Technical Review (Reactor Metallurgy). U.S.A.E.C. Report, WAPD-BT-6

BRADBURY, B. T. and HARRISON, J. W. (1961). 'A study of some structures in the uranium–oxygen system.' U.K.A.E.A. Report AERE-R-3626

BRETT, N. H. (1962). Unpublished work at A.E.R.E. Harwell

BRETT, N. H. and RUSSELL, L. E. (1960). 'The thermal expansion of $PuO_2$ and some other actinide oxides between room temperature and 1,000°C.' *Conf. Internationale sur la Metallurgie du Plutonium*. Paper No. 5 (Grenoble)

BRIGGS, A. and SCOTT, R. (1958). Unpublished work at A.E.R.E., Harwell

BRIGHT, N. F. H., GOW, K. V. and WEBSTER, A. H. (1957). 'The effect of carbon on the sintering of uranium dioxide.' Canadian Department of Mines Technical Surveys Report, MD-213

BROOKS, L. H. (1961). Unpublished work at U.K.A.E.A. Laboratories, Springfields

BUDNIKOR, P. P., TRESVYATSKII, S. G. and KUSHAKORSKII, V. I. (1958). 'Binary phase diagrams: $UO_2$–$Al_2O_3$; $UO_2$–BeO; $UO_2$–MgO.' *Proc. Second Geneva Conf.*, **6**, 125

BURDICK, M. D. and PARKER, H. S. (1956). 'Effect of particle size on bulk density and strength properties of uranium dioxide specimens.' *J. Amer. Ceram. Soc.*, **39**, 181

BYERLEY, J. J. (1960). 'The compatibility of $UO_2$ with the refractory metals and refractory metal thermocouples at temperatures above 1750°C.' Atomic Energy of Canada Ltd. Report, AECL-1126

CARMAN, P. C. (1938). 'Fundamental principles of industrial filtration.' *Trans. Inst. Chem. Engrs*, **16**, 168

CARRASCO, H. *et al.* (1959). 'Influence of lubricating agents on the sintering of $UO_2$.' (Presented at Symposium on Nuclear Materials, Salzjobaden, Sweden). U.S.A.E.C. Report, NP-9352

CASHIN, W. M. (1957). 'The fast oxide breeder—Fuel irradiation experiments.' U.S.A.E.C. Report, KAPL-1789

CASHIN, W. M. (1957). 'Irradiation experiments on a mixed plutonium–uranium oxide fast breeder fuel materials.' Paper presented at a meeting of the American Nuclear Society, Pittsburgh, Pa.

CAVALLARO, Y., MATHERN, J. P. and POWERS, R. M. (1960). Sylvania-Corning Nuclear Corp. Quarterly Progress Report, period ending March 31st 1960. U.S.A.E.C. Report, SCNC-309

CERAMIC FUELS STAFF, HANFORD (1960). 'Novel ceramic fuel fabrication processes.' U.S.A.E.C. Report, HW-64629

CHALDER, G. H. (1959). 'Fuel fabrication studies related to the N.P.D. reactor.' Atomic Energy of Canada Ltd. Report, CRFD-758

CHALDER, G. H., BRIGHT, N. F. H., PATTERSON, D. L. and WATSON, L. C. (1958). 'The fabrication and properties of uranium dioxide fuel.' *Proc. Second Geneva Conf.*, **6**, 590

CHIKALLA, T. D. (1959). 'Sintering studies on the system $UO_2 \cdot PuO_2$.' U.S.A.E.C. Report, HW-63081

CHIKALLA, T. D. (1960). 'Studies on the oxides of plutonium.' *Conf. Internationale sur la Metallurgie du Plutonium*, Paper No. 35 (Grenoble)

CHRISTIE, G. and WILLIAMS, J. (1961). 'The effect of small additions of yttria on the plasticity of uranium oxides at 940°C.' U.K.A.E.A. Report, AERE-R-3702

CLARKE, F. J. P. (1960). 'The effects of reactor irradiation on ceramic materials.' U.K.A.E.A. Report, AERE-M-659

CLAYTON, J. C. and ARONSON, S. (1958). 'Some preparation methods and physical characteristics of $UO_2$ powders.' U.S.A.E.C. Report, WAPD-178. (*J. Chem. Eng. Data*, **6**, 1960, 43)

CLAYTON, J. C. and BERRIN, L. (1960). 'A study of the sintering behaviour of some uranium dioxide powders.' U.S.A.E.C. Report, WAPD-BT-20, pp. 23–38

CURTIS, C. E. (1959). 'Thorium oxide in ceramic applications.' *Progress in Nuclear Energy*, Vol. 2, Series V. Pergamon

DAVIDSON, J. K., HAAS, W. O., JR., MEWHERTER, J. L., MILLER, R. S. and SMITH, D. J. (1957). 'The fast oxide breeder—The fuel cycle.' U.S.A.E.C. Report, KAPL-1757

DAVIDSON, J. K., MILLER, R. S. and SMITH, D. J. (1959). 'Fast oxide breeder—Fuel cycle and cost.' *Nucleonics*, January, p. 88

DEANE, A. M. (1960). 'The infra-red spectra and structures of some hydrated uranium trioxides and ammonium diuranates.' U.K.A.E.A. Report, AERE-R3411

DEEM, H. W. (1960). Unpublished work at AECL Laboratories, Chalk River. (Reported by Ross, 1960)

DEMARCO, R. E., HELLER, H. A., ABBOT, R. C. and BURKHARDT, W. (1959). 'Oxidation of $UO_2$ to $U_3O_8$.' *Ceramic Bulletin*, **38**, 360

D'EYE, R. W. M. and BLUNDELL, A. (1960). Unpublished work at U.K.A.E.A. Laboratories, Capenhurst

DRUMMOND, J. L. and WELCH, G. (1957). 'The preparation and properties of some plutonium compounds. Part VI. Plutonium dioxide.' *J. Chem. Soc.*, 4781

EHLERT, T. C. (1958). 'The melting point and spectral emissivity of $UO_2$.' M.S. Thesis, University of Wisconsin

EICHENBERG, J. D. (1958). 'An in-pile measurement of the effective thermal conductivity of $UO_2$.' U.S.A.E.C. Report, WAPD-200

EICHENBERG, J. D., FRANK, P. W., KISIEL, T. J., LUSTMAN, B. and VOGEL, K. W. (1957). 'Effects of irradiation on bulk uranium dioxide.' *Proc. Fuel Elements Conference*, Paris, Book 2, p. 616. U.S.A.E.C. Report TID-7546

EISS, A. L. (1958). 'Reactivity of certain uranium oxides with aluminium.' U.S.A.E.C. Report, SCNC-257

ELLIS, J. F., GARNER, E. V., EDWARDS, L. A. and ALLEN, P. L. (1960). Unpublished work at U.K.A.E.A. Laboratories, Capenhurst

EVANS, E. A. *et al.* (1957). 'Fabrication and enclosure of uranium dioxide.' *Proc. Fuel Elements Conf.*, Paris, Book 2, p. 414

FOX, A. and BRETT, N. H. (1962). 'Oxidation products of $PuO_2 \cdot UO_2$ solid solutions in air at 750°C.' U.K.A.E.A. Report AERE R-3937

FRANCIS, K. E. and SOWDEN, R. G. (1959). 'The microstructure of plutonium dioxide prepared by various methods.' U.K.A.E.A. Report, AERE-2939

# REFERENCES

GANGLER, J. J., SANDERS, W. A. and DRELL, I. L. (1960). 'Uranium dioxide compatibility with refractory metals, carbides, borides, nitrides and oxides between 3,500 and 5,000°F.' U.S. National Aeronautics and Space Administration, Technical Note TND-262

GILLIES, D. M. (1946). 'Some studies of the reactions of uranium oxide with hydrogen, oxygen and water.' U.S.A.E.C. Report, MDDC-647

GROCE, I. J. and SULLIVAN, R. J. (1960). 'Oxidative decladding of $UO_2$ fuel rods.' U.S.A.E.C. Report, NAA-SR-Memo-5998

GRONVOLD, F. (1955). 'High-temperature X-ray study of uranium oxides in the $UO_2$–$U_3O_8$ region.' *J. Inorg. Nucl. Chem.*, **1**, 357

HALL, A. R., SCOTT, R. and WILLIAMS, J. (1958). 'The plastic deformation of uranium oxides above 800°C.' U.K.A.E.A. Report, AERE M/R 2648

HANDWERK, J. H. (1957). 'Ceramic fuel elements in $ThO_2$.$UO_2$ and $UO_2$.$PuO_2$ systems.' *Proc. Fuel Elements Conference* (Paris), p. 526. U.S.A.E.C. Report TID-7546

HANDWERK, J. H., ABERNETHY, L. L. and BACH, R. A. (1957). 'Thoria and urania bodies.' *Bull. Amer. Ceramic Soc.*, **36**, 99

HANDWERK, J. H. and NOLAND, R. A. (1959). 'Fabrication of fuel elements for the BORAX IV reactor.' *Progress in Nuclear Energy*, V, **2**, p. 239. Pergamon

HANSON, L. A. (1959). 'Removal of irradiated $UO_2$ fuel from the cladding by controlled oxidation.' U.S.A.E.C. Report, NAA-SR-3591

HARDER, B. R. and SOWDEN, R. G. (1960). 'The oxidation of uranium dioxide by water vapour under reactor irradiation.' U.K.A.E.A. Report, AERE-M.725

HARRINGTON, C. D. (1957). 'Preparation and properties of uranium dioxide powder.' *Proc. Fuel Elements Conf.*, Paris, Book 2, p. 369

HARRINGTON, C. D. and RUEHLE, A. E. (1958). 'Preparation and properties of uranium dioxide powder.' *Chem. Eng. Progr.*, **54**, No. 3, 65–70

HARRINGTON, C. D. and RUEHLE, A. E. (1959). *Uranium Production Technology.* Van Nostrand

HARRISON, J. D. L., FOSTER, E. and RUSSELL, L. E. (1961). 'The sintering behaviour of mixed $UO_2$ and $PuO_2$ powders.' U.K.A.E.A. Report, AERE-3765

HAUTH, J. J. (1959–61). 'Vibration-compacted ceramic fuel elements.' U.S.A.E.C. Reports, HW-60346 (1959) and HW-67777 (1961)

HEDGE, J. C. and FIELDHOUSE, I. B. (1956). 'Measurement of thermal conductivity of uranium oxide.' U.S.A.E.C. Report, AECU 3381

HENDRY, I. C. (1960). Unpublished work at U.K.A.E.A. Culcheth Laboratories

HERMANS, M. E. A. (1958). 'The preparation of uranium dioxide fuel for a suspension reactor.' *Proc. Second Geneva Conf.*, **7**, 39

HOEKSTRA, H. R., SANTORIO, A. and SIEGEL, S. (1961). 'The low temperature oxidation of $UO_2$ and $U_4O_9$.' *J. Inorg. Nucl. Chem.*, **18**, 166

HOLLEY, C. E., MULFORD, R. N. R., HUBER, E. J., JR., HEAD, E. L., ELLINGER, F. H. and BORKLUND, C. W. (1958). 'Thermodynamics and phase relationships for plutonium oxide.' *Proc. Second Geneva Conf.*, **6**, 215

HOWARD, V. C. and GULVIN, T. F. (1960). 'Thermal conductivity determinations on uranium dioxide by a radial flow method.' U.K.A.E.A. Report, IG-51

HUND, F. and NIESSEN, G. (1952). 'Anomale Mischkristalle im Systeme Thoriumoxyd-Uranoxyd.' *Z. Elektrochem.*, **56**, 972

JOHNSON, R. R. and CURTIS, C. E. (1954). 'Note on sintering of thoria.' *J. Amer. Ceram. Soc.*, **37**, 611

KANE, J. (1960). 'Swaged metal fibre–$UO_2$ fuel elements final report.' U.S.A.E.C. Report MND-SF-1770

KANTAN, S. K., RAGHAVAN, R. V. and TENDULKAR, G. S. (1958). 'Sintering of thorium and thoria.' *Proc. Second Geneva Conf.*, **6**, 132

KELLY, K. K. (1949). *Bull. U.S. Bur. Mines*, 476

211

KIESSLING, R. and RUNFORS, V. (1957). 'Sintering of uranium dioxide.' *Proc. Fuel Elements Conf.*, Paris, Book 2, p. 402

KINGERY, W. D., FRANCL, J., COBLE, R. L. and VASILOS, T. (1954). 'Thermal conductivity: Data for several pure oxide materials corrected to zero porosity.' *J. Amer. Ceram. Soc.*, **37**, 107

KINGERY, W. D. (1955). 'Thermal conductivity: XII. Temperature dependence of conductivity for single-phase ceramics.' *J. Amer. Ceram. Soc.*, **38**, 251

KINZER, J. E. and MELLOT, A. N. (1960). 'Organic coolant—UO$_2$ compatibility.' U.S.A.E.C. Report, NAA-SR-Memo-5167

KITTEL, J. H. and HANDWERK, J. H. (1958). 'Preliminary irradiations of the ceramic fuels UO$_2$, UO$_2$–ZrO$_2$ and ThO$_2$–UO$_2$.' U.S.A.E.C. Report, ANL-5675

KIUKKOLA, K. and WAGNER, C. (1957). 'Measurements on galvanic cells involving solid electrolytes.' *J. Electrochem. Soc.*, **104**, 379

KNAPTON, A. G. and FINCH, T. S. (1961). Unpublished work at A.E.I.—John Thompson Nuclear Energy Co. Ltd., under contract to U.K.A.E.A.

LAMBERTSON, W. A. and HANDWERK, J. H. (1956). 'The fabrication and physical properties of urania bodies.' U.S.A.E.C. Report, ANL-5053

LAMBERTSON, W. A. and MUELLER, M. H. (1953). 'Uranium oxide phase equilibrium system, UO$_2$–MgO.' *J. Amer. Chem. Soc.*, **36**, 332

LAMBERTSON, W. A. and MUELLER, M. H. (1953). 'Uranium oxide phase equilibrium system, UO$_2$–ZrO$_2$.' *J. Amer. Ceramic Soc.*, **36**, 365

LAMBERTSON, W. A., MUELLER, M. H. and GUNZEL, F. H., JR. (1953). 'Uranium oxide phase equilibrium systems; UO$_2$.ThO$_2$.' *J. Amer. Ceram. Soc.*, **36**, 397

LANG, S. M. and KNUDSEN, F. P. (1956). 'Some physical properties of high density thorium oxide.' *J. Amer. Ceram. Soc.*, **39**, 415

LANG, S. M., KNUDSEN, F. P., FILLMORE, C. L. and ROTH, R. S. (1956). 'High temperature reactions of uranium dioxide with various metal oxides.' *U.S. Nat. Bureau of Standards Report, N.B.S. Circular* 568

LANGROD, K. (1960). 'Sintering of uranium dioxide in the range of 1,200–1,300°C.' *Amer. Ceram. Soc. Bull.*, **39**, 366

LEIPUNSKY, A. I. *et al.* (1958). 'Experimental fast reactors in the Soviet Union.' *Proc. Second Geneva Conference*, **9**, 348

LOEB, A. L. (1954). 'Thermal conductivity: VIII. A theory of thermal conductivity of porous materials.' *J. Amer. Ceramic Soc.*, **37**, 96

LOJEK, J. M., LINDSAY, W. T. and COHEN, P. (1958). 'Corrosion and erosion of sintered UO$_2$ compacts in high temperature water.' Bettis Technical Review (Reactor Chemistry and Plant Materials). U.S.A.E.C. Report, WAPD-BT-7

LYNCH, E. D., HANDWERK, J. H. and HOENIG, C. L. (1960). 'Oxidation studies of urania–thoria solid solutions.' *J. Amer. Ceram. Soc.*, **43**, 520

MacEWAN, J. R. (1961). 'Grain growth in sintered uranium dioxide.' Atomic Energy of Canada Ltd. Report, CRFD-999

MacEWAN, J. R. and LAWSON, V. B. (1960). 'Thermal simulation experiments with a UO$_2$ fuel rod assembly.' Atomic Energy of Canada Ltd. Report, CRFD-915

MacEWAN, J. R. and LAWSON, V. B. (1962). 'Grain growth in sintered uranium dioxide. II. Columnar grain growth.' *J. Amer. Ceram. Soc.*, **45**, 42

MALLETT, M. W., DROEGE, J. W., GERDS, A. F. and LEMMON, A. W. (1957). 'The zirconium–uranium dioxide reaction.' U.S.A.E.C. Report, BMI-1210

MALLETT, M. W., GERDS, A. F., LEMMON, A. W. and CHASE, D. L. (1955). 'The kinetics of the zirconium–uranium dioxide reaction.' U.S.A.E.C. Report, BMI-1028

MALLINCKRODT CHEMICAL COMPANY (1960). 'Improvements in the preparation of ammonium diuranate.' U.S. Patent Spec. No. 854, 235

MARKIN, T. L. and ROBERTS, L. E. J. (1962). Unpublished work at A.E.R.E., Harwell

MICHAUD, C. G. and BOUCHER, R. R. (1961). Unpublished work at Chalk River Laboratories, A.E.C.L.

# REFERENCES

Mizzan, E. and Chalder, G. H. (1958). 'Comparison of binder/lubricant additives in dry pressing of uranium dioxide powder.' Atomic Energy of Canada Ltd. Report CRFD-757

Mooney, R. C. L. and Zachariasen, W. H. (1949). 'Crystal structure of the oxides of plutonium.' *Natl. Nuclear Energy Series IV.–14B*, Pt. 2, Paper 20.1. McGraw-Hill

Mulford, N. R. and Ellinger, F. H. (1958). '$UO_2$.$PuO_2$ solid solutions.' *J. Amer. Chem. Soc.*, **80**, 2033

Mumpton, F. A. and Roy, R. (1960). 'Low temperature equilibrium among $ZrO_2$, $ThO_2$ and $UO_2$.' *J. Amer. Ceram. Soc.*, **43**, 234

Murray, P., Denton, I. and Wilkinson, D. (1956). 'The preparation of dense thoria crucibles and tubes.' *Trans. Brit. Ceram. Soc.*, **55**, 191

Murray, P. and Livey, D. T. (1956). 'The technology of urania and thoria.' *Progress in Nuclear Energy*, V, **1**, Pergamon

Murray, P., Pugh, S. F. and Williams, J. (1957). 'Uranium dioxide as a reactor fuel.' *Proc. Fuel Elements Conf.*, Paris, Book 2, p. 432

Murray, P., Rodgers, E. P. and Williams, A. E. (1952). 'Practical and theoretical aspects of the hot pressing of refractory oxides.' U.K.A.E.A. Report, AERE M/R893

Murray, P. and Thackray, R. W. (1952). 'Thermal expansion of sintered $UO_2$.' U.K.A.E.A. Report, AERE M/M22

Murray, P. and Williams, J. (1958). 'Ceramic and cermet fuels.' *Proc. Second Geneva Conf.*, **6**, 538

Myles, J. W. and Sayers, J. D. (1961). Unpublished work at U.K.A.E.A., Harwell

Neimark, L. A. (1961). 'Examination of an irradiated prototype fuel element for the Elk River reactor.' U.S.A.E.C. Report, ANL-6160

Neimark, L. A. and Kittel, J. H. (1959). 'Irradiation behaviour of $ThO_2$.$UO_2$ fuels.' *Nuclear Metallurgy*, Vol. VI. A Symposium on the Effects of Irradiation on Fuel and Fuel Elements, p. 83. IMD Special Report Series No. 9

Newkirk, H. W. and Anicetti, R. J. (1957). 'Fabrication of uranium dioxide fuel element shapes by hydrostatic pressing.' U.S.A.E.C. Report, HW-51770

Nicholls, R. W. (1958). 'Ceramic fuels—Properties and technology.' *Nuclear Engng*, August

Paterson, D. L. and Chalder, G. H. (1959). 'The integral fabrication of uranium dioxide fuel elements by rotary swaging.' Atomic Energy of Canada Ltd. Report, CRFD-759

Peakall, K. A. and Antill, J. E. (1960). 'Oxidation of uranium dioxide in air at 350–1,000°C.' *J. Nucl. Materials*, **2**, 194

Peakall, K. A., Antill, J. E. and Bennett, M. J. (1960). Unpublished work at A.E.R.E., Harwell

Perio, P. (1953). 'The oxidation of uranic oxide at low temperatures.' *Bull. Soc. Chim.*, **20**, 256

Perio, P. (1953). 'Observations on uranium oxides formed between $UO_2$ and $U_3O_8$.' *Bull. Soc. Chim.*, **20**, 840

Picklesimer, M. L. (1956). 'The reaction of $UO_2$ with aluminium.' U.S.A.E.C. Report, ORNL-CF-56-8-135

Pijanowski, S. W. and DeLuca, L. S. (1960). 'Melting points in the system $PuO_2$.$UO_2$.' U.S.A.E.C. Report, KAPL-1957

Placek, C. and North, E. D. (1960). 'Uranium dioxide nuclear fuel.' *Ind. Eng. Chem.*, **52**, 458

Powers, R. M. (1960). '$UO_2$ additives.' *Nucleonics*, October, p. 6

PWR Project, Technical Progress Report, August–December 1961. U.S.A.E.C. Reports WAPD-MRP-94 and WAPD-MRP-95

Rand, M. H. and Jackson, E. E. (1962). 'The oxidation behaviour of $PuO_2$ and solid solutions containing $PuO_2$.' U.K.A.E.A. Report AERE R-3636

REACTOR HANDBOOK (1955). 'General properties of materials.' U.S.A.E.C. Report AECD-3647

REISWIG, R. D. (1961). 'Thermal conductivity of $UO_2$ to 2,100°C.' *J. Amer. Ceramic Soc.*, **44**, 48

RIDAL, A. *et al.* (1961). 'Irradiation of non-stoichiometric uranium oxide for short durations.' Atomic Energy of Canada Ltd. Report, CRFD-994 (AECL-1199)

RILEY, B. (1961). Unpublished work at A.E.R.E., Harwell

ROBERTS, L. E. J., RUSSELL, L. E., ADWICK, A. G., WALTER, A. J. and RAND, M. H. (1958). 'The actinide oxides.' *Proc. Second Geneva Conf.*, **28**, 215

ROBERTS, L. E. J. and HARPER, E. A. (1952). 'The determination of oxygen in uranium oxides.' U.K.A.E.A. Report, AERE C/R885

ROBERTS, L. E. J. and WALTER, A. J. (1960). 'Equilibrium pressures and phase relations in the uranium oxide system.' U.K.A.E.A. Report, AERE-R 3345

ROBERTS, L. E. J. (1961). 'The actinide oxides.' *Quart. Rev. Chem. Soc. (London)*, **15**, 4, 442

ROBERTSON, J. A. L. (1959). '$\int k d\theta$ in fuel irradiations.' Atomic Energy of Canada Ltd. Report, CRFD-835

ROBERTSON, J. A. L. (1960). 'Concerning the effects of excess oxygen in $UO_2$.' Atomic Energy of Canada Ltd. Report, CRFD-973 (AECL-1123)

ROBERTSON, J. A. L., BAIN, A. S., BOOTH, A. H., HOWIESON, J., MORRISON, W. G. and ROBERTSON, R. F. S. (1958). 'Behaviour of uranium oxide as a reactor fuel.' *Proc. Second Geneva Conf.*, **6**, 655

ROBERTSON, J. A. L., BAIN, A. S., ALLISON, G. M. and STEVENS, W. W. (1959). 'Irradiation behaviour of $UO_2$ fuel elements.' *Nuclear Metallurgy*, Vol. VI. A Symposium on the Effects of Irradiation on Fuel and Fuel Elements, p. 45. IMD Special Report Series No. 9

ROBERTSON, J. A. L. *et al.* (1960). 'The effect of 4 mole % $Y_2O_3$ on the thermal conductivity of $UO_2$.' Atomic Energy of Canada Ltd. Report, CRFD-933

ROSE, R. G. (1958). Unpublished work at U.K.A.E.A. Culcheth Laboratories

ROSS, A. M. (1960). 'The dependence of the thermal conductivity of uranium dioxide on density, microstructure, stoichiometry and thermal neutron irradiation.' Atomic Energy of Canada Ltd. Report, CRFD-817

ROTHWELL, E. (1961). 'High temperature substoichiometry in uranium dioxide.' U.K.A.E.A. Report AERE-R 3897

RUNFORS, U., SCHONBERG, N. and KIESSLING, R. (1958). 'The sintering of uranium dioxide.' *Proc. Second Geneva Conf.*, **6**, 605

RUNNALS, O. J. C. (1959). 'Uranium dioxide fuel elements.' Atomic Energy of Canada Ltd. Report, CRL-55. (*Nucleonics*, May, p. 104)

RUSSELL, L. E. (1961). 'Sintering of plutonium dioxide.' Paper 25-X-61 presented at the Toronto meeting of the American Ceramic Society (April).

RUSSELL, L. E., BRETT, N. H., HARRISON, J. D. L., WILLIAMS, J. and ADWICK, A. G. (1960). 'Observations on phase equilibria and sintering behaviour in the $PuO_2$–$UO_2$ system.' U.K.A.E.A. Report, AERE-R3519. (Preprint). Published in *J. Nucl. Materials*, (1962) **5**, 2, 216

RYSHKEWITCH, E. (1960). *Oxide Ceramics*. Academic Press

SAYERS, J. B., MYLES, J. W. and JONES, D. V. C. (1960). Unpublished work at A.E.R.E., Harwell

SAYERS, J. B. and WORTH, J. H. (1961). 'Comparison of the irradiation behaviour of 1% $PuO_2$ in $UO_2$ and stoichiometric $UO_2$.' I.A.E.A. Symposium on Power Reactor Experiments, Paper SM-21/3 (Vienna)

SCHANER, B. E. (1959). 'Fabrication of high density $UO_2$ fuel platelets.' *Ceramic Bulletin*, **38**, 494

SCHANER, B. E. (1960). 'Metallographic determination of the $UO_2$–$U_4O_9$ phase diagram.' *J. Nucl. Materials*, **2**, 110

REFERENCES

SCHÖNBERG, N., RUNFORS, U. and KIESSLING, R. (1958). 'Production of uranium dioxide compacts for fuel elements.' *Proc. Second Geneva Conference*, **6**, 624

SCOTT, R. (1958). 'Thermal conductivity of $UO_2$.' U.K.A.E.A. Report, AERE M/R-2526

SCOTT, R. and WILLIAMS, J. (1957). 'The warm pressing (800°C) of uranium dioxide and uranium dioxide–metal mixtures.' U.K.A.E.A. Report, AERE M/R-2396

SEDDON, B. J. (1960). *Uranium ceramics data manual*. 'Properties of interest in reactor design.' (U.K.A.E.A., Risley)

SHAPIRO, W. and POWERS, R. M. (1959). 'Uranium dioxide fuel materials with improved thermal conductivity.' U.S.A.E.C. Report, SCNC-271

SHAPIRO, W. and POWERS, R. M. (1959a). 'Thoria–urania pellet preparation.' U.S.A.E.C. Report, SCNC-290

SHARPE, B., PLAIL, O. S. and PUGH, S. F. (1958). Unpublished work at A.E.R.E., Harwell

SKINNER, G. B., BECKETT, C. W. and JOHNSON, H. L. (1950). 'Thermal structural etc. properties. Part 4. Thorium and compounds.' U.S.A.E.C. Report, ATI-81813

SLOWINSKI, E. and ELLIOT, W. (1952). 'Lattice constants and magnetic susceptibilities of solid solutions of uranium and thorium dioxides.' *Acta. Cryst.*, **5**, 768

SMITH, T. D. (1960). 'Kinetics and mechanism of the oxidation of uranium dioxide and uranium dioxide plus fissia sintered pellets.' U.S.A.E.C. Report, NAA-SR-4677

SMITH, T. D. (1960a). 'Kinetics of the oxidation of a thoria–10 w/o urania sintered pellet.' U.S.A.E.C. Report, NAA-SR-Memo 5773

SMITHELLS, C. J. (1949). *Metals Reference Book*. Butterworth

SOWDEN, R. G., AINSLEY, R. and STOCKDALE, G. N. (1962). 'The preparation of $UO_2 . PuO_2$ powder for nuclear fuels.' *Progress in Nuclear Energy*. IV, **5**, 347 Pergamon

SOWDEN, R. G. and STOCKDALE, G. N. (1961). 'The characterisation of precipitates by filtration and settling parameters: a comparison of ammonium diuranate and uranium (IV) oxalate.' U.K.A.E.A. Report, AERE-R. 3767

SOWMAN, H. G. and PLOETZ, G. L. (1956). 'An investigation of the sintering of uranium dioxide.' U.S.A.E.C. Report, KAPL-1556

SPALARIS, C. N. (1961). 'Chemical stability of $UO_2$ in reactor water.' *Trans. Amer. Nucl. Soc.*, **4**, 146

STENQUIST, D. R. and ANICETTI, R. J. (1957). 'Fabrication behaviour of some uranium dioxide powders.' U.S.A.E.C. Report, HW-51748

STENQUIST, D. R., MASTEL, B. and ANICETTI, R. J. (1958). 'Note on correlation of surface characteristics of uranium dioxide powders with their sintering behaviour.' *J. Amer. Ceram. Soc.*, **41**, 273

STODDARD, S. D. and HARPER, W. T. (1957). *Bull. Amer. Ceram. Soc.*, **36**, 105

STOOPS, R. F. and HAMME, J. V. (1960). 'Study of phase relationships in the U–C–O system. Progress report.' U.S.A.E.C. Report, ORO-364

STRAUSBERG, A. and LUEBBEN, T. E. (1959). 'Chemical pulverisation of sintered uranium dioxide bodies, Part I.' U.S.A.E.C. Report, NAA-SR-3910

STRAUSBERG, S., LUEBBEN, T. and REED, D. W. (1960). 'Chemical pulverisation of sintered uranium dioxide bodies, Part II.' U.S.A.E.C. Report, NAA-SR-3911

STROMATT, R. W. and CONALLY, R. E. (1961). 'Determination of the stoichiometry of uranium dioxide by controlled potential coulometry.' *Analyt. Chem.*, **33**, 345

THACKRAY, R. W. and MURRAY, P. (1950). 'The sintering of uranium dioxide.' U.K.A.E.A. Report, AERE M/R 614

VAUGHAN, D. A., BRIDGE, J. R., ALLISON, A. G. and SCHWARTZ, C. M. (1957). 'Processing variables, reactivity and sintering of uranium dioxides.' *Ind. Eng. Chem.*, **49**, 1699

VICTOR, A. C. and DOUGLAS, T. B. (1961). 'Thermodynamic properties of thorium dioxide from 298 to 1,200°K.' *J. Res. Nat. Bur. Stand.*, **A65**, 105

215

WAIT, E. (1962). Unpublished work at A.E.R.E. Harwell

WARDE, J. M. and JOHNSON, J. R. (1955). 'Recent developments in the technology of ceramic materials for nuclear energy service.' *J. Franklin Institute*, **260**, 455

WARREN, I. H. (1960). 'New route to reactor grade $UO_2$.' *Chem. Eng. News*, **38**, No. 19, 54

WATSON, J. F. and WILDER, D. R. (1960). 'Roles of niobium pentoxide, vanadium pentoxide and titanium dioxide in the grain growth and sintering of uranium dioxide.' U.S.A.E.C. Report, 15–21

WATSON, L. C. (1957). 'Production of uranium dioxide for ceramic fuels.' *Proc. Fuel Elements Conf.*, Paris, Book 2, p. 384

WATSON, M. B. and BAIRD, J. (1961). Unpublished work at A.E.C.L. Chalk River Laboratories

WAUGH, R. C. (1959). 'The reaction and growth of uranium dioxide–aluminium fuel plates and compacts.' U.S.A.E.C. Report, ORNL-2701

WAUGH, R. C. and CUNNINGHAM, J. E. (1956). 'The application of low enrichment uranium dioxide to aluminium plate-type fuel elements.' U.S.A.E.C. Report, ORNL-CF-56-8-128

WEBB, B. A. (1959). 'Vibratory compaction and swaging of uranium dioxide to high density.' U.S.A.E.C. Report, NAA-SR-4155

WEBER, C. E. (1958). 'Radiation damage in non-metallic fuel elements.' *Proc. Second Geneva Conference*, **5**, 619

WEBSTER, A. H. and BRIGHT, N. F. H. (1957). 'The effects of additives of the sintering of uranium dioxide.' Canadian Dept. of Mines and Technical Surveys Report, MD-223

WHETSEL, H. B. and DEAN, O. C. (1960). 'Precipitation of crystalline uranium and thorium peroxide: Applications to fuel element oxides and purifications.' U.S.A.E.C. Report, ORNL-CF-60-9-5

WHITTEMORE, O. J., JR. and AULT, N. N. (1956). 'Thermal expansion of various ceramic materials to 1,500°C.' *J. Amer. Ceram. Soc.*, **39**, 443

WILLIAMS, J. (1960). 'The sintering of uranium oxides.' *J. Nucl. Materials*, **2**, 92

WILLIAMS, J., BARNES, E., SCOTT, R. and HALL, A. (1959). 'Sintering of uranium oxides of composition $UO_2$ to $U_3O_8$ in various atmospheres.' *J. Nucl. Materials*, **1**, 28

WILLIAMS, N. R., WHEATLEY, C. C. H. and LLOYD, H. (1959). Unpublished work at A.E.R.E., Harwell

WILSON, W. B. (1959). 'Stabilisation of $UO_2$ by valence compensation.' U.S.A.E.C. Report, BMI-1318

WILSON, W. B. and GERDS, A. F. (1960). 'Stabilising effects of oxide additions to uranium dioxide.' U.S.A.E.C. Report, BMI-1467

WINCHELL, R. (1958). 'Progress in the development of a process for producing $UO_2$ pellets.' U.S.A.E.C. Report, YAEC-84

WIRTHS, G. and ZIEHL, L. (1958). 'Special problems arising in connection with the production of uranium metal and uranium compounds.' *Proc. Second Geneva Conf.* **4**, 16

WISNYI, L. G. and PIJANOWSKI, S. (1956). 'The melting point of $UO_2$.' U.S.A.E.C. Report, KAPL-1658

WISNYI, L. G. and PIJANOWSKI, S. W. (1957). 'The thermal stability of uranium dioxide.' U.S.A.E.C. Report, KAPL-1702

WRINKLE, R. B. (1959). 'Sintering of $UO_2$ powders for fuel elements.' Proc. Nucl. Eng. Sci. Conf., Cleveland, Ohio. Preprint V-108

YATABE, E. and WATSON, L. C. (1958). 'Preparation of uranium dioxide for use in ceramic fuels, Part II. Continuous precipitation of ammonia diuranate.' Atomic Energy of Canada Ltd. Report, CRCE-716, Part II

YOUNG, D. A. (1958). Unpublished work at A.E.R.E., Harwell

REFERENCES

*Carbides, Nitrides, Silicides*

ACCARY, A. (1960). 'Advances in uranium carbide technology in France.' U.S.A.E.C. Report, TID-7603, p. 147

ACCARY, A. and CAILLAT, R. (1961). 'Les methodes de mise en forme du monocarbure d'uranium.' Proc. Fourth Plansee Seminar (Reutte, Austria), Paper 1

ADAM, J. and RODGERS, M. D. (1961). 'X-ray diffraction studies of fission fragment damage in uranium carbide and nitride.' *J. Nucl. Energy.* Pts. A and B, Reactor Sci. and Technol. **14**, 51

AINSLEY, R. and SOWDEN, R. G. (1961). Unpublished work at A.E.R.E., Harwell

ALBRECHT, W. M. and KOEHL, B. G. (1958). 'Reactivity of uranium compounds in several gaseous media.' *Proc. Second Geneva Conf.*, **6**, 116

ANTILL, J. E., PEAKALL, K. A., CRICK, N. and SMART, E. (1957). Unpublished work at A.E.R.E., Harwell

AUSTIN, A. E. (1959). 'Carbon positions in uranium carbides.' *Acta Cryst.*, **12**, 159

AUSTIN, A. E. and GERDS, A. F. (1958). 'The uranium–nitrogen–carbon system.' U.S.A.E.C. Report, BMI-1272

BAKER, J. (1946). 'Uranium carbide.' U.S.A.E.C. Report, NEPA-138

BARNES, E. *et al.* (1956). 'The preparation, fabrication and properties of uranium carbide and uranium–uranium carbide cermets.' *Progress in Nuclear Energy*, V, **1**, p. 448. Pergamon

BARWOOD, I. F., McLEAN-ELRICK, A., PLAIL, O. S. and ROBERTSON, J. A. L. (1957). Unpublished work at A.E.R.E., Harwell

BENZIGER, T. M. and ROHWER, R. K. (1961). 'Graphite matrix fuel bodies.' *Nucleonics*, May, p. 80

BLEIBERG, M. L. and JONES, L. J. (1958). 'The effects of pile irradiation on U₃Si.' *Trans. Met. Soc. A.I.M.E.*, **212**, 750

BOETTCHER, A. and SCHNEIDER, G. (1958). 'Some properties of uranium monocarbide.' *Proc. Second Geneva Conf.*, **6**, 561

BOLTA, C. and STRASSER, A. (1960). 'Carbide fuel development.' U.S.A.E.C. Report, NDA 2145-6

BOWMAN, M. G. (1959). 'Bonding uranium carbide to tantalum.' U.S.A.E.C. Report, AECU-4303

BRADLEY, M. J. and FERRIS, L. M. (1961). 'Processing of uranium carbide reactor fuels, 1. Reaction with water and HCl.' U.S.A.E.C. Report, ORNL-3101

BREDIG, M. A. (1960). 'The high-temperature cubic phases of uranium and lanthanum dicarbides.' *J. Amer. Ceram. Soc.*, **43**, 493

BRETT, N., LAW, D. and LIVEY, D. T. (1960). 'Some investigations on the uranium: thorium: carbon system.' *J. Inorg. Nuclear Chem.*, **13**, 44

BROWN, A. and NORREYS, J. J. (1961). 'The system thorium–silicon.' *J. Inst. Metals*, **89**, 238

BROWN, D. J. and STOBO, J. J. (1961). 'Preparation and properties of uranium monocarbide.' Proceedings of the 4th Plansee Seminar. Reutte, Austria

BROWN, F., OCKENDEN, H. M. and WELCH, G. A. (1955). 'The preparation and properties of some plutonium compounds, Part II. Plutonium nitride.' *J. Chem. Soc.*, 4196

BROWNLEE, L. D. (1958). 'The pseudo-binary systems of uranium carbide with zirconium carbide, tantalum carbide and niobium carbide.' *J. Inst. Metals*, October, p. 58

BURDICK, M. D., PARKER, H. S., ROTH, R. S. and McGANDY, E. L. (1955). 'An X-ray study of the system UC, UC₂, Be₂C.' *J. Res. Nat. Bur. Stand.*, **54**, 217

CHIOTTI, P. (1950). 'Thorium–carbon system.' U.S.A.E.C. Report, AECD-3072

CHIOTTI, P. (1951). 'Summary of research on experimental refractory bodies of high-melting nitrides, carbides and uranium dioxide.' U.S.A.E.C. Report, AECD-3204

217

CHIOTTI, P. (1952). 'Experimental refractory bodies of high-melting nitrides, carbides and uranium dioxide.' *J. Amer. Ceram. Soc.*, **35**, 123

CHUBB, W. and ROUGH, F. A. (1960). 'Research on uranium carbide and uranium carbide-base fuel materials.' U.S.A.E.C. Report, TID-7603, p. 12

CREAGH, J. W. R. (1960). 'NASA research on uranium carbide and refractory ceramics.' U.S.A.E.C. Report, TID-7603

CREAGH, J. W. R. and DRELL, I. L. (1960). 'NASA research programme on compatability of uranium monocarbide.' U.A.S.E.C. Report, TID-7589

DAYTON, R. W. and TIPTON, C. R., JR. (1959). 'Progress relating to civilian applications, August 1959.' U.S.A.E.C. Report, BMI-1377

DRUMMOND, J. L., MCDONALD, B. J., OCKENDEN, H. M. and WELCH, G. A. (1957). 'The preparation and properties of some plutonium compounds, Part VII. Plutonium carbides.' *J. Chem. Soc.*, 4785

DUBUISSON, J. *et al.* (1958). 'The preparation of uranium–uranium monocarbide cermets and stoichiometric monocarbide by sintering under stress.' *Proc. Second Geneva Conf.*, **6**, 551

ENDEBROCK, R. W. *et al.* (1961). 'Progress relating to civil applications, April.' U.S.A.E.C. Report BMI-1514 (del), and previous Progress Reports

ENGLE, G. B. (1961). 'Reaction rate studies of thorium–uranium dicarbide in moist air.' U.S.A.E.C. Report, GA-2068

FINLEY, J. J., KORCHYNSKY, M. and SARIAN, S. (1959). 'Columbium-clad uranium carbide fuel elements.' Union Carbide Quarterly Report No. 2, August 1st–October 31st. U.S.A.E.C. Report, ORO-222

FINLEY, J. J., KORCHYNSKY, M. and SARIAN, S. (1960). 'Columbium-clad uranium carbide fuel elements.' Final report, May 1st 1959–April 30th. U.S.A.E.C. Report, ORO-366

FOX, A. C. and WAIT, E. (1961). 'X-ray studies of radiation damage in fissile materials.' U.K.A.E.A. Report, AERE-R3143

GRAY, R. J., THURBER, W. C. and DUBOSE, C. K. H. (1958). 'Preparation of arc melted uranium carbides.' *Metal Progress*, **74**, 65. Preparation and Metallography of Arc-Melted Uranium Carbides. U.S.A.E.C. Report, ORNL-2446

HARE, A. W. and ROUGH, F. A. (1960). 'Irradiation effects on massive uranium monocarbide.' U.S.A.E.C. Report, BMI-1452

HARE, A. W. and ROUGH, F. A. (1961). 'The effect of high-burn-up irradiation on massive uranium carbide.' U.S.A.E.C. Report, BMI-1491

HARE, A. W., ALFANT, S., ROUGH, F. A. and SINIZER, D. I. (1961). 'Further results of irradiation of uranium carbide.' *Nucl. Sci. Engng*, **10**, 24

HARMS, W. O. and MURDOCK, R. F. (1961). Unpublished work at O.R.N.L.

HARTLEY, K. and MCLENNAN, G. (1961). 'Improvements in or relating to the processing of uranium carbide.' British Patent 858,970

HEDGER, H. J. and REGAN, C. M. (1960). 'The preparation of uranium monocarbide by reaction sintering at A.E.R.E., Harwell.' U.S.A.E.C. Report, TID-7589

HIKIDO, T. (1961). Gas Cooled Reactor Project Quarterly Progress Report, Period Ending March 31st, 1961. U.S.A.E.C. Report, ORNL-3102

HOWE, L. M. (1960). 'Irradiation behaviour of enriched $U_3Si$ elements sheathed in zircaloy-2.' Atomic Energy of Canada Ltd. Report, CR Met-904

HUNT, E. B. and RUNDLE, R. E. (1951). 'The structure of thorium dicarbide by X-ray and neutron diffraction.' *J. Amer. Chem. Soc.*, **73**, 4777

ISSEROW, S. (1956). 'The uranium silicon epsilon phase.' U.S.A.E.C. Report, NMI-1145

IVANOV, O. S. and BADAJEVA, T. J. (1958). 'Phase diagrams of certain ternary systems of uranium and thorium.' *Proc. Second Geneva Conf.*, **6**, 139

# REFERENCES

JACOBSON, E. L., FREEMAN, R. D., THARP, A. G. and SEARCY, A. W. (1956). 'Preparation, identification and chemical properties of the thorium silicides.' *J. Amer. Chem. Soc.*, **78**, 4850

KALISH, H. S., BOWMAN, F. E. and CRANE, J. (1959). 'The development of uranium carbides as a nuclear fuel.' U.S.A.E.C. Report, NYO-2684

KALISH, H. S. and LITTON, F. B. (1960). 'Development of uranium carbide as a nuclear fuel at Olin Mathieson Chemical Corporation.' U.S.A.E.C. Report, TID-7603, p. 114

KALISH, H. S. and LITTON, F. B. (1959–61). Olin Mathieson Chemical Corporation Quarterly Progress Reports. NYO-2685 (1959), NYO-2688 (1960), NYO-2691 (1961)

KATZ, J. J. and RABINOWITCH, E. (1951). *The Chemistry of Uranium*, Part I. McGraw-Hill, pp. 226–229

KAUFMANN, A., CULLITY, B. and BITSIANES, G. (1957). 'Uranium silicon alloys.' *J. Met.*, **9**, Section 2, 23

KELLER, D. L. *et al.* (1961). 'Powder metallurgy of uranium carbide and uranium nitride.' Proceedings of the 4th Plansee Seminar (Reutte, Austria)

KITTEL, J. K. and SMITH, K. F. (1960). 'Effects of irradiation on some corrosion-resistant fuel alloys.' U.S.A.E.C. Report, ANL-5640

KOENIG, N. R. (1960). '$U_3Si_2$ fuel evaluation. Part I. Oxidation characteristics.' U.S.A.E.C. Report, NAA-SR-Memo-5199

KORCHYNSKY, M. (1960). 'Columbium clad uranium carbide fuel element development at Union Carbide Metals Company.' U.S.A.E.C. Report, TID-7589, p. 70

KORCHYNSKY, M. (1960). 'Progress in technology of columbium alloy clad uranium carbide fuel elements at Union Carbide Metals Company.' U.S.A.E.C. Report, TID-7603, p. 127

KORCHYNSKY, M. *et al.* (1961). 'Columbium alloy clad uranium carbide fuel development.' U.S.A.E.C. Report, ORO-501

LIED, R. C. (1960). 'Uranium and plutonium carbide development at the Argonne National Laboratory.' U.S.A.E.C. Report, TID-7589, p. 3

LING YANG and CARPENTER, T. D. (1961). 'Materials problems in cerium ionic converters.' *J. Electrochem. Soc.*, **108**, 1079

LITZ, L. M. (1948). 'Uranium carbides—Their preparation, structure and hydrolysis.' U.S.A.E.C. Report, NP-1453

LITZ, L. M., GARRETT, A. B. and CROXTON, F. C. (1948). 'Preparation and structures of carbides of uranium.' *J. Amer. Chem. Soc.*, **70**, 1718

LOCH, L. D., ENGLE, G. B., SNYDER, M. J. and DUCKWORTH, W. H. (1956). 'Survey of refractory uranium compounds.' U.S.A.E.C. Report, BMI-1124

MALLET, M. W., GERDS, A. F. and VAUGHAN, D. A. (1950). 'Uranium sesquicarbide.' U.S.A.E.C. Report, AECD-3060

MALLET, M. W. *et al.* (1952). 'The uranium–carbon system.' *J. Electrochem. Soc.*, **99**, 197

MALLET, M. W. and GERDS, A. F. (1955). 'Reaction of nitrogen with uranium.' *J. Electrochem. Soc.*, **102**, 292

MEERSON, G. A., KOTELNIKOFF, R. B. and BESHLIKOFF, S. H. (1960). 'Uranium monocarbide.' *Atomnaya Energiya*, **9**, 387

MOREAU, C. (1960). 'Production of pure uranium monocarbide by carburisation of uranium.' *Planseeber. Pulvermet*, **8**, 22

MULFORD, R. N. R. *et al.* (1960). 'The plutonium–carbon system.' Proc. Conf. Internationale sur la Metallurgie du Plutonium (Grenoble), Paper 32

MURBACH, E. W. (1960). 'The oxidation of uranium carbide.' U.S.A.E.C. Report, NAA-SR-Memo 5494 (Rev A)

MURBACH, E. W. (1961). 'The oxidation of "reactive" uranium carbide.' U.S.A.E.C. Report, NAA-SR-6331

MURRAY, P. and WILLIAMS, J. (1958). 'Ceramic and cermet fuels.' *Proc. Second Geneva Conf.*, **6**, 538

NEWKIRK, H. W. and BATES, J. L. (1959). 'The melting points of $UO_2$, UC and UN.' U.S.A.E.C. Report, HW-59469

NEWKIRK, H. W. (1959). 'Chemical reactivity of uranium monocarbide and uranium mononitride with water at 100°C.' U.S.A.E.C. Report, HW-59408

NICHOLS, R. W. (1958). 'Ceramic fuels—Properties and technology.' *Nuclear Engineering*, August

NOWOTNY, H., KIEFFER, R., BENESOVSKY, F. and LAUBE, E. (1957). 'The binary systems: UC with TiC, ZrC, VC, NbC, TaC, $Cr_2C_3$, $Mo_2C$ and WC.' *Monatsch. Chem.*, **88**, 336. U.K.A.E.A. Report AERE Lib/Trans. 797 (1958)

NOWOTNY, H., KIEFFER, R. and BENESOVSKY, F. (1958). 'Preparation of UC and its relation to the carbides of refractory transition metals.' *Rev. Met.*, **55**, 453

OGARD, A. E., PRITCHARD, W. C., DOUGLASS, R. M. and LEARY, J. A. (1961). 'The powder metallurgy of plutonium fuel materials.' *Proc. Fourth Plansee Seminar* (Reutte, Austria), Paper 34

PAPROCKI, S. J. *et al.* (1959). 'Development of uranium nitride–stainless steel dispersion fuel elements.' U.S.A.E.C. Report, BMI-1365

PAPROCKI, S. J. *et al.* (1961). 'Progress relating to civil applications, April 1961.' U.S.A.E.C. Report, BMI-1514 (del), and previous progress reports

PASCARD, R. (1961). 'Etudes preliminaires sur le systeme plutonium–carbone et les solutions solides carbure d'uranium–carbure de plutonium.' *Proc. Fourth Plansee Seminar* (Reutte, Austria), Paper 35

PHILLIPS, G. M. (1959). Unpublished work at U.K.A.E.A. Laboratories, Windscale

PHILLIPS, W. M., CHUBB, W. and FOSTER, E. L. (1960). 'Direct casting of uranium monocarbide reactor fuel elements.' *J. Less Common Metals*, **2**, 451

PHILLIPS, W. M. and FOSTER, E. L. (1959). In U.S.A.E.C. Report, BMI-1346, p. 51

PRICE, R. B. and GOLDTHWAITE, W. H. (1958). 'Irradiation of uranium monocarbide.' U.S.A.E.C. Report, BMI-1304, p. 45

PRICE, R. B. *et al.* (1958). 'Irradiation capsule design for uranium monocarbide.' In U.S.A.E.C. Report, BMI-1259, p. 70

RAND, M. H. and KUBASCHEWSKI, O. (1960). 'The thermochemical properties of uranium compounds.' U.K.A.E.A. Report, AERE-R3487

REGAN, M. C. and HEDGER, H. J. (1961). 'The properties of uranium monocarbide fabricated by direct reaction of the elemental powders.' *Proc. Fourth Plansee Seminar* (Reutte, Austria), Paper 18

REGAN, M. C. and WILLIAMS, J. (1961). 'The sintering of uranium–carbon–iron alloys in the presence of a liquid phase.' U.K.A.E.A. Report AERE-R 3886 (Preprint). Published in *Powder Metallurgy* (1961) 8, 128

ROUGH, F. A. and CHUBB, W. C. (1960). 'An evaluation of data on nuclear carbides.' U.S.A.E.C. Report, BMI-1441

ROUGH, F. A. and CHUBB, W. (Ed.) (1960). 'Progress of the development of uranium carbide-type fuels,' Phase II. Report on the AEC Fuel-Cycle Programme. U.S.A.E.C. Report, BMI-1488

ROUGH, F. A. and DICKERSON, R. F. (1960). 'Uranium monocarbide.' *Nucleonics*, March, p. 74

ROUGH, F. A., HARE, A. W., PRICE, R. B. and ALFANT, S. (1960). 'Irradiation of uranium monocarbide.' *Nucl. Sci. Engng*, **7**, 111

RUNDLE, R. E. (1948). 'A new interpretation of interstitial compounds—Metallic carbides, nitrides and oxides of composition MX.' *Acta Cryst.*, **1**, 180

RUNDLE, R. E. *et al.* (1948). 'Studies of the carbides, nitrides and oxides of uranium.' *J. Amer. Chem. Soc.*, **70**, 99

SAMSONOV, G. V., KOSOLAPOVA, T. Ya. and PADERNO, V. N. (1960). 'Preparation of thorium carbides.' *Zhur. Prikl. Khim.*, **33**, 1661

# REFERENCES

SANTO, T., IMOTO, S. and TAKADA, Y. (1959–61). 'Research on the production of uranium monocarbide.' *Nihon Genshiryoku Cyakkai Shi*, **1**, 425 (1959) (In Japanese). U.K.A.E.A. Report, AERE Trans, 863 (1961)

SCAIFE, D. E. and WYLIE, A. W. (1958). 'The preparation of thorium carbide and some aspects of the high temperature decontamination of carbide fuels.' Australian At. Energy Symp. (Pub. Austr. A.E.C.), p. 172

SECREST, A. C., FOSTER, E. L. and DICKERSON, R. F. (1958). 'Casting techniques for the preparation of uranium monocarbide.' U.S.A.E.C. Report, BMI-1280, p. 43

SECREST, A. C., FOSTER, E. L. and DICKERSON, R. F. (1959). 'Preparation and properties of uranium monocarbide castings.' U.S.A.E.C. Report, BMI-1309

SHEINHARTZ, I. and ZAMBROW, J. L. (1958). 'Dispersion-type materials for fuel elements. Part I. Uranium mononitride and uranium silicide dispersion materials.' U.S.A.E.A. Report, SCNC-266

SIMPSON, A. M. and HEATH, B. A. (1959). Unpublished work at U.K.A.E.A. Laboratories, Dounreay

SINIZER, D. I. (1960). 'Progress in uranium carbide technology at Atomics International.' U.S.A.E.C. Report, TID-7603, p. 4

SMITH, C. A. and ROUGH, F. (1959). 'Properties of uranium monocarbide.' U.S.A.E.C. Report, NAA-SR-3625

SNYDER, M. J. and DUCKWORTH, W. H. (1957). 'Properties of some refractory uranium compounds.' U.S.A.E.C. Report, BMI-1223

SOWDEN, R. C., HODGE, N. and AINSLEY, R. (1961). Unpublished work at A.E.R.E., Harwell

STANDRING, J. and TWIGG, S. R. (1960). Unpublished work at U.K.A.E.A. Laboratories, Culcheth

STEPHAS, P. and HOYT, E. W. (1961). 'Reactive hot pressing of ZrC–UC solid solutions.' *Amer. Ceram. Soc. Bull.*, **40**, 320

STRASSER, A. (1960). 'Uranium carbide as a fuel.' *Nuclear Engng*, **5**, 353

STRASSER, A. and TAYLOR, K. (1961). 'Carbide fuel development.' Progress Report for period Feb. 1st–April 30th 1961. U.S.A.E.C. Report, NDA-2162-3

TAYLOR, K. M. (1960). 'Experimental work on uranium carbide at the Carborundum Company.' U.S.A.E.C. Report, TID-7589, p. 14

TAYLOR, K. M., LENIE, C. A. and SMUDSKI, P. A. (1959). 'Synthesis and fabrication of refractory uranium compounds.' Carborundum Co. Quarterly Progress Report, May 13th–August 31st 1959. U.S.A.E.C. Report, ORO-212

TAYLOR, K. M. and McMURTRY, C. H. (1961). 'Synthesis and fabrication of refractory uranium compounds.' U.S.A.E.C. Report, ORO-400

THURBER, W. C. and BEAVER, R. J. (1959). 'Dispersions of uranium carbides in aluminium plate-type research reactor fuel elements.' U.S.A.E.C. Report, ORNL-2618

TRIPLER, A. B., SNYDER, M. J. and DUCKWORTH, W. H. (1959). 'Further studies of sintered refractory uranium compounds.' U.S.A.E.C. Report, BMI-1313; 'A study of the effects of fabricating conditions on some properties of sintered uranium monocarbide.' U.S.A.E.C. Report, BMI-1383

WHITE, J., BARTA, J. and BRIGGS, G. (1961). 'Phase diagrams of uranium carbide-transition metal systems.' *Proc. Fourth International Plansee Seminar* (Reutte, Austria), Paper 4

WILHELM, H. A. and CHIOTTI, P. (1950). 'Thorium–carbon systems.' *Trans. Amer. Soc. Met.*, **42**, 1295

WILLIAMS, J. and SAMBELL, R. A. J. (1959). 'The uranium monocarbide–uranium mononitride system.' *J. Less Common Metals*, **1**, 217

WILLIAMS, J. *et al.* (1960). 'The variation of unit cell-edge of uranium monocarbide in arc-melted uranium carbon alloys.' U.K.A.E.A. Report, AERE M 625

221

WILSON, W. B. (1960). 'High temperature X-ray diffraction investigation of the uranium carbon system.' *J. Amer. Ceram. Soc.*, **43**, 77

WITTEMAN, W. G., LEITNAKER, J. M. and BOWMAN, M. G. (1958). 'The solid solubility of uranium monocarbide and zirconium carbide.' U.S.A.E.C. Report, LA-2159

WOLF, R. A. *et al.* (1956). 'Development of $U_3Si$ epsilon phase for use in pressurised water reactors.' U.S.A.E.C. Report, WAPD-155

ZACHARIASEN, W. H. (1949). 'Crystal chemical studies of the 5f-series of elements.' *Acta Cryst.*, **2**, 94

CHAPTER 5

# THE MIGRATION OF FISSION PRODUCTS

## 5.1 GENERAL REMARKS

THE technological consequences of the migration of fission products within nuclear fuels are of such importance that it was felt necessary to devote a special chapter to the topic. It forms a subject of considerable interest to chemists since, quite apart from the technological considerations, a comparison of rates of diffusion may lead to a better understanding of the chemical state of the fission products within the fuel and of the possibilities of their interaction one with another. Information on these matters is meagre and is difficult to obtain by other means.

Knowledge of the migration of fission products is necessary for the design of gas-cooled reactors but, insofar as migration within an intact fuel cladding is concerned, the results are also applicable to other types of reactor system. The consequences of the leakage of fission products through defects in the cladding are discussed separately in Volume 2, Chapter 7, for water-cooled reactors and in Volume 3, Chapter 1, for sodium-cooled systems. Fission product migration through graphite has been discussed in Chapter 2.

### 5.1.1 The Most Important Fission Products

In any fuel material, there will be a gradual accumulation during reactor irradiation of substantial quantities of chemically inert gas. The stable and long-lived xenon isotopes are formed to the extent of some 14 per cent by weight of uranium fissioned, while the krypton isotopes comprise approximately an additional 2 per cent. These gases can be directly responsible for a number of undesirable physical phenomena:

(a) Swelling of the fuel.
(b) Build-up of high pressures inside the cladding of ceramic fuel elements which do not have a metallurgical bond between the cladding and the fuel.
(c) Changes in thermal conductivity across the gap between the fuel and the cladding of unbonded fuel elements, leading to higher fuel temperatures and further release of gas.

From the point of view of the build-up of inert gas pressure in and around the fuel, the following fission product chains are important:

| | | | | | Yield (per 100 fissions) |
|---|---|---|---|---|---|
| | | 8·05 day | $^{131}I \rightarrow$ | $^{131}Xe$ (stable) | 2·93 |
| 77 hour | $^{132}Te \rightarrow$ | 2·3 hour | $^{132}I \rightarrow$ | $^{132}Xe$ (stable) | 4·38 |
| 44 min | $^{134}Te \rightarrow$ | 52·5 min | $^{134}I \rightarrow$ | $^{134}Xe$ (stable) | 8·06 |
| | | 83 sec | $^{136}I \rightarrow$ | $^{136}Xe$ (stable) | 6·46 |

The krypton isotopes produced in fission are considerably less important than those of xenon since their fission yield is much lower and they do not give rise to long-lived daughters of objectionable radioactivity. The following chains are significant:

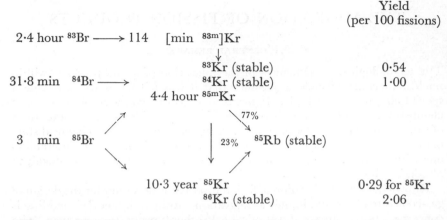

| | Yield (per 100 fissions) |
|---|---|
| 2·4 hour $^{83}$Br ⟶ 114   [min $^{83m}$]Kr | |
| $^{83}$Kr (stable) | 0·54 |
| 31·8 min   $^{84}$Br ⟶   $^{84}$Kr (stable) | 1·00 |
| 4·4 hour $^{85m}$Kr | |
| 3   min   $^{85}$Br    77%   $^{85}$Rb (stable) | |
| 23% | |
| 10·3 year $^{85}$Kr | 0·29 for $^{85}$Kr |
| $^{86}$Kr (stable) | 2·06 |

Krypton-85 will contribute little to the build-up of gas pressure, but it is important as the only radioactive isotope available for tracer studies of this element. Also, since it is the only radioactive inert gas with a half-life exceeding a few days, it is particularly valuable for long-term post-irradiation annealing studies.

Early reactor systems were designed to operate under conditions where a low release of fission products from the fuel material could be expected. The present trend of designs towards higher temperatures and longer irradiation times, however, makes a knowledge of the diffusion and emission of all fission products increasingly important. In particular, the emission of chemically reactive fission product elements, such as iodine and tellurium, may give rise to problems of compatibility with metallic components of the fuel elements. Radioactive isotopes of iodine, tellurium and strontium are also of importance from the health and safety viewpoint in the event of a fuel cladding failure, or the use of unclad fuel allowing the spread of these materials from within the confines of the reactor core.

### 5.1.2 Experimental Methods for the Measurement of Fission Product Migration

*Fuel element irradiations*

When attempts are being made to predict the behaviour of fuel in a reactor of novel design, the most realistic type of experiment is obviously the irradiation of a full-scale fuel element under the exact operating conditions envisaged. Any serious effects of the fission product gases upon performance will then become apparent. This method has many inherent difficulties, however: a large amount of irradiation space is required (perhaps even a special test reactor), both the irradiations and the subsequent examination are very expensive, and the whole operation is on such a protracted time scale that the method can be envisaged only as a final proof of fuel designs whose individual aspects have been extensively tested beforehand.

Ambiguities may arise in the interpretation of the results because so many design parameters can affect the diffusion and emission of fission products from the fuel. Since not all of the parameters can be controlled—or even measured —within sufficiently close limits, and since the results of the experiments represent an average emission over ranges of time, temperature, etc., little information is obtained concerning either the mechanism by which the fission products migrate or the rate at which they do so. The results therefore tend to be empirical and cannot be extrapolated confidently to a different set of conditions.

*Pellet irradiations*

Many laboratories have mounted experimental programmes of a wider scope involving the irradiation of small pellets of fuel material rather than the full-scale fuel rods. This method allows a wider range of parameters to be studied in a given time, but it still suffers from many of the disadvantages of the larger-scale irradiations.

Most of the work on ceramic fuels has been based upon measurement of the emitted gas confined in the space between the fuel and cladding by puncturing the cladding after irradiation. The total amount of gas is measured volumetrically after purification, and the isotopic composition is obtained by mass spectrometry (sometimes assisted by gamma spectrometry and gas chromatography).

For irradiations of long duration, where appreciable quantities of xenon will be produced in the fuel, the emission of this gas may be studied by collection and mass spectrometric analysis of the stable isotopes. The sensitivity is such that about $10^{16}$ atoms of a given isotope are necessary to achieve a precision of $\pm 5$ per cent (SLOSEK and WEIDENBAUM, 1960). A comprehensive calculation of fission product gas pressures must allow for the neutron capture reactions of the various species. In particular the capture cross-section of $^{135}$Xe for conversion to $^{136}$Xe is very high ($3 \times 10^6$ barns) and must be taken into account in the interpretation of the mass spectrometric data.

Methods in use at various establishments have been described by BOOTH *et al.* (1957); KOCH, ECK and SUSKO (1957); MORGAN *et al.* (1960); BARNES and SUNDERMAN (1960); and WOMACK (1960).

*Post-irradiation annealing experiments*

A much closer control over the experimental conditions is possible in the post-irradiation annealing technique. Small samples of the fuel material are irradiated at relatively low temperatures, and after irradiation they are heated to the temperature of interest. The emitted fission product gases are removed by a sweep gas, or by evacuation, and are analysed by gamma spectrometry. This technique has been used widely to study the emission of $^{133}$Xe from ceramic fuels as a function of temperature and of the physical characteristics of the fuel material, such as surface area and porosity. Recently the studies have been extended to the quantitative collection and measurement of iodine, tellurium, caesium and other fission products. The method is capable of giving a considerable amount of detailed information on fission product emission, and moreover of providing data much more rapidly than in-pile experiments. Furthermore, by suitable choice of irradiation and radioactive decay times the diffusion of individually chosen isotopes can be studied without interference from the simultaneous diffusion of their precursors. The disadvantages are (i) information is not obtained on the possible effects of irradiation on diffusion, (ii) application of the data to the calculation of fuel element behaviour requires a detailed knowledge of the temperature profile through the fuel: this in turn is usually the result of further calculation rather than direct measurement, (iii) if grain growth or melting occur in a fuel element the post-irradiation data afford no means of predicting the enhanced gas release which is known to occur (q.v.).

Considerable progress has been made by this method in studying the nature and extent of the diffusion of xenon from a variety of fuel materials, and the data will be discussed in detail in later sections. It is worth pointing out at once, however, that neither for metal nor for ceramic fuel materials has a true understanding of the mechanism of the diffusion yet been achieved.

Details of post-irradiation annealing techniques have been described by BOOTH and RYMER (1958), BARNES and SUNDERMAN (1960) and LINDNER and MATZKE (1959).

*In-pile annealing experiments*

A bridge between the fuel pellet irradiations in sealed capsules and the post-irradiation annealing method is provided by in-pile annealing experiments. Here a small specimen of the fuel is heated isothermally during irradiation and any emitted fission products are removed for analysis by an inert sweep gas. Details of equipment which has been used at Harwell have been given by STUBBS and WALTON (1955), at the Battelle Memorial Institute by TOWNLEY *et al.* (1960), and at Oak Ridge by CARROLL and BAUMANN (1961). Such equipment has so far been used principally to obtain data on the diffusion of xenon and krypton, and the range of temperature covered has been somewhat limited.

The experiments are much more difficult to perform than the corresponding out-of-pile annealing experiments, and furthermore the results are not easy to interpret. Accounts of the types of difficulty involved have been given by STUBBS, RUSSELL and WALTON (1959) and by CARROLL and BAUMANN (1961). Recoil of fission fragments and evaporation of uranium atoms from the surface of the fuel material to positions associated with components of the surrounding furnace give rise to a spurious release which complicates the interpretation of results. Short-lived chemically reactive species can also plate out upon the walls of the equipment and generate daughter isotopes which will be swept into the counting system.

*5.1.3 Kinetics of Fission Product Diffusion*

The emission of gaseous fission products from a nuclear fuel can occur by many means. At relatively low temperatures, all fuels will emit fission products from the free surface by recoil during each fission event near the surface: the amount emitted will be a function of the recoil range of the fission products in the fuel material. There may also be a related 'knock-out' phenomenon which is discussed below.

At low temperatures these two mechanisms predominate, but as the temperature is increased, one or more thermally activated diffusion processes become progressively more important.

Sintered ceramics have presented special problems in the interpretation of the experimental results. The difficulties arise principally from the nature and extent of residual porosity which may occur in sintered bodies. Special attention is given to such bodies on account of their outstanding importance in the future development of reactors.

Fick's general diffusion equation has many solutions according to the boundary conditions which may be applicable to each type of experiment (BARRER, 1951). Because of the porous nature of sintered ceramics, the external geometry does not define even approximately the boundaries of the units which control the diffusion. BOOTH and RYMER (1958) suggested that the emission from uranium dioxide could be analysed in terms of an assembly of uniform spheres of a radius such that the ratio of surface to volume is equal to that measured experimentally for the compacted specimen (the equivalent sphere hypothesis). It was assumed that once a diffusing gas atom reaches the surface of a pore connected with the outer surface it had, in effect, been emitted from the material. The surface area is that which is measured by gas adsorption at low temperatures using the B.E.T. technique (BRUNAUER, EMMETT and TELLER, 1938).

Most subsequent experimental data on the emission of fission products from ceramics have been analysed in terms of this concept, but it should be emphasized that the equivalent spheres are somewhat hypothetical and have no physical relationship to the grain size of the material.

In a further paper (BOOTH, 1957) it was stated that for a stable gaseous isotope initially at uniform concentration in a solid of spherical geometry, and with zero concentration at the solid/gas interface, the expression for the fraction $(f)$ emitted after post-irradiation annealing for a time $(t)$ at a fixed temperature could be simplified to:

$$f = 6\left[\frac{D \cdot t}{\pi a^2}\right]^{1/2} - 3\frac{D \cdot t}{a^2}$$

where $D$ is the diffusion coefficient of the gas and $a$ is the radius of the equivalent sphere. This expression holds for releases up to 70 per cent; when $f < 30$ per cent, the second term may be neglected. Under irradiation, for a stable species which is being produced at a constant rate, the numerical constants in the expression have the values of 4 and 3/2 for the first and second terms respectively.

Further work since that of Booth has shown that it is not necessary to assign a particular shape to the unit which controls diffusion provided that the fractional release of gas is small ( < 30 per cent). Under these conditions only gas atoms near to the surface of the diffusion units will be emitted from the sample. It is then permissible to use a solution of Fick's law for a semi-infinite solid with a surface area equal to that of the compact measured by the gas adsorption technique.

JAIN (1958) has derived expressions similar to those of Booth for diffusion in other finite shapes by considering them as special cases of diffusion from a semi-infinite slab, and an alternative derivation has been given by MILLER (1960).

Post-irradiation annealing experiments measure only the ratio $D/a^2$, usually called the 'apparent diffusion coefficient', $D'$. In order to obtain the true diffusion coefficient it is necessary to obtain $a$ from, for example, the measured surface area.

For in-pile diffusion experiments, when the half-life of the diffusing radio-active species is long compared with the time of irradiation (e.g. for $^{85}Kr$), the diffusion equations relating to stable species may still be used. On the other hand, when the isotope has a short half-life an equilibrium is set up in which the rate of formation is balanced by the rate of removal by diffusion and decay. The relationship which has been used for many years in emanation work may then be applied at any fixed temperature:

$$f = 3\left[\frac{D'}{\lambda}\right]^{1/2}$$

where $f$ is the fraction of isotope which decays externally to the fuel and $\lambda$ is the decay constant in $\sec^{-1}$. This expression is a good approximation for fractional releases up to 30 per cent, the range which is normally encountered in nuclear fuel materials.

A mathematical analysis of the in-pile release of radioactive species in terms of the equivalent sphere hypothesis has been given by BECK (1960).

Both under irradiation and out of pile, the emission of the stable gases is controlled by diffusion only within a limited range of temperature. Beyond this range much more rapid release becomes possible due to physical changes in the fuel such as grain growth, phase transformations or swelling promoted by the nucleation of gas bubbles within the fuel. Oxidation due to impurities in the surrounding gas can also enhance the release. These effects will be discussed in more detail in the appropriate sections below.

The important practical effect of the emission of stable inert gases from ceramic fuels is an increase of pressure in the gas space within the fuel cladding. The calculation of this increase using the type of approach discussed above is subject to considerable uncertainty and some attempts have been made to measure the pressure directly in the irradiation of fuel capsules of known geometry. No firm results have been reported.

A simple model suggested by BOOTH (1957), applied to the results of iso-thermal diffusion experiments, is often used to predict approximately the gas release from fuel pellets. In this model the (cylindrical) fuel is divided into an arbitrary small number of concentric skins, each assumed to be isothermal, and the fraction released from each annulus is calculated using appropriate values for the diffusion coefficient obtained from post-irradiation annealing. The total gas release is then integrated by means of Simpson's rule. Within the limits of its applicability this method gives fair agreement with the observed releases in pellet irradiations; it cannot, however, be applied effectively if a substantial portion of the fuel is at a temperature where diffusion is not the main factor controlling the release of gas (i.e. below about 1,100°C and above about 1,600°C).

*Abnormal kinetics*

Many workers have found that even in the range of temperature when it is reasonable to suppose that the emission of inert gases is primarily due to a

228

process of bulk diffusion in the solid, deviations of the rate of emission from that predicted by the appropriate solutions of Fick's law occur. These abnormal kinetics have been found for such widely different materials as metallic uranium and molybdenum, graphite, uranium dioxide and uranium carbide, both during in-pile annealing and post-irradiation annealing work.

The deviations from the strict diffusion laws normally take the form of a 'burst' of gas each time the temperature is raised stepwise (usually by 100–200°C steps). The cause of the burst release may be different in each of the systems where it occurs, and indeed it may be due to more than one mechanism in any one material. A knowledge of these causes is not only of academic interest, but may also help to decide the applicability of post-irradiation annealing studies to fuel element behaviour. At temperatures about 1,000°C in uranium dioxide, for instance, the burst release is of greater magnitude than the normal diffusional release.

A peak in the rate of emission by diffusion immediately after a temperature step is predicted by Fick's laws, but the burst release enhances the magnitude of the peak. It is normally observed as an intercept on the ordinate axis at zero time obtained by extrapolation of the linear portion of a plot of total emission against the square root of time (Fick's laws predict that this line should pass through the origin). An example is shown in *Figure 5.2*. Also, the ratio of the final rate of release at the lower temperature to the initial rate of release at the upper temperature should ideally be equal to the ratio of the diffusion constants at the two temperatures. The initial burst release can give rise to a lower ratio than anticipated. The burst release persists at higher temperatures, but its relative importance becomes less owing to more rapid release by true bulk diffusion.

Most explanations which have been offered for the burst releases attribute them to some form of inhomogeneity in the solid material. The inhomogeneities may be either chemical or physical.

A chemical effect was postulated by BARNES *et al.* (1961) for the burst release observed in post-irradiation annealing of fused uranium dioxide. Such material was found to contain inclusions of uranium metal (p. 115) and the burst release was attributed to a more rapid emission of xenon from the inclusions than from the matrix. A burst release upon *cooling* uranium dioxide which had been heated to temperatures above 1,850°C was also attributed by ROTHWELL (1961) to the formation of inclusions of metallic uranium.

Both Barnes and STEVENS *et al.* (1960) consider that surface oxidation of uranium dioxide can produce a burst release. It is known that excess oxygen over the stoichiometric amount can give rise to higher xenon diffusion rates (q.v.) and these authors attribute the burst to such excess oxygen in a surface layer, which is then removed into the interior of the oxide lattice during annealing by a diffusion process much more rapid than that of xenon. Whilst this may account for some types of burst release, it is not widely applicable since the work of LONG (1962) has shown that bursts can occur even when reducing conditions are present (e.g. the use of hydrogen as a sweep gas).

A rather different type of burst release has been observed for the emission of $^{85}Kr$ during the post-irradiation annealing of uranium metal. SCOTT and BUDDERY (1962) found a peak in the emission of gas each time the metal was heated through the $\alpha$–$\beta$ phase transformation. This was attributed to the physical changes occurring at the transformation temperature.

Long has attributed the burst release in sintered ceramic materials to the presence of physical inhomogeneities. These range from pores which are easily accessible from the outer surface, through inaccessible fine pores and grain boundaries to dislocations within the crystal lattice. There will be mobility of inert gas atoms during irradiation arising from the knock-out mechanism (see pp. 242–243) and Long suggested that this could provide opportunities for the gases to accumulate at the inhomogeneities. The rate of release from such sites during both in-pile and post-irradiation annealing at high temperatures will vary widely according to the particular nature of the imperfection. A wide range of activation energies is expected for the release from the various sites and a burst effect could be produced whenever the temperature is raised. Findlay and Laing have adopted essentially the same explanation for the burst effect which occurs during the post-irradiation annealing of xenon-impregnated graphite (see Chapter 2).

Support for the suggestion that the inert gas atoms migrate to imperfections in the material as a result of the knock-out effect may be gained from the fact that the emission of $^{222}$Rn from thoria and other oxides impregnated with trace quantities of $^{226}$Ra, but not subject to fission fragment damage, does not show a burst effect (LINDNER and MATZKE, 1960).

When in-pile annealing experiments are performed on uranium dioxide, and the sample is cooled to about 100°C, there is an unexpected burst of fission gas release (CARROLL, 1961). The 'cooling burst' is greater the higher the temperature of operation. There appears to be a store of trapped gas in the fuel material which is released during the burst, but the exact nature of the traps is not clear.

It is also of interest that in the temperature region where the burst release appears to predominate (e.g. about 1,000°C) the diffusion distance calculated for short experiments is small compared with the thickness of a grain boundary. It is often assumed that diffusion within grain boundaries is faster than in the grains themselves. As the time scale of the experiments is extended, the region surrounding the grain boundaries could become depleted of the diffusing species and the emission may then be controlled by a slower bulk diffusion. This, therefore, is another possible explanation for the initial burst release, and may be additional to that of Long where the concentration at the grain boundaries is increased during irradiation so as to produce an inhomogeneous distribution at the start of the out-of-pile annealing experiments.

## 5.2 MIGRATION IN METALLIC FUELS

One of the main limitations on the life of metallic fuel elements in power reactors is swelling of the metal. The major cause of the swelling, which becomes considerable during irradiation above about 500°C, is the production and redistribution of the inert gas fission products.

During irradiation most of the atoms of inert gas come to rest within the normal crystal structure (interstitially, or possibly on lattice sites), and if the temperature is sufficiently low, will not produce serious physical deformation until very high burn-ups have been achieved. At higher temperatures, how-ever, because of the agglomeration of the gas atoms to form bubbles, the swelling becomes more pronounced. Subsequently the growth of the bubbles is limited by surface tension, the strength of the metal matrix, and the external pressure on the system.

Reviews of the swelling phenomenon are available elsewhere (BARNES *et al.*, 1958; CHURCHMAN, 1959; BARNES, 1959) and we will confine our discussion to observations of the diffusion and emission of the inert gas atoms.

At temperatures below about 600°C the emission of fission gases from irradiated uranium is certainly low and occurs predominantly by recoil from the surface. Attempts have been made, however, by modifying the in-pile technique and by using post-irradiation annealing, to identify an emission due to diffusion. GRAY (1960) has reviewed the literature on the emission of inert gases from irradiated uranium and has summarized the results in the form shown in *Figure 5.1*. He pointed out that the post-irradiation annealing results fall into two broad groups separated by some three or four orders of magnitude in the diffusion coefficient. The upper group were obtained by a sweep-gas technique, whereas an evacuation technique was used for the lower group.

Gray calculated that in a given annealing time the depth of oxidation both in an inert gas containing trace amounts of oxygen (10–50 p.p.m.) and in an imperfect vacuum would agree reasonably well with the mean diffusion path of xenon in uranium in each of these atmospheres. This leads to the conclusion that the higher group of results may be spurious and that caution must be used even with the lower group in attributing the results to true diffusion in the uranium. The authors of the original papers do not give the limits of oxidizing impurities in their systems and usually make no observations on the state of their specimens after the experiments. WALKER (1959) noted that his specimens had a tarnish film after his experiments which were performed *in vacuo*.

The results of WALTON, STUBBS and SILVER (1958) obtained for the emission of xenon during irradiation are also shown in *Figure 5.1*. The diffusion coefficients appear to be considerably higher than would be obtained by the post-irradiation technique. These authors attempted to explain the higher figures in terms of local heating in the surface layers of the uranium caused by recoiling fission fragments. There was no quantitative agreement between the emission observed and that calculated, however. Gray suggested that here also the apparent enhancement of diffusion could have been due to surface oxidation of the metal.

The emission of fission product inert gas from a zirconium–5 per cent uranium alloy during irradiation has been studied by STUBBS and WEBSTER (1959). The release was found to be primarily by recoil below 600°C: above this temperature there was a rapid increase in emission attributed to diffusion. The calculated diffusion coefficients were similar to those obtained for un-alloyed uranium.

LECLAIRE (1954) estimated by analogy with the diffusion of argon in silver that the diffusion coefficients of the inert gases in solid solution in uranium at 800°C should be some 300 times greater than the uranium self-diffusion coefficient, i.e. about $2 \times 10^{-10}$ cm$^2$ sec$^{-1}$. The most reliable results for the emission of inert gases during post-irradiation annealing are several orders of magnitude lower than this (see *Figure 5.1*), a fact which may be attributed to the rapid agglomeration of the gas atoms into bubbles up to about 500 Å radius locked to dislocations in the uranium structure. More recently, GREENWOOD (1960) has suggested that the diffusion coefficient for the fission gas should be only ten times the self-diffusion value in gamma

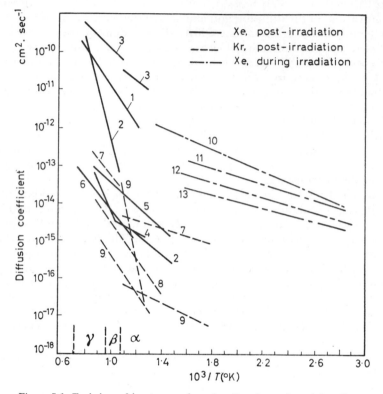

*Figure 5.1.* Emission of inert gases from irradiated uranium (after Gray, 1960).
Curve 1: Spedding, *et al.* (1952); 2 & 3: Zimen and Dahl (1957); Zimen and Schmeling (1954). 4: Bates and Clark (1955). 5, 6, 7 & 8: Curtis and Rich (1956); Curtis (1958); 9: Walker (1959). 10, 11, 12 & 13: Walton, Stubbs and Silver (1958).

uranium. This fits the experimental data more closely, and Greenwood proposed that in gamma uranium redistribution of the gas atoms takes place by re-solution from the smaller bubbles and diffusion to the larger ones.

On the other hand, at lower temperatures the mobility of the gas atoms may be insufficient to promote the formation of bubbles. BRINKMAN (1959) used the data of ZIMEN and DAHL (1957) to give an extrapolated diffusion coefficient at 400°C and calculated that bubble formation would not occur in reasonable experimental times (up to 3 months). Reference to *Figure 5.1* shows that the diffusion coefficient used by Brinkman was too high, a fact which reinforces his deduction.

Experiments relevant to reactor safety studies on the release of fission products from molten reactor fuels undergoing simultaneous oxidation have been reported by CREEK, MARTIN and PARKER (1959) and by HILLIARD (1959). The composition of the fission products released from a quiet melt-down was limited mainly to those species with boiling points lower than the melting point of the fuel. An interesting feature was that the release was considerably less than 100 per cent, even of the inert gases, for fuels with a low melting point (see Volume 2, *Table 7.6*).

In summary, it is evident that many discrepancies arise in the investigations on the diffusion and emission of fission gases in metallic fuels. Several workers have reported their results in the form of diffusion coefficients, but considerations of surface oxidation throw doubt upon the values obtained. Moreover, many of the authors themselves draw attention to the fact that the time variation of their results is not in agreement with the trend expected if the emission were in fact controlled by diffusion. In particular, solution of the diffusion equations leads to an expectation that there should be a linear variation of emission with the square root of time: this is usually not found.

## 5.3 MIGRATION IN CERAMIC FUELS

### 5.3.1 Emission of Inert Gases

#### Xenon from uranium dioxide

Results for the overall fission gas release observed in some 60 pellet irradiations of uranium dioxide at Oak Ridge, Chalk River and A.E.R.E., Harwell, have been summarized by MURRAY (1962). An upward trend in the gas release with increase in the fuel centre temperature is evident, but the results are too scattered to allow detailed deductions to be made about the mechanism of release.

Many investigations have been reported on the emission of xenon from uranium dioxide by the post-irradiation annealing technique since the latter has come to be regarded as an important method of characterizing the suitability of each type of material for use in fuel elements. The measurements are frequently either made at or extrapolated to 1,400°C for this purpose. Some workers have made measurements over a considerable range of temperature to obtain information relevant to the mechanism of the release.

If the emission of the stable inert gases is controlled by a diffusion process in the solid, the diffusion equations quoted earlier in the chapter predict that the fraction released ($f$) should be proportional to the square root of time at temperature. A typical plot obtained experimentally by LONG and DAVIES (1961) is shown in *Figure 5.2*. At the relatively high temperature of 1,600°C used for this experiment, a linear relationship was obtained after a few minutes. The significance of the intercept on the ordinate axis and of deviations from linearity at lower temperatures are discussed on pp. 229–230. Additional experiments have confirmed that the linear relationship is followed for times up to at least 300 hours at 1,400 and 1,600°C.

There is no unique relationship between $D'$ and the density of the ceramic material. Uranium dioxide of nominally the same density but prepared by different routes can have widely different values of $D'$ owing to variations in porosity and hence of surface area. However, since surface area cannot be measured routinely on large numbers of fuel pellets, the density of uranium dioxide (which can be measured relatively easily) is often used in order to specify the apparent diffusion coefficient to be expected. This may be acceptable only as long as the preparative route is not altered, but even so is subject to the further difficulty that $D'$ varies very rapidly with slight changes of density of the $UO_2$ above 10 g cm$^{-3}$.

According to the equivalent sphere hypothesis, the apparent diffusion coefficient ($D'$) should be inversely proportional to the square of the radius of the equivalent spheres (i.e. directly proportional to the square of the specific surface area). The validity of this relationship at the standard temperature of 1,400°C over a wide range of surface areas is shown in *Figure 5.3*. The scatter of results about the line of slope 2 was attributed by Long and

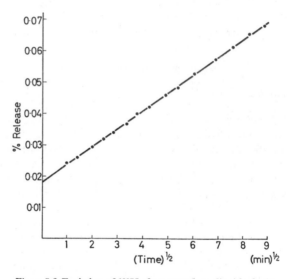

*Figure 5.2.* Emission of $^{133}$Xe from uranium dioxide during post-irradiation annealing at 1,600°C (Long and Davies, 1961).

Davies to errors introduced by the extrapolation from lower temperatures of some of the results for higher surface area samples, and to uncertainties in assigning a value of surface area at low values of this parameter, since it was then measured for a batch of pellets, rather than for the individual samples used in the diffusion measurements.

The ceramic constituent of a cermet fuel provides an interesting special case for the study of fission product diffusion. In an oxide cermet the specification may require dense oxide granules of several hundred microns diameter for dispersion in the metallic matrix. LONG and DAVIES (1961) have studied the emission of $^{133}$Xe from near-spherical granules of $UO_2$ of 300 microns diameter. The granules were of high density and essentially zero open porosity, since the B.E.T. surface area was only 25 per cent greater than that calculated from the mean radius of the granules. It was found that the results were in good agreement with those obtained on sintered pellets (*Figure 5.3*). The granules were polycrystalline, of grain size *ca.* 10 $\mu$, and so the equivalent spheres were evidently not identical with the grains. Such a result may be expected from the use of the post-irradiation annealing technique, since the diffusion length associated with experiments of short duration will be very small compared with the granule diameter, even if the diffusion is primarily via grain boundaries at a rate which is greater than lattice diffusion by some

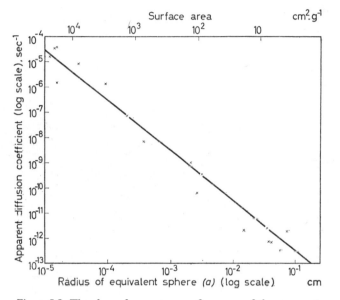

*Figure 5.3.* The dependence upon surface area of the apparent diffusion coefficient for [133]Xe in UO$_2$ at 1,400°C (Long and Davies, 1961).

two orders of magnitude. Caution is necessary, therefore, in using the short-term annealing data to predict long-term fuel performance: over long periods of time the grain boundaries could become depleted and control of the emission of xenon could be taken over by lattice diffusion throughout the material. Fortunately this effect, if substantiated, would reduce the overall emission.

The variation with temperature of the diffusion coefficient for xenon in uranium dioxide is shown in *Figure 5.4* and details of the investigations are summarized in *Table 5.1*.

There is a considerable spread of values of both the diffusion coefficient at a given temperature and of the apparent energy of activation. However, from the technological point of view the spread of values of the diffusion coefficient in sintered uranium dioxide at the temperature normally regarded as the standard for comparison, 1,400°C, is not excessive for a material with such a complex physical structure.

The spread of results when the powders and the fused material are included renders interpretation in terms of any particular diffusion model difficult.

Many factors could be responsible for this spread. The highest results, those of Booth and Rymer, are certainly subject to suspicion. COTTRELL et al. (1960) have pointed out that Booth assumed a probably erroneous value for the radius of the equivalent spheres in his material, basing it upon a sieve size rather than

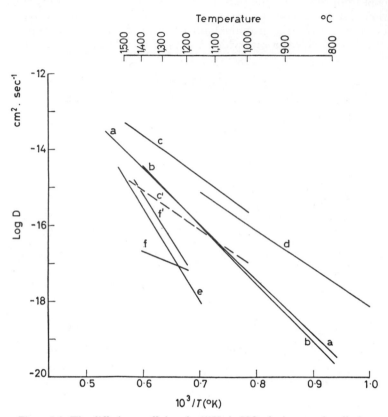

*Figure 5.4.* The diffusion coefficient for $^{133}$Xe in $UO_2$ during post-irradiation annealing (see also *Table 5.1*).

    (a)   Long and Davies (1961).
    (b)   Belle *et al.* (1960).
    (c)   Booth and Rymer (1958).
    (c′)   Booth and Rymer, corrected (see text).
    (d)   Lindner and Matzke (1959).
    (e)   Stevens, McEwan and Ross (1960).
    (f)   Barnes *et al.* (1961), fused $UO_2$.
    (f′)   Barnes *et al.* (1961), sintered $UO_2$.

upon a surface area measurement. Cottrell's suggested correction for this is plotted as curve c′ on *Figure 5.4*.

It may be significant that very good agreement was obtained in the two separate laboratories which used reducing conditions in the sweep gas (curves a and b). The results given by curves c and d may therefore be suspected of giving higher values for the diffusion coefficient due to surface oxidation of the samples. On the other hand some of the investigations which did not

236

employ reducing conditions gave low diffusion coefficients. Several investigations have shown that an increase in the oxygen content of uranium dioxide leads to an increase in the diffusion coefficient for xenon (LINDNER and MATZKE, 1959; STEVENS et al., 1960; and others).

Curve d, by Lindner and Matzke, may disagree from the others because the experiments were performed at comparatively low temperatures. Here the 'burst effect' (pp. 229–230) produces considerable deviations from the linear plot of release against $(time)^{1/2}$ and the analysis of the results in terms of the normal diffusion equations is difficult.

TABLE 5.1

SUMMARY OF POST-IRRADIATION ANNEALING EXPERIMENTS ON THE DIFFUSION OF XENON
FROM URANIUM DIOXIDE IN THE RANGE 800–1,600°C

| Material | Atmosphere during anneal | Temperature range (°C) | Diffusion coefficient at 1,400°C (cm² sec⁻¹) (× 10¹⁵) | Activation energy (kcal mole⁻¹) | Reference |
|---|---|---|---|---|---|
| Powders ($< 1\mu$) | Ar | 750–1,150 | 8 (extrap.) | 49 | Lindner and Matzke (1959–1961) |
| Sintered UO₂ | H₂ | 800–1,600 | 5 | 70 | Long and Davies (1961) |
| | H₂ | 1,400 | 0·8 | — | Scott and Toner (1960) |
| | Vac. | 1,100–1,500 | * | 90 | Stevens et al. (1960) |
| | He | 1,200–1,450 | 0·8 | 115 | Barnes et al. (1961) |
| Plate, 97% of theoretical density | H₂/He | 800–1,300 | 3 | 72 | Belle et al. (1960) |
| Fused UO₂ | He | 1,000–1,500 | 30† | 46 | Booth and Rymer (1958) |
| | Vac. | 1,200–1,500 | 0·5 | 120 | Stevens et al. (1960) |
| | He | 1,200–1,400 | 0·02 | 30 | Barnes et al. (1961) |

* Apparent diffusion coefficient, $\sim 4 \times 10^{-9}$ sec⁻¹; value of $a$ not determined.
† ORNL workers suggest that Booth and Rymer's value of $a$ was erroneous, and that $D_{1,400}$ should be $\sim 1 \times 10^{15}$ cm² sec⁻¹ (Cottrell et al., 1960).

The wide variation in the apparent activation energy indicates that we do not yet have sufficient knowledge to control all the parameters which can affect the emission of xenon. The low activation energy shown by curve f was attributed by the authors of that work possibly to inclusions of uranium nitride and of uranium metal which were known to be present in the fused UO₂.

The activation energy for the self-diffusion of uranium ion in stoichiometric material is 88 kcal mole⁻¹ (AUSKERN and BELLE, 1961) and for oxygen ion diffusion it is 65 kcal mole⁻¹ (AUSKERN and BELLE, 1961). Moreover the activation energy for oxygen ion diffusion is lowered to about 30 kcal mole⁻¹

in non-stoichiometric oxide of composition about $UO_{2.004}$ and $UO_{2.06}$. If the diffusion of xenon could take place by a mechanism similar to that proposed for oxygen (interstitialcy), then perhaps the explanation for the low activation energies observed by Lindner and Matzke and by Booth and Rymer lies in

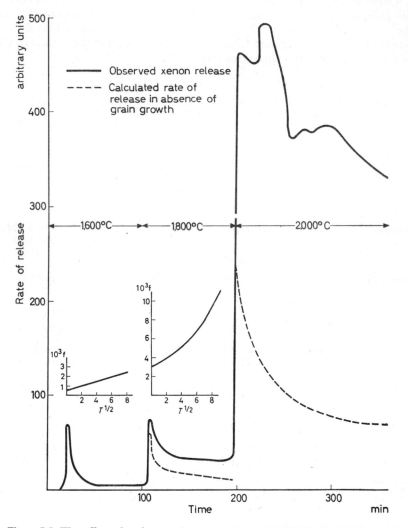

*Figure 5.5.* The effect of grain growth on the release of $^{133}Xe$ from $UO_2$ during post-irradiation annealing (Long and Davies, 1961).

partial oxidation (which need only take place in a thin surface layer). Lindner and Matzke claimed that the energy of activation for xenon diffusion was the same for $UO_{2.00}$, $UO_{2.02}$ and $UO_{2.12}$; the oxygen contents were determined by ignition and weighing, however, and this method would probably not be sufficiently sensitive to eliminate the possibility that there was further oxidation either before or during the experiments. By analogy with the results of Auskern and Belle, the oxidation of $UO_{2.00}$ might only need to proceed as far as $UO_{2.004}$ to produce marked effects on both the diffusion coefficient and the energy of activation.

Some of the higher values of the activation energy for xenon diffusion are close to that for uranium ion self-diffusion. Moreover, for the limited range of temperature in which direct comparison is possible, the diffusion coefficient of xenon is almost the same as that of the uranium ions, whereas the diffusion coefficient of oxygen is much higher. Despite some qualitative similarities between the diffusion of xenon and of oxygen, therefore, it may be necessary to postulate that xenon migration is more closely associated with the uranium lattice positions in uranium dioxide. It is difficult to visualize an atom as large as xenon diffusing through the lattice at the same rate as the much smaller uranium ions. The size of univalent xenon ions would be less than the neutral atoms, but the high ionization potential of xenon seems to render unlikely their existence in the $UO_2$ lattice. A decision on the mechanism by which xenon moves through uranium dioxide cannot yet be made.

The reader will note that the data given in *Figure 5.4* do not extend to temperatures higher than about 1,600°C. This is due to the fact that the process of bulk diffusion of xenon which appears to describe the data in the approximate range 1,100–1,600°C is no longer the controlling factor in the sintered material at higher temperatures.

For material prepared by sintering at 1,650°C, the effect of xenon release during post-irradiation annealing is shown in *Figure 5.5*. At the higher temperatures the release is greater than would be expected from normal bulk diffusion, a phenomenon which is usually attributed to the sweeping of xenon atoms to the surface by the movement of grain boundaries within the material. This enhanced rate of release has been responsible for a conservative attitude towards the design of fuel elements based on uranium dioxide. Many of these designs restrict the heat rating so that no part of the fuel will enter this grain growth region and release substantial amounts of inert gas.

*Krypton from uranium dioxide*

The emission of krypton from uranium dioxide has been studied to a much less extent than that of xenon. In the temperature range where the emission is most probably controlled by bulk diffusion (approximately 1,100–1,600°C) the available data are very scattered. BELLE (1958) has reported some results by Susko which give an activation energy of 59 kcal mole$^{-1}$ for diffusion in pellets of 97·4 per cent of theoretical density. The diffusion coefficients were rather low, however, being about $10^{-17}$ cm$^2$ sec$^{-1}$ at 1,400°C.

COTTRELL et al. (1960) have suggested that the reason why Susko's results appear to be so low lies in the fact that he used a surface area which was not measured directly but was deduced from an early curve of the variation of surface area with density. Unfortunately the surface area varies very rapidly with density about the particular value used, and Cottrell quoted more recent work which showed that Susko's surface area may have been in error by a power of ten. When this correction is applied, Susko's results for the diffusion of $^{85}$Kr lie close to the curve c′ for $^{133}$Xe on *Figure 5.4*.

Other values for the diffusion of $^{85}Kr$, obtained by Auskern, have been quoted by COTTRELL *et al.* (1960) and by BELLE *et al.* (1960). The absolute values cover about the same range as those for xenon in *Figure 5.4*, but extend up to about $10^{-12}$ cm$^2$ sec$^{-1}$ at 1,400°C. For three different types of uranium dioxide the activated energy ranged from 65·5 to 81 kcal mole$^{-1}$. BOOTH and RYMER (1958) reported that they could find no significant difference between the diffusion rates of $^{85}Kr$, $^{88}Kr$ and $^{133}Xe$, but did not quote details of the experiments on krypton. The observed differences between the diffusion of xenon and krypton mentioned above probably arise from differences in the character of the samples and in technique. LINDNER and MATZKE (1959b) have compared the diffusion rates of the two gases using the same source of uranium dioxide and the same experimental method, and have found virtually no difference between them over the range 800–1,100°C. The apparent activation energy for both gases over this range was about 48 kcal mole$^{-1}$.

For the purpose of fuel element calculations it appears reasonable to assume that the diffusion coefficients of the two elements are equal.

As would be expected, an enhanced release of $^{85}Kr$ above 1,800°C, similar to the xenon release, has been observed by ROTHWELL (1961). He noted in addition that uranium dioxide could attain sub-stoichiometric compositions at these temperatures. Upon cooling to about 1,450°C, an unexpected high release of krypton occurred which was attributed to disproportionation of the sub-stoichiometric material to a mixture of stoichiometric oxide plus uranium metal. Whilst this effect may not occur in a clad fuel element where overall loss of oxygen is prevented, the results indicate yet another feature which can complicate the interpretation of the post-irradiation annealing results in terms of any simple mechanism of emission.

*Other oxide systems*

We will record here only the data available on the diffusion of inert gases in oxides of direct interest to fuel element technology.

The emission of xenon from sintered thoria containing 5 per cent urania has been studied briefly between 1,440 and 2,015°C by SCOTT, TONER and ADAMS (1961). It appeared to be a diffusion-controlled process with an activation energy of 76 kcal mole$^{-1}$, close to the values obtained for diffusion in sintered UO$_2$ by LONG and DAVIES (1961) and by BELLE *et al.* (1960).

The diffusion of inert gases in thoria has been investigated between 1,100 and 1,500°C using both $^{133}Xe$ and $^{222}Rn$ by LINDNER and MATZKE (1960). They reported a diffusion-controlled emission process with an activation energy of 51 kcal mole$^{-1}$ for $^{222}Rn$ compared with a value of 59 kcal mole$^{-1}$ in uranium dioxide. The activation energy for xenon emission (30 kcal mole$^{-1}$) was lower than in urania, however.

The wide variations for the diffusion coefficients and the activation energies reported for xenon diffusion in uranium dioxide render further investigations on thoria highly desirable. Until closer agreement between different laboratories can be attained, a discussion of the nature of the diffusion properties and of possible differences between the various inert gases in the different oxides will not be profitable.

Measurements of the emission of xenon from lightly irradiated ZrO$_2$–25 wt. % UO$_2$ have been compared in the range 800–1,250°C with that from high density $UO_2$ by BELLE (1960b). Here a difference might be expected to arise from the differing lattice structures, and the diffusion coefficients were found to be about two orders of magnitude higher in the zirconia-rich samples.

Although plutonium may be a major constituent of oxide fuels for several advanced reactor designs, no investigations of its influence upon the diffusion of fission products have been reported. A possible effect may arise from the tendency for the presence of plutonium to stabilize phases with an oxygen:metal ratio of less than 2·00 (see Chapter 4). If the diffusion of the inert gases is associated with vacancies in the oxygen lattice, a difference from diffusion in stoichiometric urania could arise.

### Xenon from uranium carbide

The diffusion of inert gases in bulk carbide fuels has been studied much less than that in oxides. Previously unpublished results obtained at A.E.R.E., Harwell, by the post-irradiation technique using highly purified argon as a sweep gas are shown in *Table 5.2*.

TABLE 5.2

POST-IRRADIATION ANNEALING EXPERIMENTS ON THE DIFFUSION OF $^{133}$Xe IN URANIUM MONOCARBIDE (Findlay and Laing, 1961)

| Preparative route | Fabrication | Carbon content (wt.%) | Bulk density (g cm$^{-3}$) | Surface area (cm$^2$ g$^{-1}$) | Diffusion coefficient at 1,400°C ($\times 10^{16}$) (cm$^2$ sec$^{-1}$) |
|---|---|---|---|---|---|
| Reaction of uranium with carbon | Cold-pressed, sintered at 1,100°C for 2 hours | 4·8 | 12·1 | 2,230 | 8·2 |
| | | 4·8 | 12·1 | 1,645 | 2·3 |
| | | 4·8 | 12·2 | 400 | 5·3 |
| | Arc-melted | 4·6 | 13·6 | 200 | 6·1 |
| Reaction of $UO_2$ with carbon | Reacted at 1,400°C, unsintered | 4·8 | 13·0 | 1,860 | 15 |
| Reaction of uranium with carbon, iron added | UC+10% UFe$_2$ sintered at 1,100°C for 2 hours | — | — | 420 | 4·2 |

The emission of xenon at 1,400°C appears to be substantially independent of the preparative route, provided that the surface area (measured by gas adsorption) is used to evaluate the mean size of the diffusion unit. Comparison with *Table 5.1* shows that at a given temperature uranium monocarbide may have a diffusion coefficient for xenon lower by about a factor of five than that in uranium dioxide. Provided that routes can be developed for producing carbide with a specific surface area as low as that attained with oxide, then the carbide fuel could be more retentive for fission products when the operating conditions are in the range of temperature where emission is mainly by diffusion

Findlay and Laing also obtained measurements of the emission of xenon from uranium carbide over a range of temperatures. The results are not quoted here, however, since it is not certain at the time of writing whether those obtained at temperatures about 1,000°C relate to true volume diffusion. The anomalous release shown by the plot of fraction emitted against the square root of time is considerably greater than for the oxide about 1,000°C.

An activation energy of 80 kcal mole$^{-1}$ for the diffusion of krypton *into* uranium carbide has been claimed to be valid between 1,200°C and 1,500°C (RADIATION APPLICATIONS INC., 1960). The surface area was not measured in this latter work and so the true diffusion coefficient cannot be quoted.

No information is available at present on the effect of grain-growth on fission gas release from carbide fuel material, corresponding to the enhancement observed in uranium dioxide.

### The effects of irradiation

Irradiation might be expected to affect the diffusion of fission product gases in a number of different ways. Firstly, irradiation may disturb the thermal equilibrium concentration of interstitial atoms and of vacancies in the lattice, thus tending to influence the rate of diffusion if the latter proceeds by a vacancy mechanism.

Secondly, as the burn-up increases, the concentration of fission products also increases and there is a greater possibility of chemical interaction between them. This should not affect the diffusion characteristics of the inert gases directly, but there may be an indirect effect from chemical interactions of the iodine or tellurium precursors of xenon.

Thirdly, physical changes in the ceramic fuel could affect the release of the inert gases. Thus, urania irradiated at a high rate of burn-up shows considerable porosity after a burn-up of 10 per cent, regardless of temperature or other irradiation conditions (pp. 154–155). This porosity is not interconnected and may act as fission product traps, thus reducing the emission of the inert gases. The trapping of gas in closed pores which exist in sintered uranium dioxide has been demonstrated after only short irradiations by subsequently grinding the material to open up the pores (ROBERTSON et al., 1959).

Fourthly, material along the track of a fission fragment becomes very disturbed, in a manner which has been likened to the transient effects of an extremely high temperature. Within the solid material, this may lead to an enhancement of the emission of gas. Each fission fragment which is emitted into the open porosity of the ceramic material, or from the external surface, may 'knock-out' inert gas atoms which were embedded in the lattice structure of the surface layers. The effect has been discussed by WALTON et al. (1958) for the emission of fission products from metallic uranium under irradiation, and by LEWIS (1960) and LONG (1962) for emission from uranium dioxide.

Lewis considered that in some fuel specimens irradiation knock-out could be considerably more important than recoil.

Long observed that the amount of xenon emitted from samples of uranium dioxide lightly irradiated in evacuated silica ampoules at 80°C in BEPO was greater than could be attributed to recoil. From the amounts emitted it was estimated that an average of one atom of xenon (or iodine precursor) was knocked out for every $6 \times 10^3$ atoms of uranium displaced. Extending the results to fuel element operating conditions, Long showed that when the dimensions of the fuel are large compared with the recoil range the fraction of a stable isotope lost by knock-out after a long irradiation is given by

$$f = 3\delta/a$$

where $a =$ the equivalent sphere radius and $\delta =$ maximum depth from which knock-out can occur (not necessarily the full fission fragment range).

At temperatures above about 1,200°C, release by diffusion becomes more important and ultimately swamps the knock-out effect. The latter may well be of significance in some fuel element designs based upon lower centre temperatures, however, and merits more detailed experimental investigation.

Some important differences between the three modes of emission are summarized in *Table 5.3*.

TABLE 5.3

MECHANISMS FOR THE RELEASE OF INERT GASES FROM CERAMIC MATERIALS UNDER IRRADIATION

|  | *Recoil* | *Fractional release by knock-out* | *Diffusion* |
|---|---|---|---|
| Active species | Independent of half-life | Proportional to half-life | Proportional to square root of half-life |
| All stable species | Independent of rate of fission | Independent of rate of fission for long exposures | Probably independent of rate of fission |
|  | Independent of temperature | Independent of temperature | Depends on temperature |
|  | Independent of porosity | Depends on porosity | Depends on porosity |

A subsidiary effect has been postulated to arise from the passage of fission fragments through the previously evolved gas which fills the pores in the material. It was supposed that some of these gas atoms would undergo knock-on from the fission fragments and that if they attained more than about 2 keV of kinetic energy they might re-enter and become trapped in the solid surface layers. Lewis (1960) suggested that the evolution of gas by diffusion from the hottest part of the fuel, and its re-entry by knock-on in the cooler part, where it could become virtually 'fixed', could produce appreciable reductions in the pressure of fission product gases generated in a fuel element. The rate of re-entry by knock-on was considered to be given by:

$$R = 5 \cdot 2 \times 10^{-4} P\,(GK)\,V_o \text{ atoms per fission}$$

where $P$ = pressure of gas in the open pores of the ceramic material (atm)
$G$ = fraction of the knocked-on atoms which become embedded
$K$ = total number of gas atoms knocked-on per pair of fission fragment tracks
$V_o$ = volume fraction of the open porosity

From an experiment with uranium dioxide of rather low density (9·75 g cm$^{-3}$) Lewis calculated that the value of the product $GK$ was about 100 atoms per pair of fission fragment tracks. Further work involving the irradiation of sintered uranium dioxide in a mixture of natural xenon, argon and krypton at a pressure of 7 atm, followed by detailed analysis of the gas content of the solid, indicated that $GK$ may be greater than 100 and that there might be a limiting gas pressure in ceramic fuel elements. At the limiting pressure the rate of re-entry by knock-on would equal the rate of release (primarily by diffusion from the hottest zone).

If the value of $GK$ is indeed as low as 100, then the reduction of gas pressure in the void space within a ceramic fuel element up to an irradiation of 12,000 MWd/T would amount to some 20 per cent as a result of re-entry (LONG, 1962). This is not large enough to be technologically significant. The re-entry effect therefore appears to be primarily of academic interest, although further work is desirable to determine whether $GK$ can be increased with samples of different porosity from those used in the Chalk River experiments.

Unfortunately, few data are available on the release of inert gases from uranium dioxide during irradiation under closely controlled conditions.

MARKOWITZ, KOCH and ROLL (1957) measured the emission of [87]Kr and [135]Xe from uranium dioxide during irradiation up to about 500°C. They found that the emission was independent of temperature, as would be expected in this region of temperature where recoil of fission fragments from the surface and the knock-out effect should predominate over bulk diffusion.

Results up to 900°C on uranium dioxide of 91 per cent of theoretical density were obtained by STUBBS and WEBSTER (1960). They found no significant difference between the emission of [85m]Kr, [133]Xe and [135]Xe. In the temperature region (700–900°C) where the data overlapped the available out-of-pile results (curves a, b and d, *Figure 5.4*) the calculated diffusion coefficients were of comparable magnitude, and it was concluded that irradiation had no marked effect on the rate of diffusion. The in-pile results at a given temperature, however, showed considerable scatter over about four orders of magnitude.

Analysis of the gas release from 15 Shippingport PWR blanket rods at the time of the first refuelling of the seed fuel (i.e. at a burn-up of about $1 \cdot 4 \times 10^{20}$ $f$. cm$^{-3}$) confirmed that the emission of several isotopes of both krypton and xenon had been virtually identical. The average centre temperatures of the fuel had been within the range 540–735°C, and reasonable agreement between the measurements and calculated releases was obtained using a diffusion coefficient of $10^{-18}$ cm$^2$ sec$^{-1}$ over the whole of this range (RUBIN, 1961).

The emission of $^{88}$Kr and $^{85m}$Kr from uranium dioxide in an in-pile annealing experiment has been reported for the range 700–1,100°C by

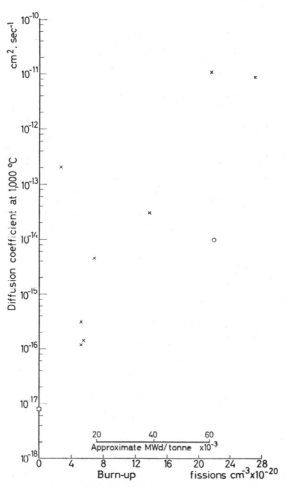

*Figure 5.6.* The diffusion of krypton in uranium dioxide as a function of burn-up.

×  Belle (1960)
○  Approximate value quoted by Bleiberg *et al.* (1960)
□  Value for xenon from *Figure 5.4.*

CARROLL and KARKHANAVALA (1961). The activation energy for the release was 40 kcal mole$^{-1}$, but the absolute values of the calculated diffusion coefficients were about two powers of ten higher than the highest out-of-pile results at the same temperatures. Results were obtained also for xenon emission which showed that the rates of release were increasing with time: this effect was attributed to possible physical changes in the oxide, such as slow grain growth or a phase change.

*Results at higher burn-up.* The post-irradiation measurement of the amount of gas evolved in capsules irradiated at Oak Ridge has shown no detectable effect of burn-up to 14,000 MWd/tonne (*ca.* $5 \times 10^{20}$ fissions per cm$^3$) (SISMAN, 1960). A large number of parameters can affect gas release in this type of experiment, however, and any effect of burn-up may have been obscured by other variations.

Preliminary results to much higher levels of irradiation have been reported by BELLE (1960) in a series of PWR Project progress reports. The quoted diffusion coefficients (for krypton) are shown in *Figure 5.6*, but it is not known what reliance may be placed upon them since details of the experiments have not yet been published. For instance, the measurements were made by a post-irradiation technique at a temperature where the 'initial burst' effect (see pp. 228–230) may easily obscure the emission by bulk diffusion. Also, the coefficients were calculated using the equivalent sphere concept, assuming that the size of the equivalent spheres did not change during irradiation.

It appears that there is a definite trend towards higher diffusion coefficients as the burn-up increases, but the scatter of the points is considerable and the exact nature of the variation remains to be clarified. BLEIBERG *et al.* (1960) have suggested, for instance, that there may be a discontinuous change in the region of $20 \times 10^{20}$ fissions cm$^{-3}$. The emission of gas during irradiation at temperatures below 1,000°C was found by these workers to be almost two powers of ten higher at this burn-up than for similar material irradiated to $8 \times 10^{20}$ fissions cm$^{-3}$.

### 5.3.2 Emission of Other Species

The high volatility and chemical inertness of xenon and krypton render measurements of their emission from ceramic materials comparatively straightforward. Measurements of the emission of the more reactive and less volatile fission products are more difficult to make and very few results are available.

LONG and DAVIES (1961) have adapted the post-irradiation annealing technique to such measurements. The diffusion coefficients for iodine, tellurium and caesium in sintered uranium dioxide over the temperature range 1,000–1,600°C were found to be of the same order of magnitude as that for xenon when the specific surface area of the samples was greater than about 700 cm$^2$ g$^{-1}$. However, when the surface area was lower ($< 200$ cm$^2$ g$^{-1}$), the diffusion of the chemically reactive fission products was much faster than that of xenon. The varying nature of the dependence on surface area indicates that the mechanisms of diffusion of xenon and the iodine groups may be different.

Strontium and barium were much more effectively retained by the uranium dioxide lattice, the diffusion coefficients being several orders of magnitude lower than that of xenon.

Results in agreement with those of Long and Davies on uranium dioxide have been reported for thorium dioxide by LINDNER and MATZKE (1960). They found that [131]I had the same energy of activation and approximately the same diffusion coefficient as [133]Xe for transport in thoria over the temperature range 700–1,200°C.

246

The behaviour of volatile fission products in uranium carbide also shows the same trends. FINDLAY and LAING (1961) found in post-irradiation annealing experiments that the relative emissions of the various fission products were as shown in *Table 5.4*. Note, however, that strontium and barium appear to be considerably more mobile in the carbide lattice than in the oxide.

TABLE 5.4

RELEASE OF FISSION PRODUCTS FROM URANIUM MONOCARBIDE AT 1,400°C,
EXPRESSED AS FRACTIONS OF THE XENON RELEASE
(Findlay and Laing, 1961)

| Xe | I | Te | Cs | Sr | Ba | Ce | Zr |
|----|-----|-----|-----|-----|-----|------|-------|
| 1 | ~1 | 0·8 | 0·5 | 0·3 | 0·3 | 0·05 | 0·003 |

An interesting aspect of the diffusion of chemically reactive fission products arises out of the changing nature of ceramic fuels with increasing burn-up. The chemical form of some of the fission products may be expected to change at high burn-ups, due to the requirement to maintain electroneutrality in the fuel. Conditions in an oxide fuel, for instance, will become progressively more reducing as irradiation proceeds inside a closed container. Such chemical changes have been discussed by ROBINSON (1958), but no relevant experimental work at high burn-up has been reported.

The substantial emission of iodine, tellurium and caesium is of considerable importance in the event of conditions which may permit the release of these species into the reactor cooling system. The physical and chemical state of the fission products after release through a defect in the fuel cladding remains a matter for speculation. Iodine, for instance, is believed to exist under such conditions in at least three forms: (a) vapour, (b) adsorbed on particles of various oxides or graphite, (c) adsorbed on Aitken nuclei. The latter nuclei are in the size range 0·01–0·1 micron, and exist to the extent of some $10^4$ per cm$^3$ in laboratory air; no information has been published concerning their concentration in reactor coolant streams.

The removal of iodine from gas streams has been studied by a number of workers (e.g. HUDSWELL *et al.*, 1960; CARDOZO and DEJONGHE, 1960; BROWNING *et al.*, 1960; SMITH and CRAWLEY, 1961), but the interpretation of results when the iodine is at very low concentrations is subject to uncertainty from the behaviour of the iodine-contaminated Aitken nuclei. The latter can carry the iodine through some of the common types of iodine-removal devices such as sodium carbonate scrubbers and copper fibre filters (CHAMBERLAIN *et al.*, 1960).

A fission product trapping system for use in the HTGR has been described by WATKINS, BUSCH and ZUMWALT (1961). Silver-coated charcoal was favoured for this system and was tested up to about 540°C (the carrier gas was helium). The removal of tellurium was also found to be efficient in this material and it was suggested that some of the results indicated that tellurium

247

and iodine were associated chemically with each other in the gas stream. Tellurium-123 removal may be important during reactor accident conditions since its release to the reactor environment could give rise to an inhalation hazard (it decays to $^{132}$I).

SMITH and CRAWLEY (1961) recommend the use of a composite bed of silvered copper mesh and activated carbon for the removal of iodine from carbon dioxide or $CO_2$–air mixtures. The bed should be preceded by mechanical filters.

#### REFERENCES

AUSKERN, A. B. and BELLE, J. (1961). 'Oxygen ion self-diffusion in uranium dioxide.' *J. Nucl. Materials*, **3**, 267

AUSKERN, A. B. and BELLE, J. (1961). 'Uranium ion self-diffusion in uranium dioxide.' *J. Nucl. Materials*, **3**, 311

BARNES, R. H., KANGILASKI, M., MELEHAN, J. B. and ROUGH, R. A. (1961). 'Xenon diffusion in single crystal and sintered $UO_2$.' U.S.A.E.C. Report, BMI-1533

BARNES, R. H. and SUNDERMAN, D. N. (1960). 'Apparatus for the study of fission gas release from fuels during post-irradiation heating at temperatures up to 1,600°C.' U.S.A.E.C. Report, BMI-1453

BARNES, R. S. (1959). 'Fundamentals of fission gas agglomeration and swelling in metals.' Met. Soc. A.I.M.E., Special Publication No. 9; Nuclear Metallurgy, Vol. 6

BARNES, R. S. *et al.* (1958). 'Swelling and inert gas diffusion in irradiated uranium.' *Proc. Second Geneva Conf.*, **5**, 543

BARNEY, W. K. (1958). 'Irradiation effects in $UO_2$.' *Proc. Second Geneva Conf.*, **6**, 677

BARRER, R. M. (1951) *Diffusion in and through solids.* Cambridge University Press

BATES, J. C. and CLARK, A. C. (1955). 'The diffusion of xenon in uranium.' U.K.A.E.A. Report, R & DB (W)-TN-200

BECK, S. D. (1960). 'The diffusion of radioactive fission products from porous fuel elements.' U.S.A.E.C. Report, BMI-1433

BELLE, J. (1958). 'Properties of uranium dioxide.' *Proc. Second Geneva Conf.*, **6**, 569

BELLE, J. (1960). Quoted in U.S.A.E.C. Reports, WAPD-MRP-84, 85, 86, 88

BELLE, J. (1960b). Quoted in U.S.A.E.C. Reports, WAPD-MRP-89, 90, 91, 92

BELLE, J., AUSKERN, A. B., BOSTROM, W. A. and SUSKO, F. S. (1960). 'Diffusion kinetics in uranium dioxide.' *Proc. Fourth Int. Symp. on Reactivity of Solids*, Amsterdam, Elsevier

BLEIBERG, M. L., MASKARINEC, G., CLARK, D. and YENISCAVICH, W. (1960). 'Burn-up limitations of bulk $UO_2$ prototype fuel elements—an interim examination of the CR-IV-X-3-1 test and of the CR-V-M experiment.' U.S.A.E.C. Report, WAPD-BT-18

BOOTH, A. H. (1957). 'A method of calculating fission gas diffusion from $UO_2$ and its application to the X-2-$f$ test.' A.E.C.L. Report, CRDC-721

BOOTH, A. H., BAIN, A. S., KERR, D. and RYMER, G. T. (1957). 'Collection and measurement of stable fission xenon in sheath puncture experiments.' A.E.C.L. Report, CRDC-719

BOOTH, A. H. and RYMER, G. T. (1958). 'Determination of the diffusion constant of fission xenon in $UO_2$ crystals and sintered compacts.' A.E.C.L. Report, CRDC-720

BRINKMAN, J. A. (1959). 'Fundamentals of fission damage.' Met. Soc. A.I.M.E., Special Publ. No. 9; Nuclear Metallurgy, Vol. 6

BROWNING, W. E., ACKLEY, R. D. and ADAMS, R. E. (1960). 'Removal of radioactive gaseous fission products from other gases.' (Part of) U.S.A.E.C. Report, ORNL-2931

# REFERENCES

BRUNAUER, S., EMMETT, P. H. and TELLER, E. (1938). 'Adsorption of gases in multi-molecular layers.' *J. Amer. Chem. Soc.*, **60**, 309

CARDOZO, R. L. and DEJONGHE, P. (1960). 'The removal of gaseous iodine from air, with particular reference to reactor accidents.' Belgian Report, BLG-53

CARROLL, R. M. (1961). Quoted in U.S.A.E.C. Report, ORNL-3166

CARROLL, R. M. and BAUMANN, C. D. (1961). 'Experiment on continuous release of fission gas during irradiation.' U.S.A.E.C. Report, ORNL-3050

CARROLL, R. M. and KARKHANAVALA, M. D. (1961). Quoted in U.S.A.E.C. Report, ORNL-3102

CHAMBERLAIN, A. C., EGGLETON, A. E. J., MEGAW, W. J. and MORRIS, J. B. (1960). 'Behaviour of iodine vapour in air.' *Disc. Faraday Soc.*, No. 30, 162

CHURCHMAN, A. T. (1959). 'Swelling and fission gas agglomeration in metal fuels.' Met. Soc. A.I.M.E., Special Publication No. 9; Nuclear Metallurgy, Vol. 6

COTTRELL, W. B., SCOTT, J. L., CULVER, H. N. and YAROSH, M. M. (1960). 'Fission product release from $UO_2$.' U.S.A.E.C. Report, ORNL-2935

CREEK, G. E., MARTIN, W. J. and PARKER, G. W. (1959). 'Experiments on the release of fission products from molten reactor fuels.' U.S.A.E.C. Report, ORNL-2616

CURTIS, G. C. (1958). Section 4.1 of 'Swelling and inert gas diffusion in irradiated uranium.' *Proc. Second Geneva Conf.*, **5**, 543

CURTIS, G. C. and RICH, J. B. (1956). Unpublished work at Windscale

FINDLAY, J. R. and LAING, T. F. (1961). Unpublished work at A.E.R.E., Harwell

GRAY, D. L. (1960). 'Release of inert gases from irradiated uranium.' U.S.A.E.C. Report, HW-62639

GREENWOOD, G. W. (1960). 'The role of fission gas re-solution during the post-irradiation heating of uranium.' U.K.A.E.A. Report, AERE-R.3572

HILLIARD, R. K. (1959). 'Fission product release from uranium heated in air.' U.S.A.E.C. Report, HW-60689

HUDSWELL, F., FURBY, E., SIMONS, J. G. and WILKINSON, K. L. (1960). 'The sorption and desorption of iodine.' U.K.A.E.A. Report, AERE-R.3183

JAIN, S. C. (1958). 'Simple solutions of the partial differential equation for diffusion or heat conduction.' *Proc. Roy. Soc.*, **A243**, 359

KOCH, R. C., ECK, J. E. and SUSKO, F. S. (1957). 'The Bettis fission gas apparatus.' *Proc. Second Nucl. Eng. and Sci. Conf.*, Philadelphia, Vol. 3, Pergamon Press

LECLAIRE, A. D. and ROWE, A. H. (1954). 'The diffusion of argon in silver.' U.K.A.E.A. Report, AERE M/R-1417

LEWIS, W. B. (1960). 'The return of escaped fission product gases to $UO_2$.' A.E.C.L. Report, DM-58

LINDNER, R. and MATZKE, H. (1959). 'The diffusion of $^{133}$Xe in uranium dioxide of varying oxygen content.' *Z. Naturf.*, **14a**, 582

LINDNER, R. and MATZKE, H. (1959b). 'The diffusion of radioactive rare gases in uranium oxides and uranium monocarbide.' *Z. Naturf.*, **14a**, 1074

LINDNER, R. and MATZKE, H. (1960). 'Diffusion of $^{133}$Xe, $^{222}$Rn and $^{131}$I in thorium dioxide.' *Z. Naturf.*, **15a**, 647

LINDNER, R. and MATZKE, H. (1960). 'The diffusion of radon in oxides.' *Z. Naturf.*, **15a**, 1082

LINDNER, R. and MATZKE, H. (1961). 'Diffusion of uniformly distributed noble gases out of solids.' *Z. Naturf.*, **16a**, 845

LONG, G. (1962). Unpublished work at A.E.R.E., Harwell

LONG, G. and DAVIES, D. (1961). Unpublished work at A.E.R.E., Harwell

MARKOWITZ, J. M., KOCH, R. C. and ROLL, J. A. (1957). 'An apparatus for the measurement of fission gas elimination from fuel materials during irradiation.' U.S.A.E.C. Report, WAPD-180

MILLER, L. (1960). 'On a method of measuring diffusion coefficients for fission products in powdered or sintered material.' U.S.A.E.C. Report, LAMS-2437

249

MORGAN, W. W., JONES, R. W. and OLMSTEAD, W. J. (1960). 'The determination of fission product xenon released by $UO_2$ in fuel elements.' A.E.C.L. Report, CRDC-969

MURRAY, P. (1962). 'Ceramic fuels.' *Nuclear Engng*, **7**, No. 69, 53

RADIATION APPLICATIONS INC. (1960). 'Brief progress report on United States–Euratom joint research contract AT (30-1) 2497.' Quoted in U.S.A.E.C. Report, EURAEC-1

ROBERTSON, J. A. L., BAIN, A. S., ALLISON, G. M. and STEVENS, W. H. (1959). 'Irradiation behaviour of $UO_2$ fuel elements.' (Part of) Nuclear Metallurgy, VI, IMD Special Report Series, No. 9

ROBINSON, M. T. (1958). 'On the chemistry of the fission process in reactor fuels containing $UF_4$ and $UO_2$.' *Nucl. Sci. Engng*, **4**, 263

ROTHWELL, E. (1962). 'The release of $^{85}Kr$ from irradiated uranium dioxide on post-irradiation annealing.' *J. Nucl. Materials*, **5**, 241

RUBIN, B. (1961). 'Fission gas release in PWR Core-1 blanket fuel rods upon conclusion of seed-1 life.' U.S.A.E.C. Report, WAPD-TM-263

SCOTT, J. L. and TONER, D. F. (1960). Quoted in Gas-cooled Reactor Project, Quarterly Progress Report for period ending December 31st, 1960. U.S.A.E.C. Report, ORNL-3049

SCOTT, J. L., TONER, D. F. and ADAMS, R. E. (1961). Quoted in Gas-cooled Reactor Programme, Quarterly Progress Report for period ending August 1961. U.S.A.E.C. Report, ORNL-3166.

SCOTT, K. T. and BUDDERY, J. H. (1962). 'Release of $^{85}Kr$ from irradiated uranium during thermal cycling through the phase changes.' *J. Nucl. Materials*, **5**, 94

SISMAN, O. (1960). Quoted in Solid State Division Annual Progress Report for Period ending August, 1960. U.S.A.E.C. Report, ORNL-3017

SLOSEK, T. J. and WIEDENBAUM, B. (1960). 'Fission gases, their measurement and evaluation.' U.S.A.E.C. Report, GEAP-3440 (Rev.)

SMITH, J. F. W. and CRAWLEY, R. H. A. (1961). 'Removing radioactive iodine from gaseous effluent.' *Nuclear Engng*, **6**, 428

SPEDDING, F. H. *et al.* (1952). 'The thermal diffusion of fission products from uranium and uranium oxide.' U.S.A.E.C. Report, MUC-NS-3067

STEVENS, W. H., MACEWAN, J. R. and ROSS, A. M. (1960). 'The diffusion behaviour of fission xenon in uranium dioxide.' (Part of) U.S.A.E.C. Report, TID-7610

STUBBS, F. J., RUSSELL, P. J. and WALTON, G. N. (1959). 'The release of fission product gases from a thin film of $U_3O_8$ during irradiation in the DIDO reactor'. U.K.A.E.A. Report, AERE-R.2983

STUBBS, F. J. and WALTON, G. N. (1955). 'Emission of active rare gases from fissile material during irradiation with slow neutrons.' *Proc. First Geneva Conf.*, **7**, 163

STUBBS, F. J. and WEBSTER, C. B. (1959). 'The release of fission product rare gas from a uranium/zirconium alloy during irradiation in the BEPO reactor.' U.K.A.E.A. Report, AERE-C/M.372

STUBBS, F. J. and WEBSTER, C. B. 'Emission of fission product gases from $UO_2$ during irradiation in a reactor.' Proc. Meeting on Irradiation Effects in $UO_2$, Hanford Laboratory, U.S.A., Oct. 1960 (to be issued).

TOWNLEY, C. D., RAINES, G. E., DIETHORN, W. S. and SUNDERMAN, D. N. (1960). 'Measuring the release of short-lived gases during capsule irradiations.' U.S.A.E.C. Report, BMI-1466

WALKER, J. F. (1959). 'The escape of krypton from irradiated uranium on heating.' U.K.A.E.A. Report, IGR-TN/W-1046

WALTON, G. N., STUBBS, F. J. and SILVER, P. (1958). Section 4.2 of 'Swelling and inert gas diffusion in irradiated uranium.' *Proc. Second Geneva Conf.*, **5**, 543

WATKINS, R. M., BUSCH, D. D. and ZUMWALT, L. R. (1961). 'Trapping fission products in the HTGR.' *Nuclear Engng*, **6**, 427

# REFERENCES

WOMACK, R. E. (1960). 'A fission gas collection system.' (Part of) U.S.A.E.C. Report, TID-7599, Bk. 2

ZIMEN, K. E. and DAHL, L. (1957). 'The diffusion of fission xenon from metallic uranium.' *Z. Naturf.*, **12a**, 167. (AERE Lib Trans. 769)

ZIMEN, K. E. and SCHMELING, P. (1954). 'Diffusion of inert gases from irradiated uranium.' *Z. Elektrochem.*, **58**, 599

# INDEX

Acetylene
  in preparation of uranium carbides, 176, 177
Adcis
  reaction with uranium monocarbide, 189
Activated nitrogen
  reaction with graphite, 49
Advanced Gas-Cooled Reactor (AGR), 2, 95, 99
Air
  as reactor coolant, 4, 12, 86
  nuclear properties, 6
  reaction with beryllium, 92, 93
    irradiated uranium, 79
    magnesium, 84–87
    mild steel, 96
    thorium dicarbide, 195
    uranium, 70–80
    uranium alloys, 74
    uranium dioxide, 140
Air-cooled reactors, 2
Aitken nuclei, 247
Alkaline earths
  diffusion in graphite, 41, 42
    uranium dioxide, 246
    uranium monocarbide, 247
Aluminium
  compatibility with graphite, 59
    uranium carbides, 182, 190
    uranium dioxide, 146
  diffusion in uranium, 146
  effect on uranium oxidation, 74
  fuel cladding, 4
  impurity in coke, 21
Aluminium alloy
  as cladding for urania–thoria, 161
Aluminium nitride
  as die material in hot pressing of silicides, 205
Aluminium oxide
  compatibility with uranium dioxide, 146
  in sintering of thoria, 159
Ammonia
  as reactor coolant, 4
  for co-precipitation of uranium and plutonium, 168–170

Ammonia—*cont.*
  in production of uranium dioxide, 135–138
    uranium nitride, 202
Ammonium diuranate (ADU)
  as source of uranium dioxide, 120, 122, 124, 126, 132, 135–137
  filtration and settling, 135–137, 169–170
Anthraquinone, 138
Argon
  as impurity in carbon dioxide, 10
  in sintering of plutonium–uranium oxides, 167
  nuclear properties, 5, 6
  purification by uranium, 78
Argon-41
  in coolant gases, 5, 6
Atmospheric gases
  adsorption on graphite, 20, 21
AVR(Krupp–Brown Boveri reactor), 3, 62

Barium
  diffusion in graphite, 41, 42
    uranium dioxide, 246
    uranium monocarbide, 247
Benzene
  as reactor coolant, 4
  as solvent for pitch, 29
  for impregnation of graphite, 22
BEPO reactor, 1, 2, 52, 54, 58
Berkeley reactors, 2
Beryllium
  as fuel cladding, 92
  compatibility with graphite, 59
    uranium dioxide, 146
    uranium monocarbide, 190
  effect on magnesium oxidation, 86–89
    uranium oxidation, 74
  failure of cladding on $UO_2$ fuel, 141
  nuclear properties, 94
  oxidation, 91–95
  reaction with carbon dioxide, 93–95
    carbon monoxide, 94
    oxygen or air, 92, 93
  world production, 91